Horizons

Mathematics 4

Teacher's Guide

Authors:

Cindi Mitchell & Lori Fowler

Editor:

Alan Christopherson

Graphic Design:

Chris Burkholder
Mark Aguilar
Lisa Kelly
JoAnn Cumming
John Charles Walker
Lisa Nelson
Annette Walker
Keith Piccolo
Robert Breen

Alpha Omega Publications, Inc.
Rock Rapids, IA

Horizons Mathematics 4 Teacher's Guide

804 N. 2nd Ave. E., Rock Rapids, IA 51246-1759

Printed in the United States of America
ISBN 978-1-58095-994-0

Contents

Introduction

Before You Start ...

THE CHALLENGE

Today's average high school graduate knows and can do less math than their counterpart of ten, fifteen, or twenty years ago. Basic math skills have deteriorated to the point that many wonder if this country can continue to be a leader in shaping the technology of the future. Unfortunately, the general trend of modern education of all types is downward. Students in private education, while they score higher overall than public school students, still do poorly in math computation skills.

THE GOAL

The goal of this curriculum is to provide the parent and teacher with a tool that will help them effectively combat this deterioration of math skills by raising the level of student performance. Research of the content and methods of other existing curriculums, the concepts evaluated by achievement tests, and typical courses of study resulted in selection of the *Scope and Sequence* starting on page 18. This curriculum was not planned around any particular group of students. Rather, it was determined that the material in this curriculum constituted a reasonable level of performance for fourth grade students. The curriculum is designed so that the teacher can adapt its use to student(s) of widely varying ability. In other words, the curriculum is a tool that is capable of performing well over a broad range of student ability to help them achieve a higher minimum level of proficiency. The two major components of the curriculum are the student text (in two volumes) and the *Teacher's Guide*. These are the absolute minimum components for accomplishing the objective of teaching the concepts in the *Scope and Sequence*. Since this handbook was designed as an integral part of the curriculum, it is absolutely necessary to use the handbook. The handbook contains activities not found in the student texts that are essential to the accomplishment of the curriculum objectives. As you will see in the following sections, this *Teacher's Guide* contains a significant number of suggestions and helps for the teacher.

THE DESIGN

Take a moment to look at the sample chart entitled, *Appearance of Concepts*, on page 22. Take note of how the curriculum concepts are developed. The first presentation is usually a brief familiarization. Then the basic teaching is accomplished as part of three to five lessons. The thoroughness of a presentation depends on how new and how important the concept is to the student's academic development.

The Development

Each concept will be reviewed for three to five lessons after the complete presentation. For the next two months the concept will be presented every two weeks as a part of two or three lessons. After a break in presentation of a few weeks, the concept will be thoroughly reviewed as part of the lesson for three to five days. This will be followed by a period where the concept will be reviewed every two weeks as part of two or three lessons. This progression continues until the student(s) have had the opportunity to thoroughly master the concept.

An Example

Some mathematics curriculums might teach *division* for two months and not go back to it again. In this curriculum it will be introduced and practiced for two weeks. For the next two months, *division* will be presented every two weeks as a part of two or three lessons to give the student(s) continual practice to develop mastery of the concept. The third month will be considered a break from presenting the concept. In the fourth month, *division* will first be thoroughly reviewed and again practiced every two weeks as a part of two or three lessons. By having a series of practices every two weeks, the student(s) will retain what they have learned to a greater degree. Short periods of exposure repeated many times is much more effective than long periods with fewer exposures. Review the chart on page 22 to see how the concepts are developed.

Readiness Evaluation

WHY EVALUATE READINESS?

Teaching could be defined as the process of starting with what a student knows and guiding him to added knowledge with new material. While this may not be a dictionary definition of teaching, it is descriptive of the processes involved. Determining a student's readiness for fourth grade mathematics is the first step to successful teaching.

TYPES OF READINESS

True readiness has little to do with chronological age. Emotional maturity and mental preparation are the main components of academic readiness. The teacher who is dealing directly with the student is best able to determine a child's emotional maturity. All emotionally immature students may need special student training in their problem areas. A child's mental *preparation* can be more easily discerned with a simple diagnostic evaluation. Observing the child's attitude of confidence or insecurity while taking the evaluation may help determine emotional readiness.

DETERMINING READINESS

The fourth grade *Readiness Evaluation* on pages 9–12 helps the teacher to determine if student(s) are ready to begin studying math at the fourth grade level. Complete this evaluation the first or second day of school.

The evaluation should take 45-60 minutes. It would be helpful to evaluate all of the students to determine what each student knows. However, you may want to evaluate only those student(s) who have not had a thorough third grade program. It is especially important to evaluate any student who is using this curriculum for the first time. The student(s) should be able to complete the test on their own with the teacher making sure they understand the directions for each individual activity.

The answer key is on page 8. Count each individual answer as a separate point. The total for the test is 102 points. The student(s) should achieve a score of 72 or more points to be ready to begin fourth grade. Be sure to note the areas of weakness of each student, even those who have scored over 72 points. If the student(s) scored under 72 points, they may need to repeat third grade math or do some refresher work in their areas of weakness. For possible review of the identified areas of weakness, refer to the chart *Appearance of Concepts* on page 22 of the *Horizons Math 3 Teacher's Guide.* It will locate lessons where the concepts were taught.

1.

32	4,267	736
7,861	86	2,815
+ 504	+ 351	+ 49
8,397	4,704	3,600

2. $\frac{3}{3}$ $\frac{4}{5}$ $\frac{6}{6}$ $\frac{3}{4}$ $\frac{5}{5}$ $\frac{5}{8}$ (answers can vary)

3. 3,814 3,734 3,559 3,086 4,503 3,119 1,553

4. < > >
< < >

5. 4,310 0
71,000 5,400
258,000 12,780
36,900 0

6. 2 r 3 7 r 3 8 r 1 3 r 2 5 r 6 3 r 6

7. 4:58 1:13 7:32 11:27 9:46

8. = = ≠ ≠

9. 190 4,240 80 23,500

10. 2,400 500 71,300 484,000

11. 8 : 3
6 : 5
22
5 : 22

12. tens | hundred millions
hundred thousands | hundreds
thousands | ones
millions | ten millions

13. 2 1/4 3 3/4 4 3/5

14. n = 6 n = 14 n = 24 n = 16

15. $\frac{7}{8}$ $\frac{6}{7}$ $\frac{7}{9}$ $\frac{8}{10}$

16. $\frac{4}{8}$ $\frac{2}{5}$ $\frac{5}{9}$ $\frac{1}{7}$ $\frac{3}{10}$ $\frac{1}{6}$ $\frac{3}{12}$ $\frac{5}{11}$

17. 2,286 89 57,363 986,654

18. 2,960 3,367 2,944 1,968 411 1,092

19. $234.00 $13.88

Passing score is 72 out of 102 possible points.

1 Write the problems vertically. Find the sum.

32 + 7,861 + 504 =	4,267 + 86 + 351 =	736 + 2,815 + 49 =

2 Reduce the fractions.

$\frac{12}{15} = \frac{12 \div \square}{15 \div \square} = \frac{\square}{\square}$ | $\frac{18}{24} = \frac{18 \div \square}{24 \div \square} = \frac{\square}{\square}$ | $\frac{25}{40} = \frac{25 \div \square}{40 \div \square} = \frac{\square}{\square}$

3 Find the difference and check.

5,970	8,075	8,900	9,007	6,080	6,900	4,006
- 2,156	- 4,341	- 5,341	- 5,921	- 1,577	- 3,781	- 2,453

4 Write < or >.

378,614 ____ 378,914	940,156 ____ 940,153	537,298 ____ 537,289
259,076 ____ 295,076	861,439 ____ 864,139	713,928 ____ 613,928

5 Find the product.

431 x 10 = ________	4,006 x 0 = ________
71 x 1,000 = ________	54 x 100 = ________
258 x 1,000 = ________	1,278 x 10 = ________
369 x 100 = ________	300,010 x 0 = ________

(6) Find the quotient.

$4\overline{)11}$ $5\overline{)38}$ $3\overline{)25}$ $7\overline{)23}$ $8\overline{)46}$ $9\overline{)33}$

(7) Write the correct time.

__________ __________ __________ __________ __________

(8) Write = or ≠.

$\frac{4}{6}$ ☐ $\frac{10}{15}$ $\frac{2}{10}$ ☐ $\frac{5}{25}$ $\frac{3}{4}$ ☐ $\frac{9}{16}$ $\frac{10}{16}$ ☐ $\frac{5}{7}$

(9) Round the numbers to the nearest 10.

(10) Round the numbers to the nearest 100.

2,386

(11) Joseph had 8 guppies, 3 red swordtails, 5 black mollies, and 6 goldfish in his fish tank.

What is the ratio of guppies to swordtails? ________

What is the ratio of goldfish to black mollies? ________

How many fish were in the tank? ________

What is the ratio of black mollies to all the fish? ________

(12) **Write the place value of the 8 in each number.**

351,643,587	________________	843,721,546	________________
529,823,146	________________	936,295,810	________________
415,498,712	________________	275,467,058	________________
168,152,364	________________	486,251,739	________________

(13) **Write the mixed number illustrated.**

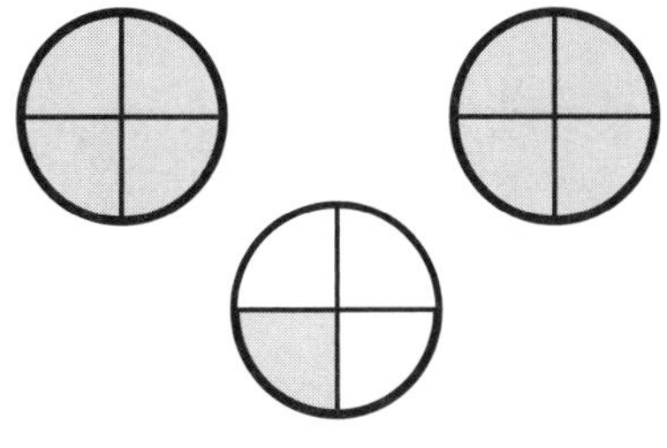

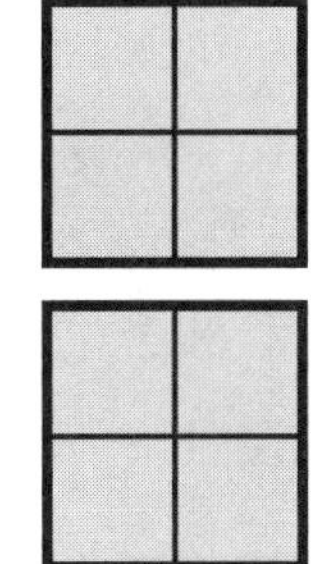

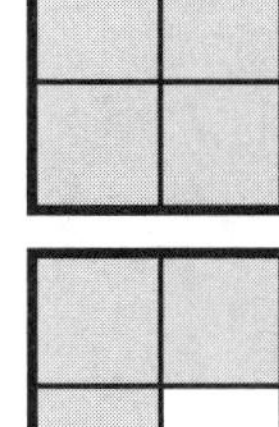

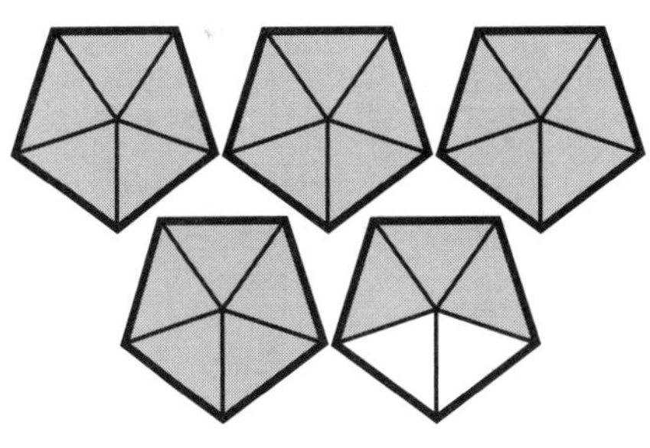

________ ________ ________

(14) **Solve the equations.**

$n + 4 = 10$	$n + 10 = 24$	$n - 8 = 16$	$n - 4 = 12$

(15) **Find the sum.**

$\frac{3}{8} + \frac{4}{8} =$	$\frac{2}{7} + \frac{4}{7} =$	$\frac{5}{9} + \frac{2}{9} =$	$\frac{7}{10} + \frac{1}{10} =$

(16) **Find the difference.**

$\frac{7}{8} - \frac{3}{8}$	$\frac{4}{5} - \frac{2}{5}$	$\frac{6}{9} - \frac{1}{9}$	$\frac{5}{7} - \frac{4}{7}$	$\frac{8}{10} - \frac{5}{10}$	$\frac{3}{6} - \frac{2}{6}$	$\frac{9}{12} - \frac{6}{12}$	$\frac{7}{11} - \frac{2}{11}$

(17) **Subtract 100 from each number.**

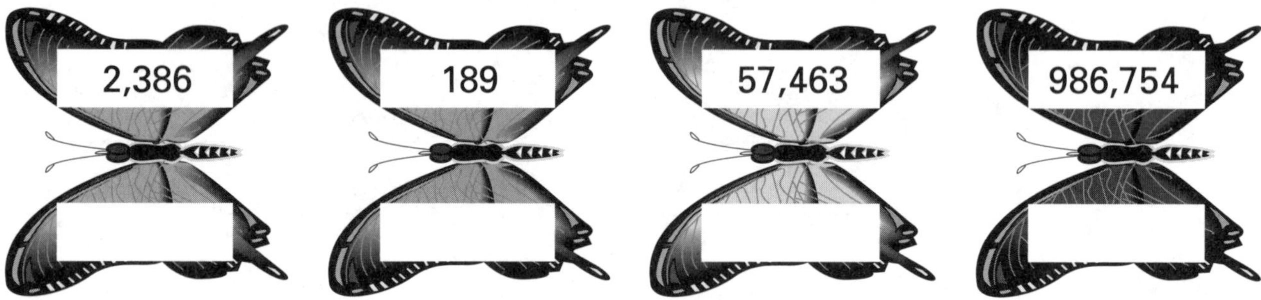

(18) **Find the product.**

592 x 5	481 x 7	736 x 4	246 x 8	137 x 3	182 x 6

(19) Karen spent 3 nights at the Sunset Hotel in Chicago.
She paid $78.00 a night.
How much did it cost her to stay at the hotel?

Frank saw a bicycle for $79.86. Two weeks later it was on sale for $65.98. How much would he save if he bought it while it was on sale?

Preparing a Lesson

GENERAL INFORMATION

There is some room on the teacher lessons for you to write your own notes. The more you personalize your teacher's guide in this way, the more useful it will be to you.

You will notice that there are 160 student lessons in the curriculum. This allows for the inevitable interruptions to the school year like holidays, test days, inclement weather days, and those unexpected interruptions. It also allows the teacher the opportunity to spend more time teaching any concept that the student(s) may have difficulty with. Or, you might wish to spend a day doing some of the fun activities mentioned in the Teaching Tips. If you find that the student(s) need extra drill, use the worksheets as extra lessons. There are no new concepts introduced after lesson 149. The last eleven lessons reinforce by application the concepts presented throughout the year.

STUDENT'S LESSONS

ORGANIZATION

The lessons are designed to be completed in forty-five to sixty minutes a day. If extra manipulatives or worksheets are utilized, you will need to allow more time for teaching. Each lesson consists of a major concept and practice of previously taught concepts. If the student(s) find the presence of four or five different activities in one lesson a little overwhelming at the beginning, start guiding the student(s) through each activity. By the end of two weeks, they should be able to work more independently as they adjust to the format. Mastery of a new concept is not necessary the first time it is presented. Complete understanding of a new concept will come as the concept is approached from different views using different methods at different intervals. Directions to the student(s) are given and examples or explanations are presented.

Tests

Starting with Lesson 10, tests are included in every tenth lesson. They should require approximately forty minutes to administer. If your daily schedule time is a major factor, the student lesson may be completed the following day. This will require efficient scheduling of the lessons throughout the year to complete the program by the end of the school year. The 16 tests, 4 quarter tests, 1 final exam, and 160 lessons each administered or taught on separate days would bring the scheduled curriculum days to a total of 181.

Do not make the test a special lesson. Allow the student(s) to perceive the test as a regular lesson with no undue pressure. The purpose of testing is not just to measure student progress, although that is an important consideration. A test is also an important teaching tool. It should be returned to the student and any missed items discussed so that it is a true learning experience. For this reason, it is important to grade and return the tests as soon as possible while the material is fresh in the student's mind.

The test structure is such that the student(s) will have had sufficient practice with a concept to have learned it before being tested. Therefore, no concept is tested until the initial presentation has been completed. For example, Test 2 in Lesson 20 covers concepts completed in Lessons 6–15. Lessons 16–19 may include the introduction of some new material which will not be covered in Test 2. Test 8 in Lesson 80 will cover Lessons 66–75. The new material from Lessons 76–79 will not be covered in Test 8.

TEACHER'S LESSONS
ORGANIZATION

Each lesson is organized into the following sections: **Concepts**; **Objectives**; **Teaching Tips**; **Materials, Supplies**, and **Equipment; Activities**; and a maxim or proverb. Each of the sections have a distinct symbol to help you locate them on the page of the teacher's lesson. To be a master teacher you will need to prepare each lesson well in advance.

Concepts

Concepts are listed at the beginning of each lesson. New concepts are listed first followed by concepts that are practiced from previous lessons. Fourth grade math has seventeen major concepts. These are developed in a progression that is designed to give the student(s) a solid foundation in the basic math skills while providing enough variety to hold the student's interest.

Objectives

The Objectives list criteria for the student's performance. They state what the student should be able to do at the completion of the lesson. You will find objectives helpful in determining the student's progress, the need for remedial work, and readiness for more advanced information. Objectives are stated in terms of measurable student performance. The teacher then has a fixed level of performance to be attained before the student(s) are ready to progress to the next level.

Teaching Tips

Each tip is related to one of the Activities in the lesson. Some Teaching Tips require the teacher to make a manipulative needed to complete the activity. Teaching Tips are activities that the teacher can do to enhance the teaching process. You will find them useful for helping the student who needs additional practice to master the concepts or for the student who needs to be challenged by extra work.

Materials, Supplies, and Equipment

Materials, Supplies, and Equipment lists the things you'll need to find before you teach each lesson. Sometimes you will also find instructions on how to make your own materials, supplies, and equipment. This section also lists the worksheets. There is approximately one worksheet for every two lessons. If worksheets are suggested in a particular lesson you will find them listed. Each worksheet has a worksheet number. The chart on pages 20-21 gives the number of the lesson with which it is associated. The **Teacher's Guide** identifies where these resource worksheets are essential to the lessons. The worksheets will be handy for many purposes. You might use them for extra work for student(s) who demonstrate extra aptitude or ability or as remedial work for the student(s) who demonstrate a lack of aptitude or ability. You may also make your own worksheets and note where you would use them in the materials section on the teacher's lesson. Some of the worksheets become manipulative aids for specific concepts.

Activities

The teacher's greatest concentration should be on the **Activities** section. Here the teacher will find directions for teaching each lesson. All activities are designed to be teacher directed both in the student lesson and in the teacher's guide. You will need to use your own judgement concerning how much time is necessary to carry out the activities. Each activity is important to the over all scope of the lesson and must be completed. Do not omit any portion of the activities, particularly the multiplication and division drill with flashcards, unless the student(s) have thoroughly mastered the concept being presented. Please do not put off looking at the activities in the lesson until you are actually teaching. Taking time to preview what you will be teaching is essential. Choose the manipulatives that fit your program best.

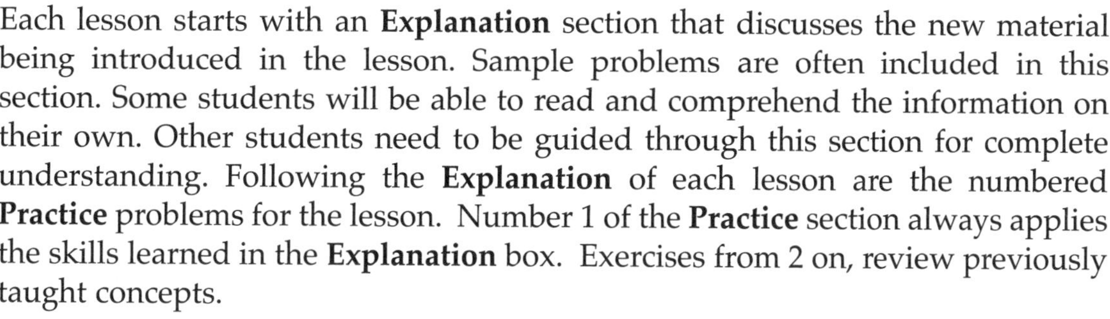

Each lesson starts with an **Explanation** section that discusses the new material being introduced in the lesson. Sample problems are often included in this section. Some students will be able to read and comprehend the information on their own. Other students need to be guided through this section for complete understanding. Following the **Explanation** of each lesson are the numbered **Practice** problems for the lesson. Number 1 of the **Practice** section always applies the skills learned in the **Explanation** box. Exercises from 2 on, review previously taught concepts.

Maxims

You will find a short maxim or proverb at the bottom of each lesson. These maxims provide a collection of various wise and pithy sayings that deal with character. They are intended for the teacher to share and discuss with the student(s). Ask the student(s) to suggest ways that they could apply the maxim to their day-to-day activities of life. Have them think of a time when their friends may have put the maxim into practice. Tell them to watch for opportunities to practice the maxim in the next week and report the incident to you. You may use or not use them as you wish.

ANSWER KEYS

The answer keys section of the **Teacher's Guide** provides answers to the student lessons. It is suggested that you give the student(s) a grade for tests only. Daily work is to be a learning experience for the student, so do not put unnecessary pressure on them. You should correct every paper, but you should not grade every paper. This means that each lesson should be marked for correct and incorrect answers, but it is not necessary to record a letter or percentage grade on every lesson. The lessons should then be returned to the student(s) so that they have the opportunity to learn from their mistakes.

WORKSHEETS

The next section contains the worksheets. They are reproducible and may be copied freely. You will find a complete listing of worksheets and where they are used on pages 20 and 21. Separate packets of all the necessary worksheets for an individual student are also available. Answer keys to the worksheets are provided in the same manner as for the student lessons.

UNIT TESTS

Quarter, Semester and Final Exam tests are provided to evaluate overall student progress. They can be administered after Lesson 40, Lesson 80, Lesson 120, and Lesson 160. Answer keys are provided for these tests.

Horizons Fourth Grade Mathematics SCOPE & SEQUENCE

1. NUMBER THEORY

word numbers through hundred billion
expanded form through hundred billion
even and odd
Roman numerals
divisibility
prime and composite
prime factorization

2. PLACE VALUE

ones, tens, hundreds
thousands, ten thousands, hundred thousands
millions, ten millions, hundred millions
billions, ten billions, hundred billions

3. NUMBER ORDER

ordinal numbers through 100
rounding to the nearest 10
rounding to the nearest 100
rounding to the nearest 1,000
greater than and less than
equal and not equal

4. ADDITION

addition properties
addition terms
basic facts
addition with two-, three-, four-, five-, and six-digit numbers with carrying
equations
add 10, 100, 1000
horizontal to vertical
column addition
missing addends
estimating
adding money

5. SUBTRACTION

subtraction properties
subtraction terms
basic facts
subtraction with two-, three-, four-, five-, and six-digit numbers with borrowing
equations
subtract 10, 100, 1000
horizontal to vertical
estimating
subtracting money

6. MULTIPLICATION

multiplication terms
basic facts
multiplication properties
triple digit times single digit without carrying
triple digit times single digit with carrying
multiplying by 10's, 100's, and 1000's
two digit times a two-digit number with carrying
three digit times a two digit with carrying
money by two-digit number
missing factors
estimating products

7. DIVISION

division terms
basic facts
division properties
one-digit divisor, one-digit quotient without remainders
one-digit divisor, one-digit quotient with remainders
one-digit divisor, two-digit quotient
dividing money
zeros in the quotient
two-digit divisor that are multiples of ten
two-digit divisors with one-digit quotients
two-digit divisor when the guess is incorrect
two-digit divisor, two-digit quotient
estimating quotients
averaging

8. TIME

terms
review telling time
A.M., P.M.
determine century
time equivalents
elapsed time
calendar
time zones

9. MONEY

money will be covered under addition, subtraction, multiplication, & division
counting change

10. GEOMETRY

shapes and solids
symmetry
congruent figures
similar figures
line, line segment, ray, endpoint
parallel, intersecting, perpendicular
angles - rays, vertex, acute, obtuse, right
circles - diameter, radius

11. PERIMETER, AREA, AND VOLUME

perimeter
area
volume

12. FRACTIONS

terms
fractional part of a whole
word fractions
part of a set
compare and order fractions with common denominators
equivalent fractions
reducing fractions
add fractions with common denominators
subtract fractions with common denominators
mixed numbers
improper fractions
add and subtract mixed numbers without regrouping
comparing fractions with unlike denominators
adding unlike fractions
subtracting unlike fractions

13. DECIMALS

fractions to decimals
word numbers to hundredths
compare decimals
order decimals
add decimals (horizontal and vertical)
subtract decimals
estimate decimals
estimate decimals with money

14. RATIO

definition
write simple ratios
multiply to find equal ratios
divide to find equal ratios

15. MEASUREMENT

standard and metric linear equivalent
standard and metric liquid equivalent
standard and metric weight equivalent
temperature reading and understanding
fahrenheit and celsius
millimeter, centimeter, decimeter, meter
decameter, hectometer, kilometer

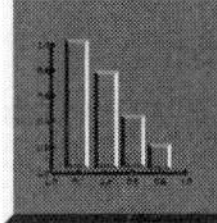

16. GRAPHS

bar
line
pictographs
circle
coordinate graphs
comparing graphs

17. EQUATIONS

addition
subtraction
multiplication
division

Worksheet Duplication Masters

Where To Use

Mathematics Worksheets

In this handbook you will find eighty worksheets to be used as ***Duplication Masters.***

This chart shows where worksheets may be used for *Horizons Math 4*.
You will need to **duplicate** any worksheet that you plan to use more than once.

No.	Concept	Lessons Where Worksheets Are Used
1	Basic addition facts	1
2	Basic subtraction facts	4
3	Even and odd numbers	8
4	Standard liquid equivalents	11
5	Place value through the hundred billions place	12
6	Roman numerals	14
7	Standard, written and expanded forms of numbers	16
8	Rounding to the 10s place	18
9	Rounding to ten, hundred, thousand	20
10	Two-digit addition	21
11	Three-digit addition	22
12	Column addition	23
13	Four-digit addition	25
14	Addition equations	26
15	Two-digit subtraction	30
16	Three-digit subtraction	31
17	Subtraction over zeros	32
18	Rounding to nearest 10, 100, 1000	33
19	Subtraction with larger numbers	34
20	Subtraction equations	35
21	Problem solving using the four step process	39
22	Basic multiplication	40
23	Multiplication table	43
24	Factor tree	44
25	Prime number table	45
26	Basic division	46
27	Three-digit by one-digit multiplication	51
28	Multiplication by multiples of 10, 100, & 1,000	52
29	Multiplication with 3-digit by 2-digit numbers	54
30	Multiplication equations	57
31	Problem solving with data from a chart	58
32	Multiplication test	60
33	Division of 2-digit numbers by a 1-digit number with remainder	61
34	Division of 3-digit numbers by a 1-digit number with remainder	62
35	Dividing numbers	63
36	Division of 4-digit numbers by a 1-digit number with remainder	65
37	Divisibility	66
38	Division equation	68

Where To Use Mathematics Worksheets, continued:

No.	Concept	Lessons Where Worksheets Are Used
39	Basic division facts	70
40	Division of 3-digit numbers by a 2-digit number with remainder	72
41	Making change	73
42	Division of larger numbers	74
43	Division of money	76
44	Problem solving using an organized list	79
45	Using a clock face to tell time	81
46	Time equivalents	84
47	Elapsed time	85
48	Problem solving/placement from given clues	88
49	Problem solving/working backward	89
50	Geometry	90
51	Congruent and similar	93
52	Lines of symmetry	94
53	Space figures	96
54	Perimeter	97
55	Grid paper	98
56	Volume	99
57	Fraction strips	100
58	Naming fractions	101
59	Fraction of a set	102
60	Equivalent fractions	103
61	Greatest common factor	104
62	Lowest terms	105
63	Comparing fractions	106
64	Mixed numbers & improper fractions	107 & 108
65	Addition of fractions with like denominators	110
66	Subtraction of fraction with like denominators	111
67	Addition of fractions with unlike denominators	113
68	Subtraction of fraction with unlike denominators	114
69	Addition of mixed fractions	116
70	Subtraction of mixed fractions	117
71	Decimal place value	121
72	Comparing decimals	122
73	Addition/subtraction of decimals	126
74	Time zones	125
75	Estimating money	128
76	Standard measurement length	131
77	Standard measurement weight	132
78	Metric measurement	136 & 137
79	Converting metric measurements	138
80	Graphing	140–144

Appearance of Concepts

Lesson 1
addition terms
value of money
write the largest number
find fractional parts
three-digit addition
three-digit subtraction
ordinal numbers

Lesson 2
addition properties
addition terms
rounding 10
write smallest number
addition puzzles
missing addends
applying addition properties
comparing whole numbers

Lesson 3
applying addition properties
problem solving and addition
round to 10
value of money
fractional parts
word problems

Lesson 4
subtraction terms
basic subtraction facts
addition terms
subtraction and addition terms
match fractions (naming)
value of money
equivalent fractions
three-digit addition

Lesson 5
subtraction properties
addition puzzle
problem solving with subtraction
terms
shapes
three-digit addition

Lesson 6
applying subtraction properties
subtraction terms
subtraction properties
basic addition facts
column addition
find products
telling time

Lesson 7
fact families
division
three-digit subtraction
value of money
product tables
shapes
rounding to 100

Lesson 8
even and odd
add and subtract
value of money
fact families
product flowers
word problems

Lesson 9
problem solving (4 step plan)
even and odd
add and subtract
basic subtraction facts
solve equations
product crossword
telling time

Lesson 10
0-100,000
ordinal numbers
even and odd
two-digit addition and subtract
simple division
shapes
equivalent fractions

Lesson 11
0-100,000,000
ordinal numbers
even and odd numbers
division
standard liquid equivalents
compare fractions

Lesson 12
0-100,000,000,000
ordinal numbers
division flowers
standard linear equivalents
mixed fractions
product table

Lesson 13
expanded form
addition properties
division crossword
add fractions
product tables
value of money

Lesson 14
Roman numerals
expanded form
subtracting fractions
word problems
write checks
ordination
product table

Lesson 15
compare and order
expanded form
Roman numerals
division riddle
equivalent fractions

Appearance of Concepts

Lesson 16
compare and order
expanded form
subtraction facts
missing addends
add and subtract fractions

Lesson 17
compare and order
shapes
expanded form
basic addition facts
compare fractions
multiplication facts
word problems

Lesson 18
rounding to 10
compare and order
basic add/subtraction facts
telling time
missing addends

Lesson 19
understand the question
read a table
column addition
smallest number
place value

Lesson 20
rounding 10, 100, 1000
p. solv. understand question
place value >, <, =
mult facts
add fractions
value of money

Lesson 21
two-digit addition
round to 10
round to 100
round to 1,000
place value
even and odd
basic facts

Lesson 22
addition with three digits
addition with two digits
standard form
even and odd
rounding to 1,000
word problems

Lesson 23
column addition
addition with three digits
word problems
addition with two digits
rounding to 1,000
standard form
expanded form

Lesson 24
estimating sums
addition with 2 and 3 digits
column addition
standard form
add fractions
missing numbers

Lesson 25
adding greater numbers
round to ten and estimate sums
rounding numbers
column addition
compare and order
Roman numerals

Lesson 26
equations
round to 100
round to 10
column addition
logical reasoning
adding greater numbers

Lesson 27
add money
write checks
adding money
add greater numbers
rounding 100
add 100

Lesson 28
estimate money
equations
horizontal/vertical addition
add greater numbers
rounding 100
write checks
add 1,000

Lesson 29
problem solving What operation?
adding money
equations
horizontal/vertical add of $
rounding 1000
missing addends

Lesson 30
subtract with two digits
estimate money
place value
rounding 100
problem solving
equations

Appearance of Concepts

Lesson 31
subtract with 3 digits
subtract with 2 digits
add money
even and odd
place value
rounding 1,000

Lesson 32
subtract across zeros
subtract with 2 and 3 digits
estimate money
expanded form
problem solving

Lesson 33
estimate differences
subtract across zero
subtract with 2 and 3 digits
standard form
expanded form
rounding 1,000

Lesson 34
subtract greater numbers
estimate differences
subtract across zeros
compare and order
estimate sums
money

Lesson 35
subtraction equations
subtract greater numbers
subtract across zeros
compare and order
estimate sums
addition puzzles
shapes

Lesson 36
subtract money
subtract equations
add and subtract
subtract greater numbers
subtract 10
estimate and subtract

Lesson 37
estimate money
subtract money
subtract equations
add and subtract
addition equations
add 100
subtract greater numbers

Lesson 38
counting change
subtract money
subtract equations
subtract greater numbers
three step equations
subtract 1,000

Lesson 39
problem solving
counting change
estimate money
subtract money
subtraction equations
place value

Lesson 40
multiplication terms
counting change
estimate money
even and odd
standard form
expanded form
subtract with 5 digits

Lesson 41
multiplication properties
multiplications terms
counting change
estimate money
place value
even and odd
subtract with 5 digits

Lesson 42
applying multiplication properties
multiplication
subtraction with 5 digits
mystery numbers
standard form
problem solving

Lesson 43
fact table
factors
mystery numbers
multiplication terms
multiplication properties
even and odd

Lesson 44
factor trees
prime and composite
basic multiplication facts
standard form
addition with 2 digits
problem solving

Lesson 45
prime numbers
prime factors
basic mult. facts
compare and order
addition with 2 digits
mystery numbers

Appearance of Concepts

Lesson 46
division terms
prime and composite
factors
basic multiplication facts
addition with 3 digits
place value
compare and order

Lesson 47
division properties
division facts
missing factor
prime and composite
column addition
addition of equations
subtract across zeros

Lesson 48
applying basic division facts
division terms
missing factor
addition equations
definitions
problem solving

Lesson 49
problem solving
basic division facts
subtract with 2 digits
subtraction equations
counting change
place value

Lesson 50
multiplication
division
even and odd
place value
round 10
subtract with 3 digits
division terms

Lesson 51
multiplication with carrying
multiplication
basic division
even and odd
problem solving
place value
round 10
subtract across zeros

Lesson 52
multiply 10, 100, 1,000
multiplication with carrying
subtraction
ordination
expanded form
round 100

Lesson 53
multiplication by 2 digits
multiplication 10, 100, 1,000
multiplication
standard form
expanded form
round 100

Lesson 54
multiplication by 2 digits
multiplication
multiplication 10, 100, 1,000
estimate and multiply
compare and order
mult. properties

Lesson 55
multiplication
multiplication by 2 digits
multiply and check
compare and order
round 1,000
multiplication terms

Lesson 56
estimating products
multiplication 10, 100, 1,000
multiplication with carrying
addition equations
multiplication missing numbers
definitions

Lesson 57
multiplication of equations
estimating products
multiplication by multiples of 10
addition equations
definitions
multiplication missing numbers

Lesson 58
problem solving- money
multiplication of equations
estimating products
subtract with 2 digits
division terms

Lesson 59
problem solving (guess & check)
subtraction of equations
missing numbers
Roman numerals
shapes

Lesson 60
division
subtract across zeros
multiplication of equations
estimating products
even and odd

Appearance of Concepts

Lesson 61
division with remainders
division
estimating products
subtraction
multiplication
prime numbers
mystery numbers

Lesson 62
division
division with remainders
division
problem solving
even and odd
multiplication

Lesson 63
dividing money
division
odd and even
problem solving
multiplication of equations
sequences

Lesson 64
zeros in the quotient
dividing money
division
division with remainders
round 10
sequence

Lesson 65
dividing larger numbers
zeros in the quotient
dividing money
round 10
sequence
shapes

Lesson 66
divisibility 2, 5, 10, 3
dividing larger numbers
zeros in the quotient
dividing money
rounding
addition equations
definitions

Lesson 67
averaging
divisibility 2, 5, 10, 3
dividing larger numbers
word problems
addition equations
rounding 1,000

Lesson 68
division equations
averaging
divisibility 2, 5, 10, 3
dividing money
missing numbers
subtraction equations

Lesson 69
problem solving
division equations
averaging
divisibility 2, 5, 10, 3
column addition
prime and composite

Lesson 70
division
equations - division
averaging
subtraction with 2 digits
multiplication
patterns

Lesson 71
division - 2-digit divisor
division
equations
subtraction with 2 digits
patterns
multiplication

Lesson 72
division and estimation
1-digit quotients
division
subtraction with 3 digits
ordinal numbers
multiplication equations

Lesson 73
changing estimates
division - 2-digit divisor
1-digit quotients
subtract across zeros
counting change
mystery number

Lesson 74
2-digit quotients
changing estimates
division
quotients counting change
word problems

Lesson 75
zeros in quotient
division
changing estimates
1-digit quotients
money
shape recognition

Appearance of Concepts

Lesson 76
dividing money
zeros in quotient
changing estimates
money
story problems

Lesson 77
estimation
dividing money
zeros in quotient
changing estimates
money
time

Lesson 78
problem solving - division
estimation
dividing money
zeros in quotient
place value
subtract equations

Lesson 79
problem solving (organized list)
place value
time
prime and composite
subtract equations
shape recognition

Lesson 80
time definitions
equations
estimation
dividing money
standard form
subtraction and multiplication

Lesson 81
time
equations
standard form
subtraction
multiplication
definitions

Lesson 82
A.M., P.M.
time definitions
compare and order
subtract with 3 digits
multiplication equations
division

Lesson 83
century
A.M., P.M.
compare and order
subtract across zeros
division
averaging

Lesson 84
time equivalents
A.M., P.M.
division - 1-digit divisor
division - 2-digit divisor
magic number

Lesson 85
elapsed time
time equivalents
A.M., P.M.
divisibility 2, 5, 10, 3
division - 2-digit divisor
change

Lesson 86
calendar
elapsed time
time equivalents
century
division - 2-digit divisor
change

Lesson 87
time zones
time equivalents
elapsed time
time equivalents
place value
subtraction equations

Lesson 88
problem solving
time zones
calendar
elapsed time
place value
subtract equations

Lesson 89
problem solving (work backwards)
standard form
expanded form
multiplication
addition of fractions
compare whole numbers

Lesson 90
geometric terms
problem solving
time zones
calendar
standard form

Appearance of Concepts

Lesson 91
rays and angles
geometric terms
problem solving
time zones
multiplication
addition

Lesson 92
polygons
averaging
rays and angles
geometric terms
problem solving
column addition

Lesson 93
congruent and similar
polygons
geometric terms
subtract with 3 digits
division
geometric shapes

Lesson 94
symmetry
polygons
rays and angles
congruent and similar
division
time definitions
quadrilaterals

Lesson 95
circles
symmetry
congruent and similar
geometric terms
polygons
division
time definitions

Lesson 96
space figures
circles
symmetry
congruent and similar
rounding 10
divisibility 2, 5, 10, 3

Lesson 97
perimeter
space figures
circles
symmetry
rounding 100
prime and composite
division equations

Lesson 98
area
perimeter
space figures
circles
rounding 100
addition equations
division

Lesson 99
volume
perimeter and area
space figures
rounding 100
addition equations
averaging
division

Lesson 100
fractions
volume
perimeter and area
place value
rounding 100
multiplication

Lesson 101
word fractions
fractions
volume
place value
rounding 1,000
multiplication

Lesson 102
part of a set
word fractions
fractions
standard form
multiplication equations
expanded form

Lesson 103
equivalent fractions
part of a set
word fractions
fraction terms
standard form
division

Lesson 104
GCF - (Greatest Common Factor)
equivalent fractions
part of a set
word fractions
compare and order
subtract across zeros
division

Lesson 105
reduce fractions
equivalent fractions
fractions on a number line
compare and order
division

Appearance of Concepts

Lesson 106
compare and order fractions
reduce fractions
GCF
equivalent fractions
prime and composite
divisibility 2, 5, 10, 3
subtraction

Lesson 107
mixed numbers
compare and order
reduce fractions
equivalent fractions
addition equations
division equations
shapes and solids

Lesson 108
improper fractions
mixed numbers
compare and order
reduce fractions
rounding 100
addition equations
averaging
shapes and solids

Lesson 109
problem solving - make it simpler
improper fractions
mixed numbers
compare and order
symmetry
division

Lesson 110
adding like fractions
problem solving
improper fractions
mixed numbers
division
symmetry

Lesson 111
subtracting like fractions
adding like fractions
problem solving
improper fractions
addition with 2 digits
multiplication
congruent/similar

Lesson 112
add and subtract like fractions
subtract like fractions
add like fractions
problem solving
multiplication
division
congruent and similar

Lesson 113
addition of unlike fractions
add and subtract like fractions
subtract like fractions
add like fractions
column addition
subtract with 2 digits
division
geometric symbols

Lesson 114
subtract unlike fractions
add unlike fractions
add and subtract like fractions
rounding 10
subtract across zeros
equations
geometric symbols

Lesson 115
word problems
add and subtract unlike fractions
rounding 10
division
prime and composite
geometric terms

Lesson 116
add mixed numbers
word problems
add unlike fractions
add and subtract like fractions
divisibility 2, 5, 10, 3
A.M., P.M.
geometric terms

Lesson 117
subtract mixed numbers
add mixed numbers
word problems
add and subtract unlike fractions
angles
addition equations
multiplication of equations
averaging

Lesson 118
add and subtract mixed numbers
add mixed numbers
subtract mixed numbers
subtraction of equations
counting change
century
angles

Lesson 119
problem solving-logical reasoning
counting change
time equivalents
circles
equivalent fractions
reduce fractions
compare and order fractions

Lesson 120
fractions to decimals
add and subtract mixed numbers
subtract mixed numbers
add mixed numbers
time equivalents
circles
reduce fractions

Appearance of Concepts

Lesson 121
hundredths
reading/writing decimals
add and subtract mixed numbers
subtract with 3 digits
divide
century
perimeter and area

Lesson 122
compare decimals
reading decimals
missing numbers
subtract across zeros
division
century
perimeter and area

Lesson 123
order decimals
compare decimals
reading decimals
place value
round 10
subtract equations
division
volume

Lesson 124
estimate decimals
compare decimals
writing decimals
round 10
subtract equations
division
volume

Lesson 125
add decimals
estimate decimals
order decimals
round 100
averaging
time zones
add and subtract like fractions

Lesson 126
subtract decimals
add decimals
estimate decimals
order decimals
round 100
addition equations
time zones
add and subtract like fractions

Lesson 127
estimate to add/subtract decimals
add and subtract decimals
missing numbers
estimate decimals
round 1,000
addition equations
time definitions
place value

Lesson 128
estimate with money
add and subtract decimals
round 1,000
properties
A.M., P.M.
place value

Lesson 129
problem solving-draw a picture
counting change
A.M., P.M.
geometry definitions
equivalent fractions
reduce fractions
compare and order fractions
add and subtract unlike fractions

Lesson 130
measurement 1/2", 1/4"
estimate with money
subtract decimals
subtract
division
counting change
equivalent fractions

Lesson 131
ft, yd, mile
measurement 1/2", 1/4"
estimate with money
add and subtract decimals
subtract across zeros
division
century
reduce fractions

Lesson 132
oz, lb, ton
ft, yd, mile
inch, half, quarter
estimate with money
subtract equations
division
century
reduce fractions

Lesson 133
cup, pint, qt, gal
oz, lb, ton
ft, yd, mile
inch, half, quarter
subtract equations
division
add and subtract unlike fractions

Lesson 134
temp. Fahrenheit
cup, pint, qt, gal
oz, lb, ton
ft, yd, mile
addition with 2 digits
averaging
add and subtract mixed numbers

Lesson 135
temp. Celsius
temp. Fahrenheit
cup, pint, qt, gal
oz, lb, ton
addition with 3 digits
write decimals

Appearance of Concepts

Lesson 136
cm, mm
temp. Celsius
temp. Fahrenheit
cup, pint, qt, gal
column addition
fractions as decimals
compare decimals

Lesson 137
metric conversion
cm, mm
temp. Celsius, temp. Fahrenheit
addition equations
angles
order fractions

Lesson 138
liter
metric conversion
temp. Celsius
addition equations
geometry definitions
compare and order fractions

Lesson 139
weight
liquid
metric conversion
multiplication
compare decimals
add decimals

Lesson 140
bar graph
weight
liquid
metric conversion
subtract with 3 digits
subtract equations
multiplication

Lesson 141
line graph
bar graph
weight
liquid
subtract across zeros
subtract equations
reduce fractions

Lesson 142
pictographs
line graph
bar graph
weight
prime and composite
multiplication equations
reduce fractions

Lesson 143
circle graphs
pictographs
line graph
bar graph
averaging
division
equations

Lesson 144
coordinate graphs
circle graphs
pictographs
line graph
addition equations
missing numbers

Lesson 145
define ratio
coordinate graphs
circle graphs
pictographs
addition equations
counting change
order fractions

Lesson 146
ratio tables
define ratio
coordinate graphs
circle graphs
division
counting change
compare fractions

Lesson 147
multiply ratios
ratio tables
define ratio
coordinate graphs
division
geometry definitions
compare fractions

Lesson 148
divide ratios
multiply ratios
define ratio
multiplication
geometry definitions
equivalent fractions

Lesson 149
problem solving
equivalent fractions
ratio
subtract equations
multiplication
fractions
divide ratios

Lesson 150
ratios
ratio table
divide ratios
subtract with 3 digits
reduce fractions
add and subtract unlike fractions

Appearance of Concepts

Lesson 151
prime/composite
A.M., P.M.
subtract equations
reduce fractions
ratio tables
crossword
add and subtract fractions

Lesson 152
A.M., P.M.
add and subtract like fractions
averaging
division
add and subtract decimals
temp. Fahrenheit

Lesson 153
fractions to decimals
temp. Celsius
equations
century decimals_
add and subtract like fractions
division
inch, half, quarter

Lesson 154
decimals to fractions
century
ft, yd, mile
division
counting change
equations

Lesson 155
oz, lb, ton
counting change
add and subtract mixed numbers
compare fractions
division
mathematical terms

Lesson 156
compare fractions
weight conversion
cm, mm
cup, pint, qt, gal
add and subtract fractions
add and subtract decimals

Lesson 157
cm, mm
geometric definitions
metric conversions
reduce fractions
addition with 2 digits
multiplication
equivalent fractions
multiply ratios

Lesson 160
decimals as fractions
subtract across zeros
equivalent fractions
multiplication equations
add and subtract unlike fractions
ratios

Lesson 158
ratios
geometric terms
geometry definitions
equivalent fractions
multiplication
even numbers
addition

Lesson 159
column addition
subtract equations
mystery numbers
temperature
century
meters, liters, grams
reduce fractions

Development of Concepts

GENERAL PATTERN:

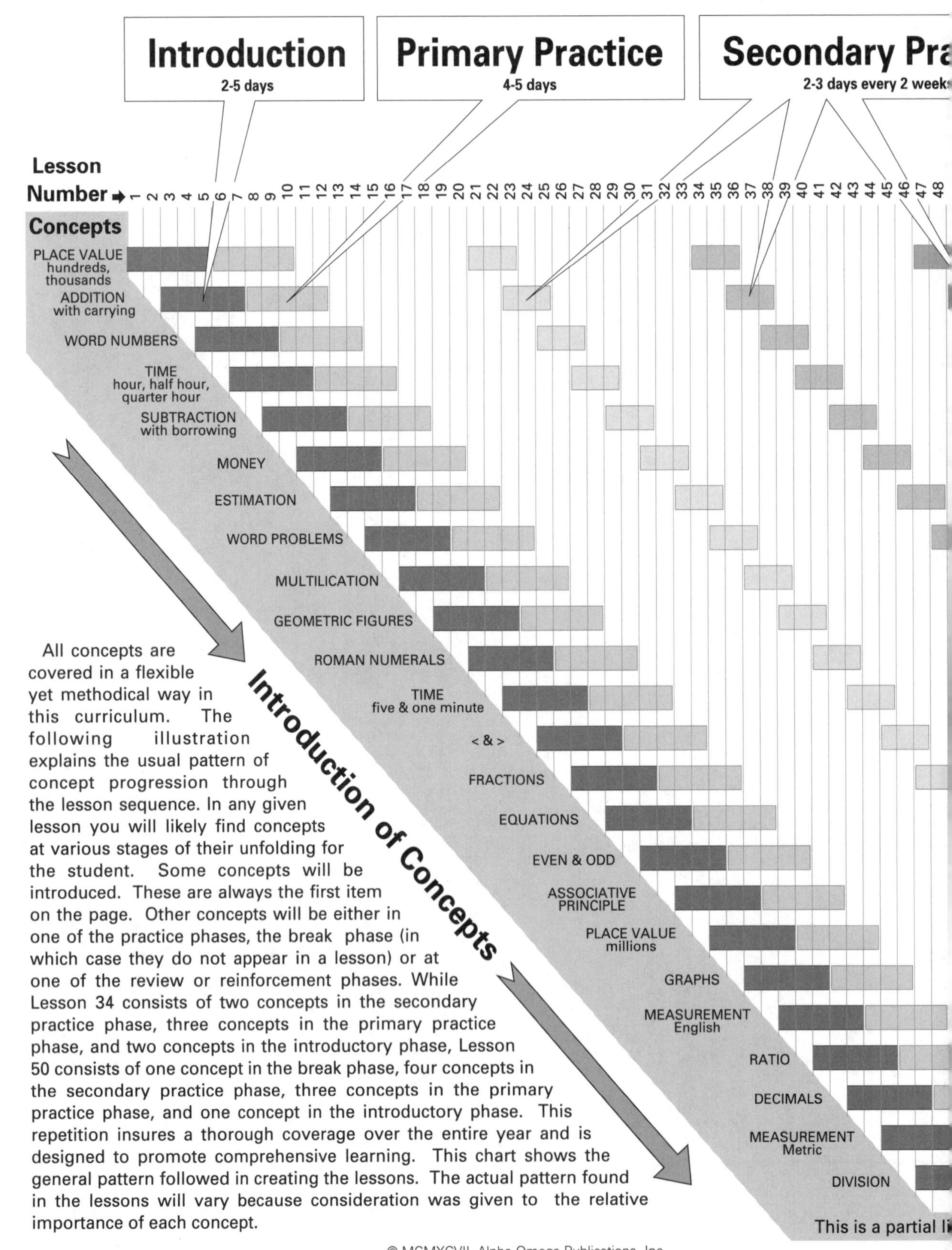

All concepts are covered in a flexible yet methodical way in this curriculum. The following illustration explains the usual pattern of concept progression through the lesson sequence. In any given lesson you will likely find concepts at various stages of their unfolding for the student. Some concepts will be introduced. These are always the first item on the page. Other concepts will be either in one of the practice phases, the break phase (in which case they do not appear in a lesson) or at one of the review or reinforcement phases. While Lesson 34 consists of two concepts in the secondary practice phase, three concepts in the primary practice phase, and two concepts in the introductory phase, Lesson 50 consists of one concept in the break phase, four concepts in the secondary practice phase, three concepts in the primary practice phase, and one concept in the introductory phase. This repetition insures a thorough coverage over the entire year and is designed to promote comprehensive learning. This chart shows the general pattern followed in creating the lessons. The actual pattern found in the lessons will vary because consideration was given to the relative importance of each concept.

Grades 3-6

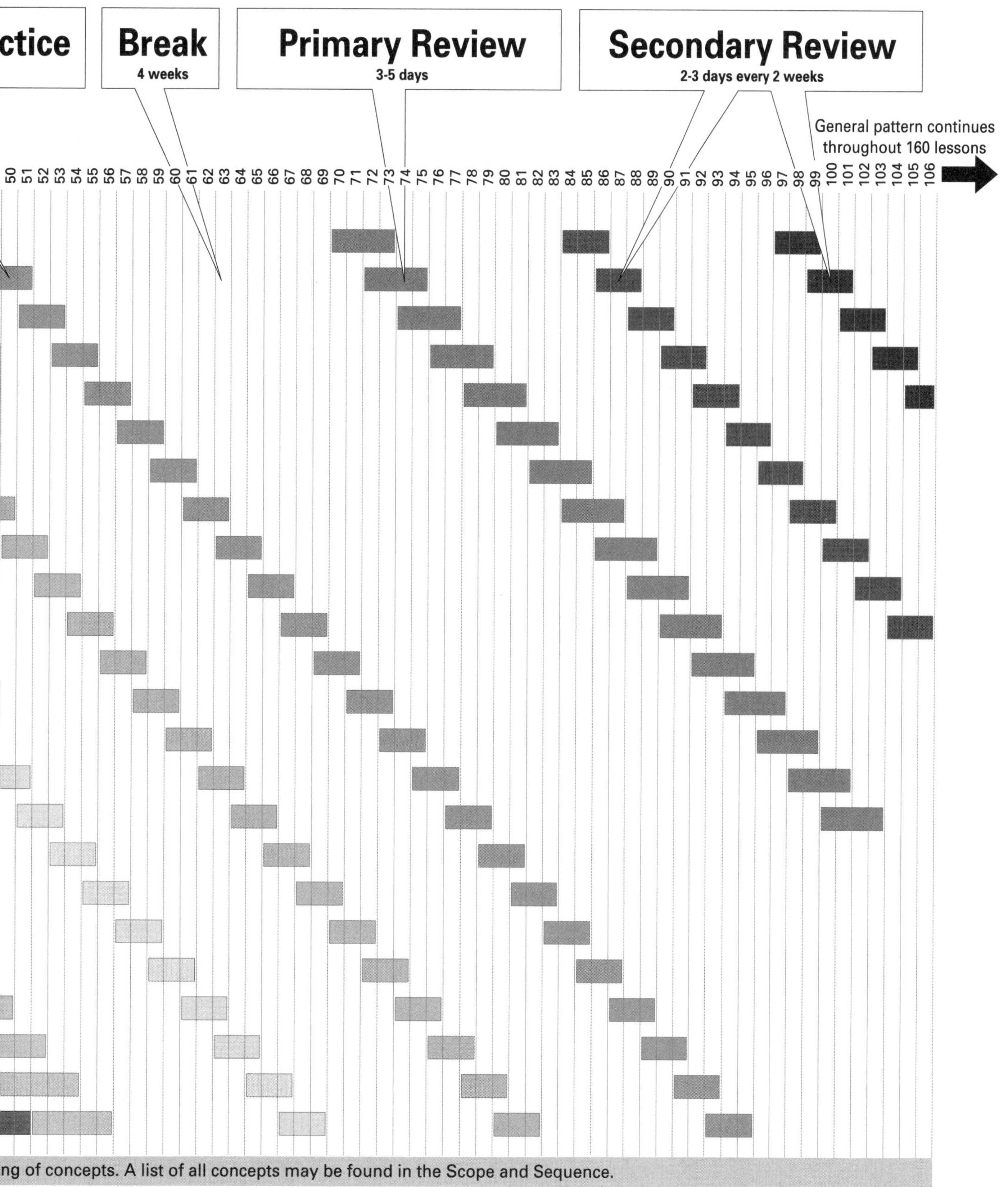

ng of concepts. A list of all concepts may be found in the Scope and Sequence.

Lessons

Lesson 1

Concepts:

Addition terms, money, ordering, fractional parts, addition, subtraction, ordinal numbers

Objectives:

1. The student will be able to write the name of the terms in an addition problem.
2. The student will be able to write the value of a given number of various coins and bills.
3. The student will be able to write the largest possible number when given five digits.
4. The student will be able to shade the fractional part of a circle
5. The student will be able to write the sum of two triple-digit numbers that involve trading in the ones' place. The student will be able to place the corresponding letter in the message box.
6. The student will be able to write the difference of two triple-digit numbers that involve borrowing from the tens' place. The student will be able to place the corresponding letter in the message box.
7. The student will be able to correctly place a set of letters numbered ordinally on blanks corresponding to the appropriate ordinal numbers.

Teaching Tips:

Students should have little difficulty with the concept of addition. They may need repeated drill to memorize the addition terms. Drill basic addition and subtraction skills with flashcards.

Materials, Supplies, and Equipment:

1. Beans, pennies, counters or similar items that can be easily counted and grouped
2. *Worksheet 1*
3. Addition and subtraction flashcards

Activities:

1. Place 4 counters in one group, and 7 counters in another group. Ask the students how many counters are in each group. Write the numbers beside each group.
2. Ask the students how many counters are in both groups combined. Combine the counters into one group and write the number 11 beside the group.
3. Direct the students' attention to **Lesson 1 Explanation**. Define the terms addend and sum. Emphasize vertical and horizontal forms of writing addition.
4. The students should be able to complete **Lesson 1 Practice** independently.
5. **Lessons 1-10** review many of the skills covered in previous *Horizons Math* workbooks. Any students new to the *Horizons Math* program can be helped through these review exercises by discussing the **Explanations** for these problems that appear later in the student book. For example, an explanation for the geometry shapes reviewed in **Lessons 5 & 10** can be found in **Lesson 92 & Lesson 96 Explanations**.

Setting an example is not the main means of influencing another, it is the ONLY means.

Albert Einstein

Lesson 2

Concepts:

Addition properties, addition, rounding, ordering, missing addends, applying properties, comparing numbers

Objectives:

1. The student will be able to match the addition property to the corresponding numerical example.
2. The student will be able to write the names of the terms in an addition problem.
3. The student will be able to round two and three-digit numbers to the nearest 10. The student will be able to match the rounded number to a corresponding letter and place it on a line provided.
4. The student will be able to write the smallest possible number when given five digits.
5. The student will be able to find the missing sums to solve a magic square.
6. The student will be able to identify the missing addend given six addends and the sum.
7. The student will be able to write the correct symbol (< or >) between two triple-digit numbers.

Teaching Tips:

Give the students the opportunity to use the counters and prove to themselves that the properties are true. Drill basic addition and subtraction skills with flashcards.

Materials, Supplies, and Equipment:

1. Beans, pennies, counters or similar items that can be easily counted and grouped
2. Chart paper and markers
3. Addition and subtraction flashcards

Activities:

1. Write each of the addition properties on the board and challenge the students to prove that they are true using counters. Demonstrate the Order Property of Addition.

   4 + 6 = 10   6 + 4 = 10

   oooo oooooo = 10   oooooo oooo = 10

2. The students might prove the Zero Property of Addition as follows:

   8 + 0 = 8

   oooooooo + (no counters) = 8

3. The students might prove the Grouping Property of Addition as follows:

   (5 + 2) + 1 = 8   5 + (2 + 1) = 8

   (ooooo + oo) + o = 8   ooooo + (oo + o) = 8

   7 + 1 = 8   5 + 3 = 8

4. Have the students restate the addition properties in their own words and write them on the chart paper. Keep this for future use.
5. The students should be able to complete **Lesson 2 Practice** independently.

Short arm needs man to reach to Heaven, so ready is Heaven to stoop to him.
Francis Thompson

Lesson 3

Concepts:

Applying addition properties, addition, rounding, money, fractions, word problems

Objectives:

1. The student will be able to add two and three, one-digit numbers and obtain the sum.
2. The student will be able to add two, two-digit numbers and obtain the sum.
3. The student will be able to round two-, three-, and four-digit numbers to the nearest 10.
4. The student will be able to determine the combination of bills and coins needed to find a given sum of money.
5. The student will be able to divide a circle into 3, 4, 6, and 8 equal parts. The student will be able to shade the fraction of the circle given.
6. The student will be able to solve a story problem involving the addition of 2 and 4 addends.

Teaching Tips:

Students will have little difficulty reviewing the properties of addition. Drill basic addition and subtraction skills with flashcards.

Materials, Supplies, and Equipment:

1. Chart completed in Lesson 2 with addition properties
2. Counters
3. Addition and subtraction flashcards

Activities:

1. Review the Addition Properties written on the chart paper from Lesson 2.
2. Ask the students to demonstrate each property using counters.
3. The students should be able to complete **Lesson 3 Practice** independently.
4. **Lessons 1-10** review many of the skills covered in previous *Horizons Math* workbooks. Any students new to the *Horizons Math* program can be helped through these review exercises by discussing the **Explanations** for these problems that appear later in the student book. For example, an explanation for the geometry shapes reviewed in **Lessons 5 & 10** can be found in **Lesson 92 & Lesson 96 Explanations**.

If you have knowledge, let others light their candle at it.
Margaret Fuller

Lesson 4

Concepts:

Subtraction properties, subtraction, addition and subtraction terms, fractions, money, equivalent fractions, addition

Objectives:

1. The student will be able to write the names of the terms in a subtraction problem and find the difference.
2. The student will be able to identify the missing numbers to complete the magic square.
3. The student will be able to identify the names of terms in both addition and subtraction problems.
4. The student will be able to draw a line between the fractional part given and its written name.
5. The student will be able to determine the smallest number of coins and largest number of coins (excluding pennies) to make the dollar amount given.
6. The student will be able to identify the fractional part of a circle that is highlighted.
7. The student will be able to find the sum of two, three-digit numbers that involves carrying in the ones' place. The student will be able to place the corresponding letter on the line of numbers to solve a riddle.

Teaching Tips:

Students will have little difficulty reviewing subtraction. They may need repeated drill to memorize subtraction terms. Drill basic addition and subtraction skills with flashcards.

Materials, Supplies, and Equipment:

1. Counters
2. *Worksheet 2*
3. Addition and subtraction flashcards

Activities:

1. Place 8 counters in one group. Take 2 counters away. Ask the students how many counters are left. **(6)**
2. Direct the students' attention to **Lesson 4 Explanation**. Define the terms minuend, subtrahend and difference. Emphasize vertical and horizontal forms of writing subtraction.
3. The students should be able to complete **Lesson 4 Practice** independently.

Kind words can be short and easy to speak, but their echoes are truly endless.
Mother Teresa

Lesson 5

Concepts:

Subtraction properties, addition, subtraction, geometric shapes, rounding

Objectives:

1. The student will be able to identify the sum and difference of the numbers given.
2. The student will be able to identify the missing numbers to complete the magic square.
3. Given the difference, the student will be able to identify the correct minuend and subtrahend from a selection of five numbers.
4. The student will be able to identify the following shapes: triangle, circle, cylinder, square, diamond, sphere, cube, hexagon, oval, rectangular pyramid, pentagon, and cone.
5. The student will be able to find the sum given two, three-digit addends.

Teaching Tips:

Give the students the opportunity to use the counters and prove to themselves that the properties are true. Drill basic addition and subtraction skills with flashcards.

Materials, Supplies, and Equipment:

1. Counters
2. Chart paper and markers
3. Addition and subtraction flashcards

Activities:

1. Write each of the subtraction properties on the board and challenge the students to prove that they are true using counters. Demonstrate the Zero Property of Subtraction.

   8 – 0 = 8

   oooooooo – (take away none) = 8
2. The students might demonstrate the opposites property as follows:

   7 + 2 = 9, so 9 – 2 = 7

   ooooooo + oo = 9, ooooooooo – oo = 7
3. Challenge the students to determine why the Order Property of Addition does not apply to subtraction.

   The students might demonstrate as follows:

   5 – 2 = 3 2 – 5 ≠ 3

   ooooo – oo = 3 oo – ooooo ≠ 3
4. Have the students restate the subtraction properties in their own words and write them on the chart paper. Keep this for future use.
5. The students should be able to complete **Lesson 5 Practice** independently.
6. **Lessons 1-10** review many of the skills covered in previous *Horizons Math* workbooks. Any students new to the *Horizons Math* program can be helped through these review exercises by discussing the **Explanations** for these problems that appear later in the student book. For example, an explanation for the geometry shapes reviewed in **Lessons 5 & 10** can be found in **Lesson 92 & Lesson 96 Explanations**.

One person can make a difference and every person should try.
John F. Kennedy

Lesson 6

Concepts:

Applying subtraction properties, mystery numbers, subtraction, column addition, multiplication, telling time

Objectives:

1. The student will be able to identify the sum and difference of the numbers given. The student will be able to apply the Opposites Property and check each problem.
2. The student will be able to write a number sentence and identify missing numbers when given numbers and number terms.
3. The student will be able to find the sum and difference, given two, one-digit numbers. The student will be able to place the corresponding letter on the number answer line to solve a riddle.
4. The student will be able to identify the sum, given a list of four single-digit addends.
5. The student will be able to complete a product table.
6. The student will be able to identify the time, to the minute, on ten clocks.

Teaching Tips:

Students will have little difficulty reviewing the properties of subtraction. Drill basic addition and subtraction skills with flashcards.

Materials, Supplies, and Equipment:

1. Chart completed in Lesson 5 with subtraction properties
2. Counters
3. Addition and subtraction flashcards

Activities:

1. Review the Subtraction Properties written on the chart paper from Lesson 5.
2. Ask the students to demonstrate each property using counters.
3. The students should be able to complete **Lesson 6 Practice** independently.

I can do everything through him who gives me strength.
Philippians 4:13

Lesson 7

Concepts:

Fact families, missing numbers, division, subtraction, change, multiplication, geometric shapes

Objectives:

1. The student will be able to identify the sum, difference, and missing numbers given fact families.
2. The student will be able to divide a one or two-digit dividend by a one-digit divisor.
3. The student will be able to find the difference given two, three-digit numbers that require borrowing from the tens' place.
4. The student will be able to determine the value of a set of coins.
5. The student will be able to complete a product table.
6. The student will be able to identify the following figures: parallelogram, trapezoid, rhombus, rectangular prism.
7. The student will be able to determine if a given number will round to 100. The student will shade the numbers that round to 100 and solve for a message.

Teaching Tips:

Students will have little difficulty understanding fact families. Drill basic addition, subtraction, multiplication, and division skills with flashcards.

Materials, Supplies, and Equipment:

1. Addition and subtraction flashcards

Activities:

1. Direct students to **Lesson 7 Explanation**. Review each of the four facts.
2. Ask: **If we know that 8 + 7 = 15, what other facts do we know? (7 + 8 = 15, 15 – 7 = 8, and 15 – 8 = 7)**
3. Ask: **If we know that 8 + 2 = 10, what other facts do we know? (2 + 8 = 10, 10 – 8 = 2, and 10 – 2 = 8)**
4. The students should be able to complete **Lesson 7 Practice** independently.
5. **Lessons 1-10** review many of the skills covered in previous *Horizons Math* workbooks. Any students new to the *Horizons Math* program can be helped through these review exercises by discussing the **Explanations** for these problems that appear later in the student book. For example, an explanation for the geometry shapes reviewed in **Lessons 5 & 10** can be found in **Lesson 92 & Lesson 96 Explanations**.

My God is my rock.
2 Samuel 22:3

Lesson 8

Concepts:

Even and odd numbers, addition and subtraction, money, fact families, multiplication, word problems

Objectives:

1. The student will be able to identify an even and an odd number given any number.
2. Given an addition or subtraction problem, the student will be able to **find** the sum or difference and determine if it is odd or even. The student will shade the problems with even answers and find their way through a maze.
3. The student will be able to determine the quantity of bills and coins necessary to make a dollar amount given.
4. The student will be able to find each missing numbers in the fact families.
5. The student will be able to **find** the product given who single-digit numbers.
6. The student will be able to solve a story problem given two addends. The student will be able to determine if the sum is odd or even. The student will be able to determine if those numbers can be paired evenly.

Teaching Tips:

Students will have little difficulty understanding even and odd numbers. Drill basic addition, subtraction, multiplication, and division skills with flashcards.

Materials, Supplies, and Equipment:

1. *Worksheet 3*
2. Addition, subtraction, multiplication and division flashcards

Activities:

1. Direct students to **Lesson 8 Explanation.**
2. Students should be able to complete **Lesson 8 Practice** independently.

The greatest mistake a man can make is to be afraid to make one.
Elbert Hubbard

Lesson 9

Concepts:

Problem solving, even and odd numbers, addition and subtraction, fact families, equations, multiplication, telling time

Objectives:

1. The student will be able to solve story problems using *Four Steps to a Solution.*
2. The student will be able to determine if the sum and difference of the number sentences are odd or even. The student will be able to write an example of the number sentence.
3. The student will be able to find the sum or difference of two one-digit numbers.
4. The student will be able to find the missing numbers in the fact families.
5. The student will be able to solve the addition equations and check their answers.
6. The student will be able to find the product of two, one-digit numbers, and one example of a two-digit and one-digit problem.
7. The student will be able to identify the times on the clocks to the minute.

Teaching Tips:

Students are successful at problem solving if they understand the four steps to a solution. Drill basic addition, subtraction, multiplication, and division skills with flashcards.

Materials, Supplies, and Equipment:

1. Addition, subtraction, multiplication and division flashcards

Activities:

1. Direct students to **Lesson 9 Explanation** and read orally.
2. Have the students write the four steps to a solution.
3. Read the first problem in **Lesson 9 Practice** orally. Work the problem following each step carefully.
4. Students should be able to complete **Lesson 9 Practice** independently.

Nothing great was ever achieved without enthusiasm.
Ralph Waldo Emerson

Lesson 10

Concepts:

Place value, ordinal numbers, odd numbers, addition, subtraction, division, standard liquid measure, fractions

Objectives:

1. The student will be able to identify place value through the hundred thousands' column when given a number.
2. The student will be able to use ordinal numbers to solve a given message.
3. The student will be able to identify even and odd numbers.
4. The student will be able to add two-digit numbers.
5. The student will be able to subtract two-digit numbers which do not require regrouping.
6. The student will be able to solve division problems containing a one-digit divisor, one-digit dividend, and yielding a one-digit quotient.
7. The student will be able to identify and label given geometric shapes.
8. The student will be able to write an equivalent fraction and shade a corresponding picture when given a reduced fraction and corresponding picture.

Teaching Tips:

Give the students the opportunity to make their own place value chart which they can keep for easy reference. This chart needs to allow room for additional columns which will be discussed in Lessons 11 & 12. Drill basic addition, subtraction, multiplication, and division skills with flashcards.

Materials, Supplies and Equipment:

1. Centimeter graph paper
2. Beans, pennies, place value blocks, or any other item that can be easily counted and grouped
3. Addition, subtraction, multiplication and division flashcards

Activities:

1. Have the student cut the centimeter graph paper into as many 100 squares, 10 strips and individual squares as possible (at least five of each type).
2. Demonstrate the relationship between each of the three items by having the student count how many squares in each strip, how many strips in each large 100 square, and how many individual squares in the 100 square.
3. Have the students trade 100 squares for equal numbers of strips or squares, trade strips for equal numbers of individual squares, and so on.
4. Practice writing numbers, using the place value chart and the centimeter squares. Use a three-digit number, such as 451, and illustrate it using four of the 100 square, 5 of the ten strips, and 1 individual square.
5. Write several three, two, and one-digit numbers down, and instruct the student to illustrate each number the same way with a partner.
6. Have the students get into groups of three. Have them to stack 10 of the 100 squares together and imagine they form a block. Ask them how many individual squares would it take to form this block? Relate the concept that 10 of 100 squares is a 1,000 square block. Proceed to have the students illustrate 4-digit numbers using this 1,000 block along with the 100 squares, 10 strips and individual squares. By this point the students should be grasping the concept enough to use only the place value chart to identify the value of a number.

7. Continue to practice placing larger (4-digit - 6-digit numbers) on the place value chart and working with their value. The student should be given several of these types of numbers and asked to write them on his/her place value chart, as well as identifying the value of various digits within each number.
8. The student should be able to complete **Lesson 10 Practice** independently.
9. **Lessons 1-10** review many of the skills covered in previous *Horizons Math* workbooks. Any students new to the *Horizons Math* program can be helped through these review exercises by discussing the **Explanations** for these problems that appear later in the student book. For example, an explanation for the geometry shapes reviewed in **Lessons 5 & 10** can be found in **Lesson 92 & Lesson 96 Explanations**.

The eyes of the Lord keep watch over knowledge.
Proverbs 22:12

Lesson 11

Concepts:

Place value, ordinal numbers, odd and even, division, standard linear measure, fractions

Objectives:

1. The student will be able to identify place value through the hundred millions' column and write a given written number through the hundred millions' column in standard form.
2. The student will be able to use ordinal numbers to put a given set of events in chronological order.
3. The student will be able to identify odd and even numbers.
4. The student will be able to solve division problems containing a one-digit divisor, one-digit dividend, and yielding a one-digit quotient.
5. The student will be able to use standard liquid equivalents to calculate equal measurements using gallons, quarts, pints, and cups.
6. The student will be able to compare and state whether two fractions are equivalent or not equivalent.

Teaching Tips:

Allow the students to use their place value charts if necessary, but stress the importance of knowing the value of a number without a chart.

Materials, Supplies, and Equipment:

1. Place value chart for reference
2. Centimeter place value squares/strips (place value blocks or any other counting items)
3. *Worksheet 4*

Activities:

1. Review place value from Lesson 10 by writing a 3-digit number down and having the student demonstrate it using the place value squares and strips. Stress how that number is pronounced:

Example: 354

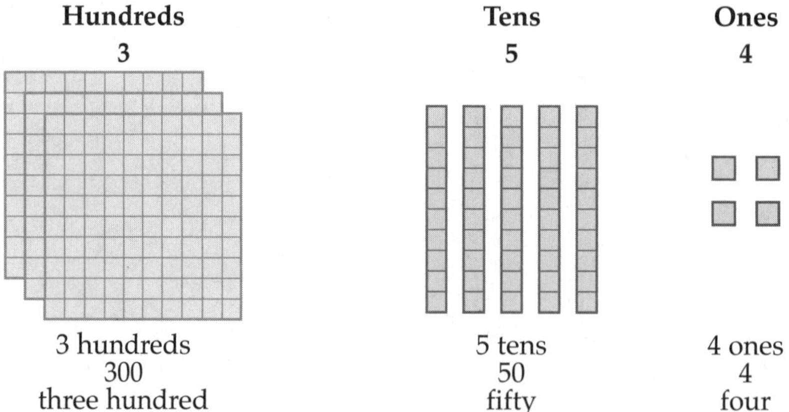

2. Write down several numbers and have the student pronounce the numbers and write each number on written form.
3. Have the student read a written number and then write it in standard form.
4. The student should be able to complete **Lesson 11 Practice** independently.

The righteous will live by faith.
Habakkuk 2:4

Lesson 12

Concepts:

Place value, ordinal numbers, division, standard linear measure, fractions, multiplication

Objectives:

1. The student will be able to identify place value through the hundred billions' column.
2. The student will be able to use ordinal numbers to complete a connect the dot.
3. The student will be able to find the quotient when given a one-digit divisor and a two-digit dividend.
4. The student will be able to use standard linear equivalents to identify equal measurements using yards, feet, and inches.
5. The student will be able to write a mixed fraction when given a picture representation of that number.
6. The student will be able to complete a multiplication table containing multiples of 4, 5, 6, 7, and 8.

Teaching Tips:

The students should have a good grasp of the place value concept. Place Value Charts should be made available only if absolutely necessary. If needed, continue to drill basic skills with flashcards.

Materials, Supplies, and Equipment:

1. Place value chart—only if absolutely necessary
2. Place value squares—only if absolutely necessary
3. *Worksheet 5*
4. Addition, subtraction, multiplication, and division flashcards

Activities:

1. Give the students a set of numbers (example: 2, 3, 5, 6, 7) and have them create the largest number possible, the smallest number possible, a number with a 2 in the tens' place, a number with a 5 in the thousands' place, and so on.
2. The students should be able to complete **Lesson 12 Practice** independently.

Go and make disciples of all nations, baptizing them in the name of the Father, and of the Son, and of the Holy Spirit.
Matthew 28:19

Lesson 13

Concepts:

Place value, expanded form, addition properties, division, fractions, multiplication, money

Objectives:

1. The student will be able to write given standard numbers in expanded form.
2. The student will be able to give examples of each addition property; the Zero Property, the Order Property, and the Grouping Property.
3. The student will be able to complete a division crossword by solving division problems containing one and two-digit quotients
4. The student will be able to write and solve a fractional addition equation with like denominators when given a pictorial representation of that equation.
5. The student will be able to complete a multiplication table containing multiples of 4, 5, 6, and 7.
6. The student will be able to calculate a total dollar amount when given a specified number of coins and bills.

Teaching Tips:

Refer to Lesson 11, if necessary, to remind students that each number in the place value chart have a specific value. This can be demonstrated through the use of place value blocks, or squares. If needed, continue to drill basic skills with flashcards.

Materials, Supplies, and Equipment:

1. Index cards
2. Addition, subtraction, multiplication and division flashcards

Activities:

1. Have each student write several numbers (in standard form) on a index cards (one number per card). Mix the cards onto one stack. Divide the students into two teams. Each team takes a turn pulling a card and then writing that number in both expanded and written form. Another variation is to have the students write numbers on the index cards in written or expanded form and then have each team write the standard number.
2. The students should be able to complete **Lesson 13 Practice** independently.

Commit to the Lord whatever you do and your plans will succeed.
Proverbs 16:3

Lesson 14

Concepts:

Roman numerals, expanded form, subtract fractions, word problems, writing checks, ordinal numbers, multiplication

Objectives:

1. The student will be able to identify, read, and write Roman numerals.
2. The student will be able to write given standard numbers in expanded form.
3. The student will be able to subtract fractions with like denominators.
4. The student will be able to solve given word problems containing addition of money and check writing.
5. The student will be able to use ordination to put the books of the New Testament in order.
6. The student will be able to complete a multiplication table contain multiples of 7, 8, 9, and 10.

Teaching Tips:

Stress the use of Roman Numerals in every day life. Have the students name the different areas and items which contain or use Roman Numerals. This concept is much easier to understand once the student understands that Roman Numerals follow place value just like regular standard (Arabic) numbers. Each Roman Numeral has its place on the place value chart.

Materials, Supplies and Equipment:

1. Place value chart
2. Index cards.
3. *Worksheet 6*

Activities:

1. Have each student write down the basic Roman numerals (given in the text) on an index card. These may be used as a reference while instructing.
2. Demonstrate how each Roman Numeral has a place value and coordinates with the place value chart.

Example:

	Hundreds	Tens	Ones
XIX = 19		X	IX
		1	9
CXXV = 125	C	XX	V
	1	2	5

Make up several numbers, have the students make up numbers also, and place them on the place value chart (like above) as both Roman numerals and Standard Arabic numbers.

3. Use the index cards to create a Roman numeral concentration game for the students. If you would like, the students can pair up and create their own concentration games in pairs. Choose several Roman numerals and write them on cards (each numeral needs to be written on two cards to make a pair or "match.") Allow the students to play several games of Concentration.
4. The students should be able to complete **Lesson 14 Practice** independently.

For God, who said, "Let light shine out of darkness," made His light to shine in our hearts to give us the light of knowledge of the glory of God in the face of Christ.
2 Corinthians 4:6

Lesson 15

Concepts:

Place value, comparing numbers, ordering numbers, expanded numbers, Roman numerals, fractions, division

Objectives:

1. The student will be able to compare two numbers to determine which number is larger.
2. The student will be able to put a given set of numbers in order from largest to smallest.
3. The student will be able to write a given standard number in expanded form.
4. The student will be able to add and subtract fractions with common denominators which are written in Roman numeral form.
5. The student will be able to write and shade an equivalent fraction, when given a fraction in reduced form.
6. The student will be able to solve division problems containing a one-digit divisor, two-digit dividend, and a one-digit quotient.

Teaching Tips:

The students should have little difficulty with this concept. Explain that they compare numbers each time they keep score to see who wins when playing a game, or when they argue over who has more of something. If needed, continue to drill basic skills with flashcards.

Materials, Supplies, and Equipment:

1. Place value chart
2. The sports page from your local paper
3. Addition, subtraction, multiplication and division flashcards

Activities:

1. Write the numbers 2,068 and 2,078 on the board. Have the students write each of these numbers on the place value chart. Beginning with the thousands' column, and working over toward the ones' column, have the student compare each number to see which is larger. Since the thousands' and hundreds' columns are the same, the tens' column is the first column where there is a difference in the numbers. 7 is larger than 6, therefore, 2,078 is larger than 2,068.
2. Have the students go through the sports pages from a local news paper. Chose several scores from competing teams in local sports events (baseball, football, basketball, hockey, etc.) Have them write the scores on the place value chart and then compare to see which number is larger, which team won?
3. The students should be able to complete **Lesson 15 Practice** independently.

A friend loves at all times.
Proverbs 17:17

Lesson 16

Concepts:

Comparing numbers, ordering numbers, expanded numbers, subtraction, addition, addition and subtraction of fractions

Objectives:

1. The student will be able to identify place value through the hundred billions' and compare whether two numbers are equal or not equal.
2. The student will be able to compare and order a given set of numbers from the smallest to the largest.
3. The student will be able to identify and match a given standard number to its appropriate expanded form.
4. The student will be able to solve simple subtraction problems and identify place value through the hundred billions' to solve a given problem.
5. The student will be able to identify and solve for missing addition terms.
6. The student will be able to add fractions with like denominators.

Teaching Tips:

Review with the students writing numbers in standard, expanded and written form at the beginning of the lesson. This will help when comparing written numbers and standard numbers. Some activities in this lesson will require some additional preplanning before the lesson can be presented.

Materials, Supplies, and Equipment:

1. Index cards
2. Markers
3. *Worksheet 7*

Activities:

1. Review the steps for comparing numbers (Lesson 15.) Explain that numbers can be compared when written in standard form and written form.

   Example: 100 = one hundred
   250 = two hundred, fifty
   150 ≠ fifteen
2. Give each student an index card and have them write a standard number on it (at least a three-digit number.) Then have the students trade cards and instruct them to write the equivalent written number.
3. Prior to the lesson, create a Comparison Bingo game. Create several game boards that contain standard numbers written in each square (see below). For each number on the bingo card, create a display card with written numbers that correspond to the standard numbers (see below.)

Bingo card:

325	9,851	21	792	150
498	2,063	390	12,513	784
56,851	198	85	891	54
22	57	1,003	45	65,127
706	405	395	518	30

Play a game of Comparison Bingo.

4. The student should be able to complete **Lesson 16 Practice** independently.

Display card: three hundred, twenty-five

Seek first His kingdom, and His righteousness,
and all these things will be given unto you as well.
Matthew 6:33

Lesson 17

Concepts:

Comparing numbers, geometric shapes, expanded forms, fractions, multiplication, work problems

Objectives:

1. The student will be able to compare two numbers and create a mathematical sentence using the terms greater than >, less than <, and equal to =.
2. The student will be able to name and label, given geometric shapes.
3. The student will be able to write a given number in expanded form.
4. The student will be able to compare fractions and order them from the smallest to the largest.
5. The student will be able to solve for multiplication facts contained in a word search.
6. The student will be able to solve given word problems which require addition.

Teaching Tips:

If the student is having difficulty comparing numbers, take them back to Lesson 16 and review the steps in comparing numbers.

Materials, Supplies, and Equipment:

1. Place value chart
2. Place value squares from Lessons 10 & 11

Activities:

1. Have the students write the number 1,676 and 1,686 on the place value chart. Then have them illustrate the number using the centimeter place value squares. They may do this in groups of three or four in order to "pool" the 100 square pieces and have enough to make enough square pieces.

Example:

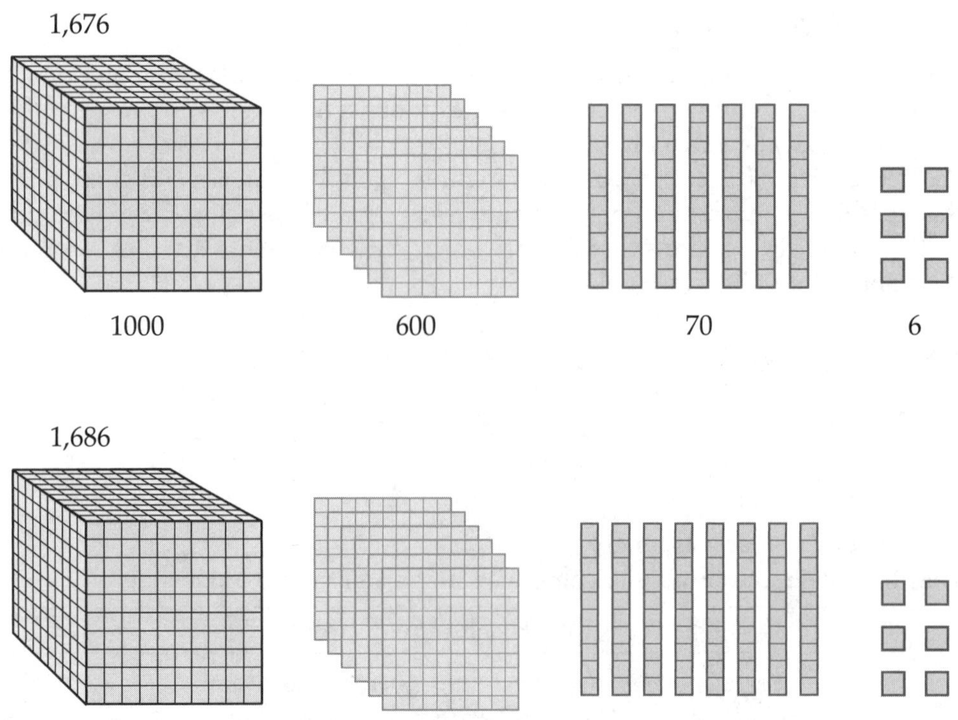

This visual makes it easy to see which number is larger, and at which place value column the difference occurs. Introduce the concept of writing a mathematical sentence using the greater than >, less than <, and equal to = symbols; 1,676 < 1,686.

2. Practice using a mathematical sentence and comparing numbers using the following number comparisons: 743 O 753 ; 15,368 O 15,768 ; 4,796 O 4,980 ; 8,822 O 8,823. The student may use the place value chart or squares, but should try to complete these comparisons without the use of manipulative or visual aids.
3. The student should be instructed to complete **Lesson 17 Practice** independently.

For we walk by faith, not by sight.
2 Corinthians 5:7

Lesson 18

Concepts:

Rounding numbers, comparing numbers, money, addition and subtraction, telling time, missing addends

Objectives:

1. The student will be able to round numbers to the tens' place.
2. The student will be able to compare numbers which have been rounded to the 10s' place and complete a mathematical sentence using >, <, and =.
3. The student will be able to calculate a total dollar amount, when given a specified number of coins and bills.
4. The student will be able to complete a string of addition and subtraction problems.
5. The student will be able to read a clock face and tell the time shown.
6. The student will be able to solve for a missing addend in an equation.

Teaching Tips:

Once again, it is important that the student understand that rounding is a skill that is used regularly. Give examples of everyday activities that use rounding, such as estimating prices when shopping at a store.

Materials, Supplies, and Equipment:

1. A centimeter ruler or meter stick for each child (or 1 for every 2 children)
2. *Worksheet 8*

Activities:

1. Have each student look at the centimeter ruler. They should note that the centimeter markings for 10, 20, and 30 are written larger than the other numbers. Instruct them to notice numbers 10 - 20. When looking at the numbers 11 - 14, they are closer to the 10 than to the 20. When looking at numbers 16 - 19, they are closer to the 20. When rounding numbers instruct the student that they are estimating which number a given number is closer to. 13 is closer to 10 so it would round to 10. 17 is closer to 20, so it would round to 20. When looking at 15 instruct the students that because this is the half way point (middle) we round up.
2. Have the students draw number lines from 30 - 50. Practice rounding numbers between 30 and 50 using this number line for assistance.
3. Explain that larger numbers can be rounded to specific places (tens', hundreds', thousands'.) Practice this process by making up, and rounding, several 4-digit numbers to the tens' place.
4. Complete the example problems in the text **Lesson 18 Explanation**.
5. The student should complete **Lesson 18 Practice** independently.

We can make our plans, but the final outcome is in God's hands.
Proverbs 16:1

Lesson 19

Concepts:

Problem solving, word problems, using tables, addition, comparing numbers, standard form, place value

Objectives:

1. The student will be able to understand the question being asked in a given word problem.
2. The student will be able to determine if a question can be answered using a given amount of data.
3. The student will be able to formulate a question when given a specific set of data.
4. The student will be able to use a data table to answer questions concerning that information.
5. The student will be able to round an addition problem to the nearest 10 and find the sum.
6. The student will be able to create the smallest number possible when given a series of 4 digits.
7. The student will be able to match a number presented in written form with its standard form. If needed, continue to drill basic skills with flashcards.

Teaching Tips:

If the student is having difficulty understanding the problem, have them read it several times (out loud if necessary) to themselves and then restate it in their own words.

Materials, Supplies, and Equipment:

1. Pencil and paper

Activities:

1. Teacher instruction is of the utmost importance when discussing word problems. Read **Lesson 19 Explanation** with the students. Answer any questions they may have.
2. The students should be instructed to complete **Lesson 19 Practice** independently.

Therefore, come out from them and be separate.
2 Corinthians 6:17

Lesson 20

Concepts:

Rounding to ten, hundred, and one thousand, even and odd numbers, money, adding fractions, multiplication, comparing numbers, word problems

Objectives:

1. The student will be able to round a four-digit number to the tens', hundreds', and thousands' place.
2. The student will be able to count the number of digits in a word and determine if the number of digits is odd or even.
3. The student will be able to write the number of quarters, dimes, nickels, and pennies equivalent to a sum of money.
4. The student will be able to add two fractions with common denominators.
5. The student will be able to find the product of two, one-digit numbers.
6. The student will be able to compare two digits up to the hundred billions' place and determine which number has the greater value, or if the numbers are equal.
7. Given a solution to a story problem, the student will be able to determine if the person who solved the problem understood the question.

Teaching Tips:

Allow the students to work through many problems while viewing a number line. When the student thoroughly grasps the concept move on to the abstract.

Materials, Supplies, and Equipment:

1. *Worksheet 9*

Activities:

1. Draw the number line on the board.

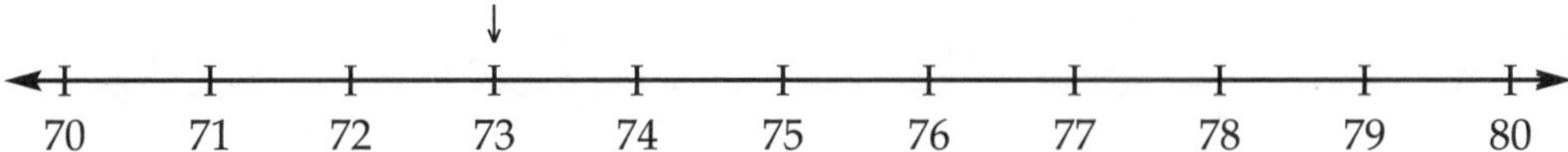

2. Tell the students that sometimes we don't want or need to use exact numbers. We want to use approximate numbers that are easy to add, subtract, multiply, and divide. Tell the students, **We are going to approximate or round 73 to the nearest ten. Is 73 closer to 70 or 80? (70)**

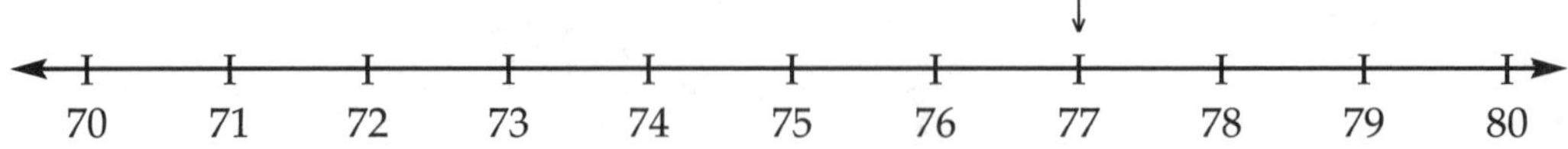

3. Tell the students, **We are going to approximate or round 77 to the nearest ten. Is 77 closer to 70 or 80? (80)**

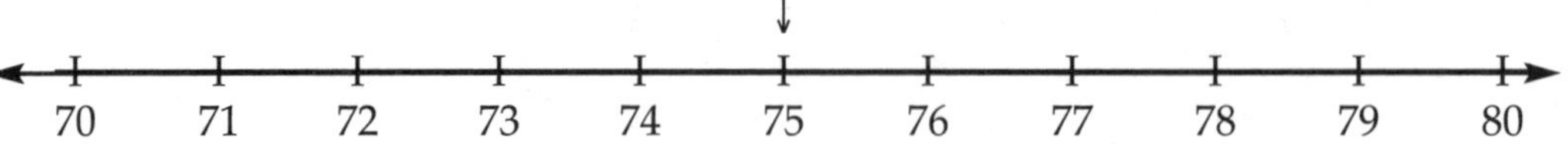

4. Tell the students, **We are going to approximate or round 75 to the nearest ten. Is 75 closer to 70 or 80? (75 is in the middle. We round numbers that end in 5 to the higher number, so 75 rounds to 80.)**

5. Tell the students, **Round 78 to the nearest ten. (80)**
   Tell the students, **Round 71 to the nearest ten. (70)**
   Tell the students, **Round 74 to the nearest ten. (70)**
   Tell the students, **Round 79 to the nearest ten. (80)**
6. Direct the students' attention to **Lesson 20A Explanation.** Read the directions orally.
7. Work through **Lesson 20 Practice** with the students applying the steps outlined in the explanation.

I will lift up my eyes to the mountains; From whence shall my help come?
My help comes from the Lord, Who made heaven and earth.
Psalm 121:1,2

Lesson 21

Concepts:

Addition, rounding to ten, hundred, and one thousand, place value, multiples, addition

Objectives:

1. The student will be able to find the sum of two, two-digit numbers which requires regrouping from the ones' to tens' place.
2. The student will be able to round two and three-digit numbers to the nearest ten and place them in a puzzle using logical reasoning.
3. The student will be able to round numbers to the nearest hundred and find them in a puzzle to solve a riddle.
4. The student will be able to find numbers in a number list given place value information.
5. The student will be able to write numbers in multiples of three and five. The student will be able to find even numbers in these multiples and see a pattern.
6. The student will be able to find the sum of two, one-digit numbers quickly with accuracy.

Teaching Tips:

Allow the students to work through many problems using manipulatives. When the student thoroughly grasps the concept, move on to the abstract.

Materials, Supplies, and Equipment:

1. Base ten blocks
2. *Worksheet 10*

Activities:

1. Tell the students, **We are adding two-digit numbers today. It is important that you can rename numbers as tens and ones. For instance, 13 has 1 ten and 3 ones.** (Demonstrate by showing one ten rod and three cubes.) Tell the students, **Rename the following as tens and ones and demonstrate with rods: 27, 38, 45, 21, 40, 53, 67, and 91.**
2. Have the students demonstrate 28 + 14 using base ten blocks.
3. Direct the students' attention to **Lesson 21 Explanation**. Direct the students' attention to **Lesson 23 Explanation**. Read orally.
4. Have the students demonstrate 37 + 48 using base ten blocks. Check to see that the students are renaming correctly.
5. Allow the students to use base ten blocks as they complete **Lesson 21 Practice.**

Some books are to be tasted; others swallowed; and some to be chewed and digested.
Francis Bacon

Lesson 22

Concepts:

Addition, place value, even numbers, rounding numbers, problem solving

Objectives:

1. The student will be able to find the sum of two, three-digit numbers where regrouping is required in the ones' and tens' place.
2. The student will be able to read and write numbers to the hundred billions' place.
3. The student will be able to determine if numbers are odd or even. The student will be able to compare numbers to the millions' place and group them from smallest to largest.
4. The student will be able to round numbers to the thousands' place and find them in a puzzle.
5. Given a set of five numbers, the student will be able to use logical reasoning and determine which two numbers would equal a specified sum.

Teaching Tips:

Allow the students to work through many problems using manipulatives. When the student thoroughly grasps the concept, move on to the abstract.

Materials, Supplies, and Equipment:

1. Base ten blocks
2. *Worksheet 11*

Activities:

1. Tell the students, **We are adding three-digit numbers today. It is important that you can rename numbers as hundreds, tens, and ones. For instance, 131 has 1 hundred, 3 tens, and 1 one.** (Demonstrate by showing one hundred flat, three ten rods and one cube.) Tell the students, **Rename the following as hundreds, tens, and ones and demonstrate with rods: 221, 238, 405, 241, 407, 353, 617, and 191.**
2. Have the students demonstrate 164 + 157 using base ten blocks.
3. Direct the students' attention to **Lesson 22 Explanation**. The students should check their model against the one represented in the exercise.
4. Have the students demonstrate 377 + 161 using base ten blocks. Check to see that the students are renaming correctly.
5. Allow the students to use base ten blocks as they complete **Lesson 22 Practice.**

The journey of a thousand miles begins with one step.

Lao-tse

Lesson 23

Concepts:

Column addition, addition, problem solving, rounding numbers, place value, expanded form

Objectives:

1. The student will be able to find the sum of three or four, two-digit numbers that require regrouping in the ones' and tens' place.
2. The student will be able to find the sum of two, three-digit numbers that require regrouping in the ones', tens', and hundreds' place. The student will be able to match each sum with a corresponding letter to solve a puzzle.
3. Given a set of ten numbers, the student will be able to determine what addends equal a given sum. Given addends, the student will be able to find the sum.
4. The student will be able to find the sum given two, two-digit numbers that require regrouping in the ones' and tens' place.
5. Given numbers with up to six digits, the student will be able to round to the nearest thousand.
6. Given a number written in words and one written in numerals, the student will be able to determine if the two are equal or not equal.
7. Given a number written in words, the student will be able to write the number in expanded notation.

Teaching Tips:

Allow the students to work through many problems using manipulatives. When the student thoroughly grasps the concept move on to the abstract.

Materials, Supplies, and Equipment:

1. Base ten blocks
2. *Worksheet 12*

Activities:

1. Direct the students' attention to **Lesson 23 Explanation**. Read orally.
2. This exercise should require no additional explanation if the student comprehends regrouping.
3. Allow the students to work **Lesson 23 Practice** independently. If they find the manipulatives helpful, encourage the students to use them.

The mind of man plans his way, but the Lord directs his steps.
Proverbs 16:9

Lesson 24

Concepts:

Rounding and addition, addition, column addition, place value, expanded form, rounding and column addition, standard from, addition of fractions, missing numbers

Objectives:

1. The student will be able to estimate sums by rounding.
2. The student will be able to find the sum of two and three-digit numbers and solve a crossword puzzle.
3. The student will use rounding to estimate the sum of three, two-digit numbers.
4. Given a number written in words, the student will be able to write the number in standard form. Using logical reasoning, the student will determine where to place each number in a puzzle.
5. Given numbers written in words, the student will be able to write the number in expanded form.
6. Given two fractions with common denominators, the student will be able to find the sum.
7. Given two, four-digit numbers and their sums, the student will be able to identify missing digits.

Teaching Tips:

This exercise combines the skill of rounding and regrouping. Allow the students to use number lines and manipulatives for reinforcement.

Materials, Supplies, and Equipment:

1. Base ten blocks
2. Number line

Activities:

1. Draw a number line on the board.

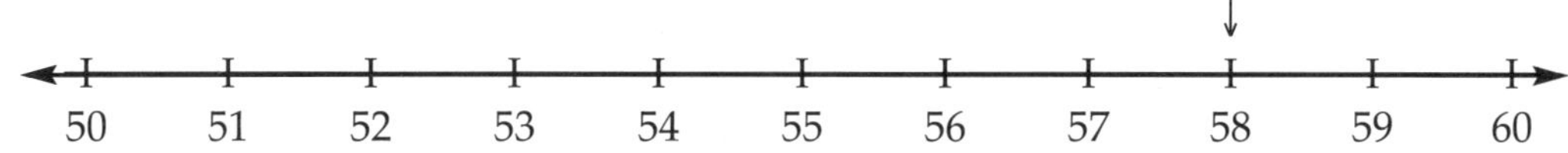

2. Ask the student, **58 rounds to 50 or 60?(60)**

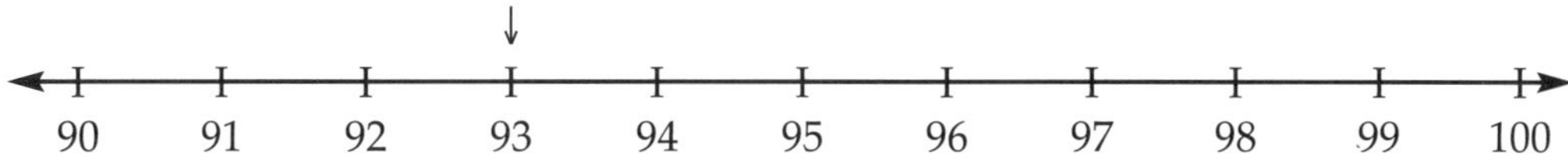

3. **Ask the student, 93 rounds to 90 or 100?(90)**
4. Direct the students to find the sum of the rounded numbers. 60 + 90 = 150
5. Direct the students' attention to **Lesson 24 Explanation**. Read orally. The students should check their model against the one represented in the exercise.
6. Allow the students to work **Lesson 24 Practice** independently.

And be sure of this—that I am with you always, even to the end of the world.
Matthew 28:20

Lesson 25

Concepts:

Addition, rounding and addition, rounding, column addition, ordering numbers, Roman numerals

Objectives:

1. The student will be able to find the sum of two, four-digit numbers that require regrouping in the ones', tens', and hundreds' places.
2. Given a set of numerals, the student will be able to find a number that could be rounded to a specified number.
3. Given three, two-digit numbers the student will be able to find the sum.
4. Given populations in a table, the student will be able to compare and order populations from smallest to largest.
5. Given Roman numerals, the student will be able to write the corresponding Arabic numeral.

Teaching Tips:

The most common errors involve misalignment of digits. Have students check their work carefully.

Materials, Supplies, and Equipment:

1. Base ten blocks
2. *Worksheet 13*

Activities:

1. Direct the students' attention to **Lesson 25 Explanation**. Read orally.
2. This exercise should require no additional explanation if the student comprehends regrouping. Allow them to use the thousand block when regrouping hundreds if they are using manipulatives.
3. Allow the students to work **Lesson 23 Practice** independently. If they find the manipulatives helpful, encourage the students to use them.

My presence shall go with thee, and I will give thee rest.
Exodus 33:14

Lesson 26

Concepts:

Equations, rounding numbers, comparing numbers, add 10, column addition, mystery numbers, addition

Objectives:

1. The student will be able to find the value of a variable given an addition equation.
2. Given a table of numbers, the student will be able to round each number to the nearest 100, and rank the numbers from highest to lowest.
3. Given a set of numbers, the student will be able to add 10 to each numeral. The student will be able to color shapes that are greater than 100 to solve a puzzle.
4. The student will be able to find the sum of five, two-digit numbers that require regrouping.
5. Given clues, the student will be able to use the problem solving skill of elimination and determine the value of a given number.
6. The student will be able to find the sum of two, six-digit numbers that require regrouping.

Teaching Tips:

Allow the students the opportunity to work equations at the concrete level first. Emphasize that both sides of the equation are always equal.

Materials, Supplies, and Equipment:

1. Beans, counters, or any item easy to count
2. *Worksheet 14*

Activities:

1. Tell the students, **An equation is a number sentence where both sides are equal. A variable is a letter that stands for a number.**
2. Have the students work the problems at their desks with counters, as you demonstrate at the board. Use the following examples:

   1. ☆☆☆☆☆☆☆☆ = ☆☆☆☆☆ + n
   2. ☆☆☆☆☆☆☆☆☆☆☆☆☆☆ = ☆☆ + n
   3. ☆☆☆ + n = ☆☆☆☆☆☆
   4. ☆☆☆ + n = ☆☆☆☆☆☆☆☆☆☆☆☆☆☆☆☆☆☆

   Ask the students, **If N is the variable, how many stars would we need to put in its place to make the equation equal? (1. 3, 2. 12, 3. 3, 4. 15)**
3. Demonstrate that it is easy to check to see if an equation is correct. Replace n with the stars and show that both sides are equal.
4. Direct the students' attention to **Lesson 26 Explanation**. Read orally. Emphasize that an equation is a number sentence where both sides are equal.
5. Supervise the students as they complete **Lesson 26 Practice**.

They that wait upon the Lord shall renew their strength;
they shall mount up with wings as eagles;
they shall run, and not be weary:
and they shall walk, and not faint.
Isaiah 40:31

Lesson 27

Concepts:

Adding money, writing checks, adding decimals, addition, rounding numbers, word problems, add 100

Objectives:

1. The student will be able to find the sum of money given two dollar amounts not to exceed $999.99.
2. Given a blank check, the student will be able to correctly complete the name of business, date, sum of money, and signature.
3. The student will be able to find the sum of money and complete a puzzle.
4. The student will be able to find the sum of two, six-digit numbers with regrouping.
5. Given a table of miles, the student will be able to round the land area to the nearest 100 miles and answer questions that require knowledge of comparing and ordering numbers.
6. Given up to six-digit numbers, the student will be able to add 100 to each number.

Teaching Tips:

Students should have little difficulty adding decimals.

Materials, Supplies, and Equipment:

Activities:

1. Direct the students' attention to **Lesson 27 Explanation**. Read orally.
2. This exercise should require no additional explanation if the student comprehends regrouping. Emphasize that the decimal points need to be in a straight line.
3. Allow the students to work **Lesson 27 Practice** independently. Students who have alignment problems may want to use paper with vertical lines.

Anything is possible if you try.
Terry Fox

Lesson 28

Concepts:

Estimating sums, equations, addition, rounding to 100, writing checks, add 1,000

Objectives:

1. The student will be able to estimate amounts of money by rounding.
2. The student will be able to find the value of a variable given an addition equation.
3. The student will be able to find the sum of two, two-digit numbers that require regrouping.
4. The student will be able to find the sum of two, six-digit numbers that require regrouping.
5. Given up to a six-digit number, the student will be able to round to the nearest hundred and solve a puzzle.
6. Given a blank check, the student will be able to correctly complete the name of business, date, sum of money, and signature.
7. The student will be able to add 1,000 to each number to find his way through a maze.

Teaching Tips:

Students having difficulty with rounding money are often successful using play money.

Materials, Supplies, and Equipment:

Activities:

1. Point out to students that sometimes we need exact amounts and at other times we need estimates. Have them tell some instances when estimates would be appropriate. Tell the students that there are different ways to estimate depending on your needs. Today they will be rounding to the nearest dollar or the nearest hundred.
2. Ask the student, **What are the following numbers rounded to the nearest dollar? $.75, $1.82, $4.12, and $7.38 ($1, $2, $4, $7).**
3. Ask the student, **What is the sum of the rounded numbers? ($14)**
4. Ask the student, **What are the following numbers rounded to the nearest 100? 465, 132, and 547 (500, 100, 500)**
5. Ask the student, **What is the sum of the rounded numbers? (1,100)**
6. Direct the students' attention to **Lesson 28 Explanation**. Read orally.
7. Allow the students to work **Lesson 28 Practice** independently.

There is no achievement without goals.
Robert J. McKain

Lesson 29

Concepts:

Problem solving, addition of decimals, equations, addition of money, round to 1,000, missing numbers

Objectives:

1. The student will be able to read a story problem and use key words to determine what operation to use.
2. The student will be able to find the sum of money given two dollar amounts not to exceed $999.99.
3. The student will be able to find the value of a variable given an addition equation.
4. The student will be able to add money to find their way through a puzzle maze.
5. Given up to a six-digit number, the student will be able to round to the nearest thousand and solve a puzzle.
6. The student will be able to find the missing addend given six addends and the sum.

Teaching Tips:

Materials, Supplies, and Equipment:

Activities:

1. Direct the students' attention to **Lesson 29 Explanation**. Read orally.
2. Have students write their own simple story problems that require one operation. Use the problems to play **STUMPER**.
3. **<u>STUMPER</u>** Choose a student to be the head of the class. The class is going to try and stump that person. The head of the class may choose any student to read their problem. If he/she gets the answer right, he/she stays in the game. If he/she loses, the person who stumped him/her comes to the head of the class. If a person stays at the head of the class for five questions in a row, they get their name in the HALL OF FAME. The HALL OF FAME is a poster prominently placed in the room bearing the names of students who have accomplished exceptional feats in the classroom.
4. Students should be able to complete **Lesson 29 Practice** independently.

Thy word is a lamp unto my feet, and a light unto my path.
Psalm119:105

Lesson 30

Concepts:

Subtraction, rounding money, place value, round 100, word problems, equations

Objectives:

1. The student will be able to subtract two-digit numbers using the regrouping process, if necessary.
2. The student will be able to round a given dollar amount to the nearest dollar.
3. The student will be able to identify place value through the hundred billions' column.
4. The student will be able to round given numbers to the nearest 100s'.
5. The student will be able to complete a given problem solving equation.
6. The student will be able to solve given addition equations for a value named *n*.

Teaching Tips:

If the students are having difficulty keeping columns aligned, try the following: turn a piece of notebook paper sideways to use the lines for an aid, use graph paper or write the place value columns above each problem. Remind them that each row of numbers in the problem has a value on the place value chart.

Materials, Supplies, and Equipment:

1. Poster board
2. Markers
3. Centimeter place value squares (from Lesson 10)
4. *Worksheet 15*

Activities:

1. Draw a place value chart (through the 100 thousands' column) on the poster board. Make each column large enough to fit one 1000 square centimeter block. Write the problem 39-27 down on the chalkboard for the students to see. Then illustrate the problem on the place value chart with the centimeter place value squares.

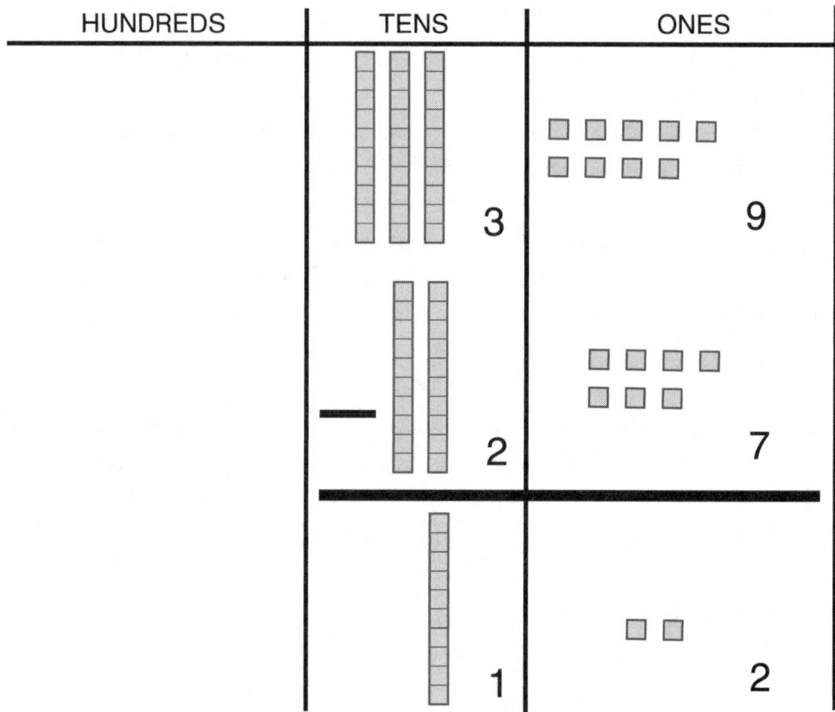

This is a very helpful visual illustration of the subtraction process. Try several more problems both together as a group and independently.

2. The students might chose to work the subtraction problems on the place value chart.
3. The student should be able to complete **Lesson 30 Practice** independently.

Do not be overcome with evil, but overcome evil with good.
Romans 12:21

Lesson 31

Concepts:

Subtraction with borrowing, subtraction, adding decimals, odd and even numbers, place value, round the thousands

Objectives:

1. The student will be able to subtract three-digit numbers using the regrouping process, if necessary.
2. The student will be able to subtract two-digit numbers using the regrouping process, if necessary.
3. The student will be able to add given sums of money.
4. The student will be able to identify odd and even numbers.
5. The student will be able to identify place value through the hundred billions' place.
6. The student will be able to round numbers to the nearest 1000.

Teaching Tips:

Review the concept that each row in a subtraction problem represents a column on the place value chart.

Materials, Supplies, and Equipment:

1. Posterboard place value chart
2. Centimeter place value squares (from Lesson 30)
3. *Worksheet 16*

Activities:

1. Use the poster board place value chart from Lesson 30. Write the problem 930 – 912 on the board and illustrate it on the place value chart with the centimeter square pieces. Show the regrouping process with the squares and then solve.

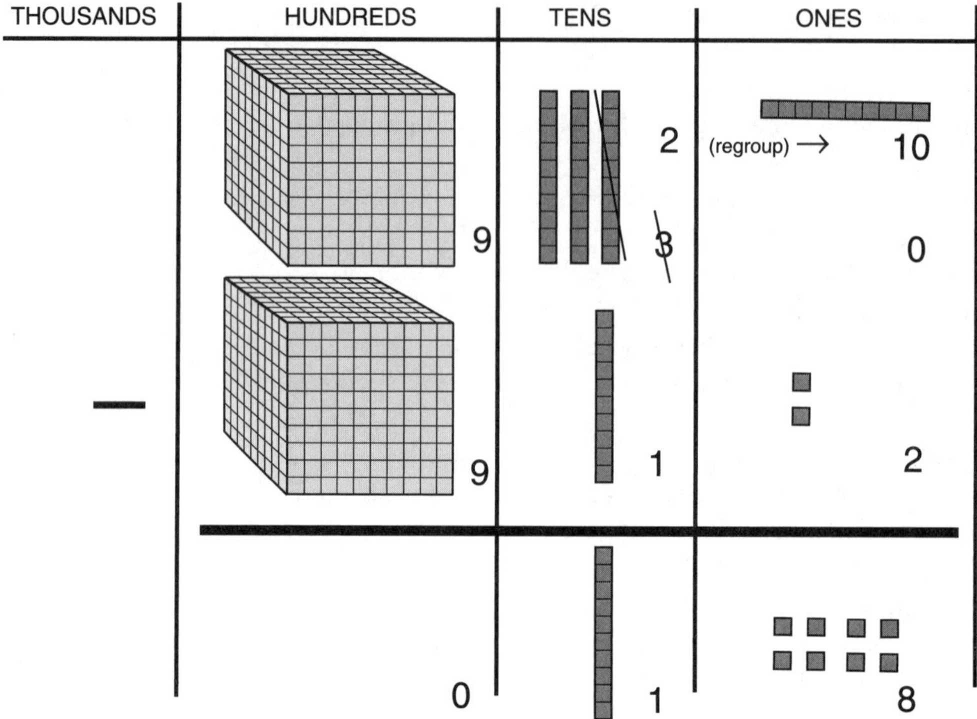

   The drawing illustrates the regrouping process in which you will actually exchange place value squares and strips.
   Work several problems with regrouping to insure that the students understand the concept.
2. The student should be able to complete **Lesson 31 Practice** independently.

Do not be conformed any longer to the pattern of this world,
but be transformed by the renewing of your mind.
Romans 12:2a

Lesson 32

Concepts:

Subtraction with borrowing, subtraction, even and odd numbers, estimating money, expanded numbers, word problems

Objectives:

1. The student will be able to complete subtraction problems requiring regrouping across zeros.
2. The student will be able to subtract three-digit numbers using the regrouping process, if necessary.
3. The student will be able to subtract two-digit numbers using the regrouping process, if necessary.
4. The student will be able to identify odd and even numbers.
5. The student will be able to round a given dollar amount to the nearest dollar.
6. The student will be able to read a number presented in written form and write it in expanded form.
7. The student will be able to use the four steps of problem solving to solve given word problems.

Teaching Tips:

Review the concept that each row in a subtraction problem represents a column on the place value chart.

Materials, Supplies, and Equipment:

1. Poster board place value chart
2. Centimeter place value squares (from Lesson 30)
3. *Worksheet 17*

Activities:

1. Use the poster board place value chart from Lesson 31. Write the problem 103 – 59 on the board and illustrate it on the place value chart with the centimeter square pieces. Show the regrouping process with the squares and then solve (like Lessons 30 & 31.)

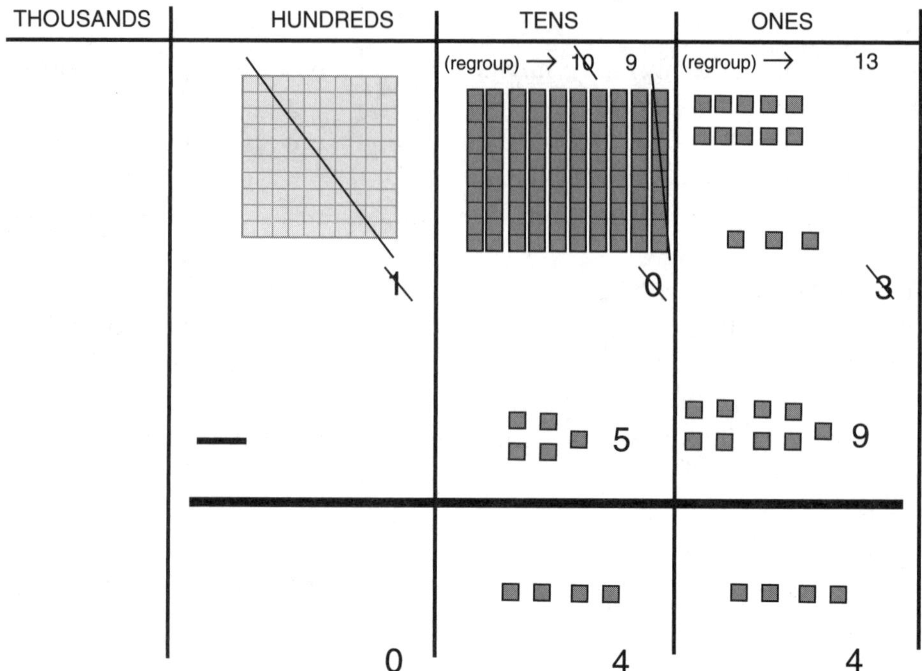

The drawing illustrates the regrouping process where the exchanging of place value squares and strips will take place during the teacher explanation.

2. Have the students practice several problems.
3. The students should be able to complete **Lesson 32 Practice** independently.

Blessed is the man who trusts in the Lord, whose confidence is in him.
Jeremiah 17:7

Lesson 33

Concepts:

Round the nearest 10, 100, and 1,000, subtraction, standard numbers, expanded numbers

Objectives:

1. The student will be able to estimate differences by rounding each subtrahend and minuend to the nearest 10, 100, or 1,000 and then subtracting.
2. The student will be able to complete subtraction problems requiring regrouping across zeros.
3. The student will be able to subtract two and three-digit numbers requiring the regrouping process, if necessary.
4. The student will be able to match numbers given in written form with the same number in standard form.
5. The student will be able to write a given number in expanded form.
6. The student will be able to round numbers to the nearest 1,000.

Teaching Tips:

It is important that the student understand that rounding is a skill that is used regularly. Give examples of everyday activities that use rounding such as estimating prices when shopping at a store. Remind them of the rounding from Lesson 18. Explain that in estimating you round each individual number before adding or subtracting.

Materials, Supplies, and Equipment:

1. A centimeter ruler or meter stick for each child (or 1 for every 2 children)
2. *Worksheet 18*

Activities:

1. Have each student look at the centimeter ruler. They should note that the centimeter markings for 10, 20, and 30 are written larger than the other numbers. Instruct them to notice numbers 10 - 20. When looking at the numbers 11 - 14, they are closer to the 10 than to the 20. When looking at numbers 16 - 19, they are closer to the 20. When rounding numbers instruct the student that they are estimating which number a given number is closer to. 13 is closer to 10 so it would round to 10. 17 is closer to 20, so it would round to 20. When looking at 15 instruct the students that because this is the half way point (middle) we round up.
2. Have the students draw number lines from 30 - 50. Practice rounding numbers between 30 and 50 using this number line for assistance.
3. Explain that larger numbers can be rounded to specific places (tens', hundreds', thousands'.) Practice this process by making up, and rounding, several 4-digit numbers to the tens' place, hundreds' place, and thousands' place.
4. Complete the example problems in the text **Lesson 33 Explanation** together.
5. The student should complete **Lesson 33 Practice** independently.

You are all sons of God through faith in Christ Jesus.
Galatians 3:26

Lesson 34

Concepts:

Subtraction with borrowing, round and subtract, comparing numbers, estimate and add, money

Objectives:

1. The student will be able to subtract larger numbers (four digits and larger) using the regrouping process if necessary.
2. The student will be able to estimate differences by rounding each subtrahend and minuend to the nearest 10, 100, or 1,000 and then subtracting.
3. The student will be able to subtract three-digit numbers and complete subtraction problems requiring regrouping across zeros.
4. The student will be able to create the smallest number possible when given a series of 5 digits.
5. The student will be able to solve given word problems which require estimating the problem by rounding each addend to the nearest dollar before adding.
6. The student will be able to write the number of coins and bills needed to make a given sum of money.

Teaching Tips:

Review the concept that each row in a subtraction problem represents a column on the place value chart. When subtracting larger numbers, keeping all columns straight becomes imperative and difficult for some students.

Materials, Supplies, and Equipment:

1. Centimeter squares, if necessary. (*Worksheet 55*)
2. Chalkboard and chalk or dry erase board and markers
3. *Worksheet 19*

Activities:

1. Read **Lesson 34 Explanation** with the students. Use graph paper, turn a piece of notebook paper sideways, or draw in place value columns so that the students keep all rows straight.
2. Continue to use the centimeter squares if necessary.
3. Have the students make up several problems and work them together. You may choose to play a game by dividing the students in half. The students take turns going two at a time. Each student makes up a problem (no larger than 4 digits by 3 digits), they swap problems, work them, compare them and then tell which answer is larger by writing it down as a mathematical sentence using >, <, & =. The students are given one point for answering the problem correctly and one point for writing the mathematical sentence correctly. See example:

$$\begin{array}{r} 1{,}645 \\ -\ 235 \\ \hline 1{,}410 \end{array} \qquad \begin{array}{r} 1{,}890 \\ -\ 378 \\ \hline 1{,}512 \end{array}$$

1,410 < 1,512 or 1,512 > 1,410

4. The students should be able to work **Lesson 34 Practice** independently.

When you pray, if you hold anything against anyone, forgive him, so that your father in heaven may forgive you your sins.
Mark 11:25

Lesson 35

Concepts:

Equations, subtraction, comparing and ordering, addition of decimals, missing numbers, geometric shapes

Objectives:

1. The student will be able to solve a subtraction equation by solving for the value *n.*
2. The student will be able to subtract larger numbers (four digits or larger) using the regrouping process if necessary.
3. The student will be able to compare and order a given set of numbers from the largest to the smallest.
4. The student will be able to estimate addition problems containing money by rounding each addend to the nearest dollar and then adding.
5. The student will be able to use problem solving techniques to solve for missing numbers within an addition puzzle.
6. The student will be able to draw and correctly label listed geometric shapes.

Teaching Tips:

Explain to the students that doing a subtraction equation is as simple as creating an addition problem.

Materials, Supplies, and Equipment:

1. Pencil and paper
2. *Worksheet 20*

Activities:

1. Read **Lesson 35 Explanation** together. Solve the example problem together. Then do the following problems as practice: n – 20 = 50; n – 15 = 30; n – 50 = 100.
2. Students should be able to complete **Lesson 35 Practice** independently.

For he bore the sin of many, and made intercession for the sinners.
Isaiah 53:12

Lesson 36

Concepts:

Subtracting money, equations, addition and subtraction, subtract 10, estimate and subtract

Objectives:

1. The student will be able to complete subtraction problems involving money.
2. The student will be able to solve subtraction equations by solving for a value of n.
3. The student will be able to write addition and subtraction problems vertically and solve.
4. The student will be able to subtract larger numbers (four digits or larger) using the regrouping process if necessary.
5. The student will be able to find a new number by subtracting 10 from a given number.
6. The student will be able to estimate subtraction problems by rounding each subtrahend and minuend to the nearest 1,000 and then subtracting.

Teaching Tips:

Emphasize that subtracting money is done like subtracting larger numbers. The only difference is that the decimal needs to be lined up and placed in the answer first. Then the student will subtract just as normal.

Most students will understand this immediately and need little explanation.

Materials, Supplies, and Equipment:

1. Place value chart

Activities:

1. Now is an excellent time to remind the students that there are two sides to a place value chart, the whole number side (green money) and the decimal side (change). Have them copy the place value chart and the example problem below. This will remind them that each number holds a place value and that the decimal serves as a breaking point between the whole number side and the decimal side. Make sure that they remember that on the place value chart the decimal always goes between the ones' and tenths' columns.

WHOLE NUMBER SIDE			DECIMAL SIDE	
INDREDS	TENS	ONES	TENTHS	HUNDREDTH
	$5	7	.7	0
	— 1	5	.0	0
	$4	2	.7	0

2. Students may complete each problem on the place value chart, graph paper, or vertically lined paper in order to keep columns and decimals lined up.
3. The student should be able to complete **Lesson 36 Practice** independently.

God is everywhere. Throughout the universe. He is a person, He is a Spirit. He can be on Mars at the same time He's on Earth. God is from everlasting to everlasting.

Billy Graham

Lesson 37

Concepts:

Estimate and subtract money, subtract money, vertical addition and subtraction, equations, add 100, subtraction

Objectives:

1. The student will be able to estimate addition and subtraction problems containing dollar amounts by rounding each subtrahend, minuend, and addend to the nearest dollar.
2. The student will be able to complete subtraction problems containing money.
3. The student will be able to write a subtraction and addition problem vertically and then solve.
4. The student will be able to solve a multi-step addition equation by solving for a value of *n*.
5. The student will be able to add 100 to a give number to reveal a new number.
6. The student will be able to subtract larger numbers (4 digits or larger) and use the regrouping process if necessary.

Teaching Tips:

A quick review of rounding to the nearest dollar might be appropriate before beginning the lesson.

Materials, Supplies, and Equipment:

Activities:

1. Tell the students that a stereo system costs \$589 and a computer system costs \$1,579. If tax is included in theses prices, can both of these times be purchased for \$2000? (No) Ask the students to explain how they could answer this question without adding the exact numbers. (Round both figures and estimate the total \$600 + \$1,600 = \$2,200)
2. After discussing the above example, practice estimating the example problem in **Lesson 37 Explanation**. The students should be able to grasp this concept easily. They might need another example or two for practice.
3. The student should be able to complete **Lesson 37 Practice** independently.

Trust in the Lord forever, for the Lord is the rock eternal.
Isaiah 26:4

Lesson 38

Concepts:

Money, subtract money, equations, subtraction, equations, subtract 10

Objectives:

1. The student will be able to calculate and count the change due from a given purchase or transaction.
2. The student will be able to write a subtraction problem vertically and complete subtraction problems containing money.
3. The student will be able to solve a subtraction equation by solving for the value *n*.
4. The student will be able to subtract three and four-digit problems and use the regrouping process if necessary.
5. The student will be able to solve a multi-step addition equation by solving for a value of *n*.
6. The student will be able to subtract 1,000 from a given number to reveal a new number.
7. The student will be able to match the name of a mathematical property, or term, with its definition.

Teaching Tips:

Most students know their coins and bills but cannot count back change. Try to give examples of times when a student would need to count back change without the assistance of a calculator or computer (concessions stands at a ball field, cashiering during a power outage, making sure a cashier gave you the correct change.)

Materials, Supplies, and Equipment:

1. Play money and coins

Activities:

1. Review the value of coins: pennies, nickels, dimes, quarters and half dollars. The ask the following types of questions:
   1 quarter, 5 dimes. How much altogether?
   17 pennies, 3 dimes, 5 pennies. How much altogether?
   3 quarters, 1 dime, 3 pennies. How much altogether?
2. Read **Lesson 38 Explanation** together. Go through each step and actually do the problem with the aid of play money and coins. Have several students experience counting the change. Create several new problems and allow several more students to count change.
3. Break the students into pairs, have them work the first two problems on **Lesson 38 Practice** together with the play money and coins. Check their answers.
4. The students should be able to complete the rest of **Lesson 38 Practice** independently.

Fine counsel is confusing, but an example is always clear.
Charles L. Allen

Lesson 39

Concepts:

Problem solving, change, money, subtraction, equations, place value

Objectives:

1. The student will be able to read a word problem and its answer and evaluate if the answer is reasonable or not.
2. The student will be able to calculate and count the change due from a given purchase or transaction.
3. The student will be able to estimate given word problems and use the 4 steps of problem solving to solve them.
4. The student will be able to complete a subtraction problem containing money.
5. The student will be able to solve a subtraction equation by solving for a value of n.
6. The student will be able to identify place value through the hundred thousands' place.

Teaching Tips:

If the student is having difficulty, have them read the problem several times and restate it in their own words. Then have them state what options they have for solving the problem.

Materials, Supplies and Equipment:

1. *Worksheet 21*

Activities:

1. Read **Lesson 39 Explanation** with the students.
2. The students should be able to complete **Lesson 39 Practice** with little or no assistance.

A wise man controls his temper, he knows that anger causes mistakes.
Proverbs 14:29

Lesson 40

Concepts:

Multiplication terms, making change, estimate money, odd and even numbers, mystery numbers, expanded numbers, missing numbers

Objectives:

1. The student will be able to identify the name of terms in a multiplication problem.
2. The student will be able to subtract three-digit numbers with decimals that require borrowing.
3. The student will be able give change using the least number of coins in amounts less than one dollar.
4. The student will be able to estimate the cost of items and add those estimates.
5. The student will be able determine if an estimated sum is greater or less than a given amount.
6. The student will be able to recognize odd numbers and follow odd numbers through a maze from beginning to end.
7. The student will be able to recognize place value through the hundred billions' place.
8. The student will be able to write numbers in expanded form through the millions' place.
9. The student will be able to find missing digits in a subtraction problem given clues.

Teaching Tips:

1. Some students will grasp this concept looking at it once visually, others will need to work each problem with the aid of beans, pennies, or counters.

Materials, Supplies, and Equipment:

1. Multiplication Chart for reference
2. Beans, pennies, counters, or similar item that can be easily counted and grouped
3. *Worksheet 22*

Activities:

1. Tell the students that there are five packages of cookies with two cookies in each package. Ask for a volunteer to show this relationship with counters. They should group five sets of two counters. Point out that sets are groups of objects. Write an addition sentence as follows: 2 + 2 + 2 + 2 + 2 = 10.
2. We can multiply to show this relationship because there are the same number of objects in each set.
   Write a multiplication sentence as follows: 5 x 2 = 10 (There are five sets of 2).
3. Reinforce the terms multiplicand, multiplier and product.
4. Point out examples of problems written vertically and horizontally.
5. Tell the students that there are two packages that contain five plastic spiders. Ask for a volunteer to show this relationship with counters. They should group two sets of five counters. Write an addition sentence as follows: 5 + 5 = 10.
6. Write the multiplication sentence 2 x 5 = 10. (There are two sets of 5)
7. Continue grouping objects until the students have mastered the concepts.
8. The students should be able to complete **Lesson 40 Practice** independently.

The only limit to our realization of tomorrow will be our doubts of today.
Franklin D. Roosevelt

Lesson 41

Concepts:

Multiplication properties, making change, odd and even numbers, estimating money, mystery numbers, missing numbers

Objectives:

1. The student will be able to match the multiplication property to the corresponding numerical example.
2. The student will be able to write the name of the terms in a multiplication problem.
3. The student will be able to determine the cost of several items using multiplication.
4. The student will be able to give change using the least amount of coins in amounts less than one dollar.
5. The student will be able to color even numbered stripes red and odd numbered stripes white.
6. The student will be able to color multiples of three white and multiples of 10 blue.
7. The student will be able to estimate the cost of items and add those estimates.
8. The student will be able to recognize place value through the hundred billions' place.
9. The student will be able to find missing digits in a subtraction problem given clues.

Teaching Tips:

1. Give the students an opportunity to use the counters and prove to themselves that the properties are true.

Materials, Supplies, and Equipment:

1. Multiplication Chart for reference
2. Beans, pennies, counters, or similar item that can be easily counted and grouped
3. Chart paper

Activities:

1. Write each of the multiplication properties on the board and challenge the students to prove that they are true using counters. Demonstrate with the Order Property of Multiplication.

3 x 2 = 6	2 x 3 = 6
oo	**ooo**
oo	**ooo**
oo	

2. The students might prove The Grouping Property of Multiplication as follows:

a. Work inside the brackets first.

(**2 x 4**) x 3 = 24	2 x (**4 x 3**) = 24
oooo	**ooo ooo**
oooo	**ooo ooo**
8	**12**

b. Work outside the brackets next.

(2 x 4) x 3 = 24	2 x (4 x 3) = 24
8 x 3	**2 x 12**
ooo ooo ooo ooo	**oooooooooooo**
ooo ooo ooo ooo	**oooooooooooo**
24	**24**

3. The students might prove the One Property of Multiplication as follows:

5 x 1 = 5 (five groups of one) **o o o o o = 5**

7 x 1 = 7 (seven groups of one) **o o o o o o o = 7**

4. The students might prove the Zero Property of Multiplication as follows:
   5 x 0 = 0 (five sets of zero) You have no counters to use, so the answer is 0.
5. Have the students restate the multiplication properties in their own words and write them on the chart paper. Keep this for future reference.
6. The students should be able to complete **Lesson 41 Practice** independently.

The grass withereth, the flower fadeth: but the word of God shall stand forever.
Isaiah 40:8

Lesson 42

Concepts:

Applying multiplication properties, multiplication, subtraction, mystery numbers, problem solving, standard form, word problems

Objectives:

1. The student will be able to multiply one-digit numbers applying the four rules of multiplication: Order Property, Grouping Property, One Property, Zero Property.
2. The student will be able to multiply two, one-digit numbers and identify the terms used in multiplication.
3. The student will be able to find the difference of two, five-digit numbers that require borrowing.
4. Given clues, the student will be able to use the problem solving skill of elimination and determine the value of a given number.
5. The student will be able to recognize even numbers and follow them through a maze.
6. Given a number written in words, the student will be able to write the number in standard form.
7. The student will be able to solve story problems using multiplication of two, one-digit numbers.

Teaching Tips:

1. Some students confuse the additive and multiplicative properties. If you note confusion, contrast 6 + 0 = 6, but 6 x 0 = 0 and 6 + 1 = 7, but 6 x 1 = 6.

Materials, Supplies, and Equipment:

1. Multiplication Chart for reference
2. Chart paper with multiplication rules

Activities:

1. Review the four properties of multiplication on their chart paper: Order Property, Grouping Property, One Property, Zero Property.
2. Place the following four examples on the board and ask the students to identify which property applies.

   2 x (3 x 5) = 30 so, (2 x 3) x 5 = 30 (Grouping Property of Multiplication)
   7 x 0 = 0 (Zero Property of Multiplication)
   4 x 5 = 20 and 5 x 4 = 20 (Order Property of Multiplication)
   5 x 1 = 5 (One Property of Multiplication)
3. The students should be able to complete **Lesson 42 Practice** independently.

The best thing about the future is that it comes one day at a time.
Abraham Lincoln

Lesson 43

Concepts:

Multiplication tables, multiples, mystery numbers, multiplication terms, multiplication properties, multiplication

Objectives:

1. The student will be able to complete a multiplication table.
2. The student will be able to find multiples and factors on a multiplication table.
3. Given clues, the student will be able to use the problem solving skill of elimination and determine the value of a given number.
4. The student will be able to identify the terms of a multiplication problem.
5. The student will be able to give an example of each of the four rules for multiplication.
6. The student will be able to multiply two, one-digit numbers and solve a riddle.

Teaching Tips:

1. Allow a little extra time for this activity. Students enjoy completing the table, but it is time consuming.

Materials, Supplies, and Equipment:

1. Multiplication Chart (*Worksheet 23*)
2. Markers
3. Rulers

Activities:

1. Read through lesson **43 Explanation** with the students.
2. Give each student a multiplication chart, a ruler, and marker. Demonstrate use of the chart with the problem 3 x 5 = 15. Have the students find the 3 across the top line and put a marker line on that number. Then have them find the 5 on the vertical column and place a marker line on that number. As they follow the lines, they will see that the lines intersect at the 15. 3 x 5 = 15. Let them draw over these lines with markers.
3. Repeat the procedure with the following problems:
   2 x 3 = 6, 1 x 1 = 1, 3 x 4 = 12, 5 x 4 = 20, and 0 x 1 = 0.
4. Have the students find the multiples of 3. (3, 6, 9, 12, 15)
5. Have the students find the multiples of 4. (4, 8, 12, 16, 20)
6. Assist the students as they complete the multiplication table on **Lesson 43 Practice**.

Best friends, bring out the best in you.
Author Unknown

Lesson 44

Concepts:

Prime and composite, prime factors, multiplication, place value, addition, word problems

Objectives:

1. The student will be able to complete a factor tree.
2. Given a composite number, the student will be able to find the prime factors.
3. The student will be able to multiply two, one-digit numbers and identify the terms used in multiplication.
4. Given a number written in words and a number written in numerals, the student will be able to determine if the two are equal or not equal.
5. The student will be able to find the sum of two, two-digit numbers.
6. The student will be able to solve a two step story problem. He/She will add three, four-digit numbers with decimal points to obtain a sum. The sum will be subtracted from a given number to determine the difference.

Teaching Tips:

1. Allow the students to use the multiplication chart for additional assistance.

Materials, Supplies, and Equipment:

1. Multiplication Chart
2. Markers
3. Chart paper
4. *Worksheet 24*

Activities:

1. Read **Lesson 44 Explanation** with the students. Have the students define prime numbers and composite numbers in their own words and write them on the chart paper. Give at least 5 examples of each type of number.
2. Give the students the opportunity to make factor trees using the factors 4 x 3. (The prime numbers are 2, 2, and 3.)
3. Allow them to continue making factor trees until they are confident and ready to work independently. Possible examples follow:

   4 x 7 (The prime factors are 2, 2, 7.)
   3 x 8 (The prime factors are 3, 2, 2, 2.)
   4 x 9 (The prime factors are 2, 2, 3, 3.)
   4 x 6 (The prime factors are 2, 2, 2, 3.)

I can start my day over again any time I choose.
Author Unknown

Lesson 45

Concepts:

Prime numbers, prime factors, multiplication, compare and order, addition, mystery numbers

Objectives:

1. The student will be able to use a prime number table to find prime and composite numbers.
2. The student will be able to find prime numbers in a table and shade them in to find a message.
3. The student will be able to find the prime factors of composite numbers.
4. The student will be able to order numbers ranging from two digit to six digit.
5. The student will be able to find the sum or two, two-digit numbers.
6. Given clues, the student will be able to use the problem solving skill of elimination and determine the value of a given number.

Teaching Tips:

1. Students who would like to complete a prime number table on their own may use Worksheet 25.

Materials, Supplies, and Equipment:

1. Poster from Lesson 44 Explanation
2. *Worksheet 25*

Activities:

1. Review the poster from **Lesson 44 Explanation** defining prime and composite numbers.
2. Read **Lesson 45 Explanation** with the students.
3. Call out the following numbers one at a time, and have the student tell if they are prime or composite: 3, 4, 6, 10, 11, 12, 13, 15, 17. (They may refer to the chart in **Lesson 45 Explanation** when necessary.)
4. The students should be able to complete **Lesson 45 Practice** independently. Assist the students as they complete **Lesson 45-2 Practice.**

Sticks and stones will break my bones, but words will wound forever.
Author Unknown

Lesson 46

Concepts:

Division terms, division, prime numbers, prime factors, product table, addition, place value, compare and order

Objectives:

1. The student will be able to write the name of terms in a division problem.
2. The student will be able to locate prime numbers in a table of numbers and shade them to find a message.
3. Given a composite number, the student will be able to find the prime factors.
4. The student will be able to complete a product table.
5. The student will be able to add two, three-digit numbers that require regrouping.
6. Given two numbers, the student will be able to determine their relationship using: < , > , and = .
7. The student will be able to order numbers ranging from three digit to seven digit.

Teaching Tips:

1. If students are having difficulty with division, take them back to the manipulative stage to reinforce the basic concepts.

Materials, Supplies, and Equipment:

1. Beans, pennies, counters, or similar item that can be easily counted and grouped
2. Overhead projector, transparent counters (for group instruction)
3. *Worksheet 26*

Activities:

1. Place ten counters randomly on the desk or overhead. Ask the students to rearrange the counters so that they are in even groups with none left over. Encourage them to discover all of the possible answers as follows:

   oo oo oo oo oo   **ooooo ooooo**   **oooooooooo**

2. Have the students say the division fact represented in each array as follows:

   oo oo oo oo oo (10 ÷ 2 = 5); ooooo ooooo (10 ÷ 5 = 2); oooooooooo (10 ÷ 1 = 10)

3. Give each student 20 counters and have them solve each division problem using the manipulatives.

   20 ÷ 5 = ooooo ooooo ooooo ooooo   20 ÷ 5 = **4**
   1 2 3 4

   20 ÷ 10 = oooooooooo oooooooooo   20 ÷ 10 = **2**
   1 2

   15 ÷ 3 = ooo ooo ooo ooo ooo   15 ÷ 3 = **5**
   1 2 3 4 5

   12 ÷ 4 = oooo oooo oooo   12 ÷ 4 = **3**
   1 2 3

4. Read **Lesson 46 Explanation** with the students. Review the division terms encouraging the student to memorize them.
5. The students should be able to complete **Lesson 46 Practice** independently. They may use counters to help them visualize the process.

He who has imagination without learning has wings and no feet.
Joseph Joubert

Lesson 47

Concepts:

Division properties, division, equations, prime factors, column addition, equations, subtraction

Objectives:

1. The student will be able to divide one-digit dividends by one-digit divisors applying the four rules of division: Division by One, Division by a Number Itself, Multiplication and Division are Related, Division by Zero.
2. The student will be able to divide one-digit dividends by one-digit divisors.
3. The student will be able to find a missing number in a multiplication number sentence.
4. The student will be able to determine if a number is prime or composite. If the number is composite, the student will be able to find the prime factors and shade them to spell a message.
5. The student will be able to find the sum of a column of four, two-digit numbers.
6. The student will be able to solve addition equations.
7. The student will be able to find the difference of two, four-digit numbers.

Teaching Tips:

1. If students are having difficulty with division properties, take them back to the manipulative stage to reinforce the basic concepts.

Materials, Supplies, and Equipment:

1. Poster paper
2. Markers

Activities:

1. Read **Lesson 47 Explanation** with the students. Have the students write the rules for division in their own words on poster paper.
2. Apply the property stating that multiplication and division are related. Give the students these three division problems to solve:

   $21 \div 7 = \mathbf{3}$ $\quad$ $4 \div 2 = \mathbf{2}$ $\quad$ $9 \div 3 = \mathbf{3}$

   Ask the students if anyone can check these problems using multiplication? The response should be as follows:

   $21 \div 7 = \mathbf{3}$ **(3 x 7 = 21)** $\quad$ $4 \div 2 = \mathbf{2}$ **(2 x 2 = 4)** $\quad$ $9 \div 3 = \mathbf{3}$ **(3 x 3 = 9)**

3. The students should be able to complete **Lesson 47 Practice** independently.

Courage is resistance to fear, mastery of fear—not absence of fear.
Mark Twain

Lesson 48

Concepts:

Application of division properties, division, equations, definitions, problem solving

Objectives:

1. The student will be able to divide one-digit dividends by one-digit divisors applying the four rules of division: Division by One, Division by a Number Itself, Multiplication and Division are Related, Division by Zero.
2. The student will be able to find a missing number in a multiplication number sentence.
3. The student will be able to solve addition equations.
4. The student will be able to define all addition, subtraction, multiplication and division terms.
5. The student will be able to solve story problems that involve addition of two and three, two-digit numbers.

Teaching Tips:

1. If students are having difficulty with division properties, take them back to the manipulative stage to reinforce the basic concepts.

Materials, Supplies, and Equipment:

1. **Lesson 47 Explanation**

Activities:

1. Review **Lesson 47 Explanation**.
2. Place the following four examples on the board and ask the students to identify which property applies:

$9 \div 9 = 1$	Division of a Number by Itself
$4 \div 1 = 4$	Division by One
$25 \div 5 = 5$ so, $5 \times 5 = 25$	Multiplication and Division are Related
$0 \div 7 = 0$ $7 \div 0 =$ is impossible	Division by Zero

3. The students should be able to complete **Lesson 48 Practice** independently.

Before I say something about someone else I should ask:
Is it true? Is it kind? Is it necessary?
Author Unknown

Lesson 49

Concepts:

Problem solving, division, subtraction, equations, word problems, place value

Objectives:

1. The student will be able to determine if there is too much or too little information given in a story problem.
2. The student will be able to divide one-digit dividends by one-digit divisors.
3. The student will be able to find the difference of two, two-digit numbers that require borrowing.
4. The student will be able to solve subtraction equations.
5. The student will be able to determine the cost of several items using multiplication, subtract it from a dollar amount, and determine the most reasonable amount of change to be given.
6. Given a number written in words, the student will be able to write it in numerals placing each digit in a box. The student will shade the boxes with zeros to spell a message.

Teaching Tips:

1. If the student is having difficulty, have them read the problem several times and restate it in their own words.

Materials, Supplies, and Equipment:

None

Activities:

1. Read **Lesson 49 Explanation** with the students.
2. The students should be able to complete **Lesson 49 Practice** with a little assistance.

All good is not God's will, but God's will is always good.
Watchman Nee

Lesson 50

Concepts:

Multiplication with carrying, division, addition, place value, round to ten, subtraction, definitions

Objectives:

1. The student will be able to multiply a three-digit number by a one-digit number with no carrying.
2. The student will be able to divide a one-digit divisor by two-digit dividend to yield a one-digit quotient.
3. The student will be able to identify the following division terms: divisor, dividend, and quotient.
4. The student will be able to identify odd and even sums.
5. The student will be able to identify place value up to the hundred billions' place.
6. The student will be able to round numbers to the nearest 10.
7. The student will be able to subtract a three-digit number from a three-digit number using the regrouping (borrowing) process.

Teaching Tips:

Remind the students that multiplication is really an easier way to do repeated addition.

Materials, Supplies, and Equipment:

1. Place value chart

Activities:

1. Read **Lesson 50 Explanation** together. Have the students write the example problem (121 x 3) on the place value chart. Remind them that each number stands for a specific value.

Thousands'	Hundreds'	Tens'	Ones'
	1	2	1
X			3
	3	6	3

2. Use graph paper, turn a piece of notebook paper sideways, or draw in place value columns so that the students keep all rows straight.
3. Continue to use the centimeter squares if necessary.
4. Have the students make up several problems and work them together. You may choose to play a game by dividing the students in half. The students take turns going two at a time. Each student makes up a problem (no larger than 4 digits by 1 digit), they swap problems, work them, compare them and then tell which answer is larger by writing it down as a mathematical sentence using >, <, & =. The students are given one point for answering the problem correctly and one point for writing the mathematical sentence correctly. See example:

$$\begin{array}{r} 235 \\ \times \quad 6 \\ \hline 1{,}410 \end{array} \qquad \begin{array}{r} 378 \\ \times \quad 4 \\ \hline 1{,}512 \end{array}$$

$1{,}410 < 1{,}512$ or $1{,}512 > 1{,}410$

5. The students should be able to complete **Lesson 50 Practice** independently.

Set your minds on things that are above, not on things that are on earth.
Colossians 3:2

Lesson 51

Concepts:

Multiplication with carrying, multiplication, division, odd and even, word problems, place value, round to 10, subtraction

Objectives:

1. The student will be able to multiply a three-digit number by a one-digit number using the regrouping process.
2. The student will be able to multiply a three-digit number by a one-digit number without using the regrouping process.
3. The student will be able to divide a one-digit divisor by a two-digit dividend yielding a one-digit quotient.
4. The student will be able to identify odd and even numbers.
5. The student will be able to solve multiplication word problems.
6. The student will identify place value through the billions' place
7. The student will be able to round given numbers to the tens' place.
8. The student will be able to subtract three-digit numbers, and larger, which require regrouping (borrowing) across zeros.

Teaching Tips:

Remind the students that each number has a specific place value. Remind them that when regrouping occurs you are regrouping a set of numbers, not one individual number.

Materials, Supplies, and Equipment:

1. Place value chart if necessary
2. Place value squares if necessary
3. *Worksheet 27*

Activities:

1. Read **Lesson 51 Explanation** together. Complete the example problem either on the place value chart or with the place value squares. This will give the student a visual representation of the regrouping process.
2. The students should be able to complete **Lesson 51 Practice** independently after completing the sample problem together. If students need additional assistance, continue using the place value chart, or squares.

A cheerful heart is good medicine.
Proverbs 17:22a

Lesson 52

Concepts:

Multiplication of 10, 100, and 1,000, multiplication, subtraction, ordinal numbers, expanded form, round to 100

Objectives:

1. The student will be able to use mental math to find products of basic facts and multiples of 10, 100, or 1,000 when one or both of the factors are multiples of 10, 100, or 1,000.
2. The student will be able to multiply a three-digit number by a one-digit number using the regrouping process.
3. The student will be able to multiply a three-digit number by a one-digit number with no carrying.
4. The student will be able to divide a one-digit divisor by two-digit dividend to yield a one-digit quotient.
5. The student will be able to recognize ordinal numbers by correctly completing a connect the dot.
6. The student will be able to recognize and correctly match given standard numbers and their expanded equivalents.
7. The student will be able to round numbers to the nearest 100.

Teaching Tips:

Materials, Supplies, and Equipment:

1. Place value chart if necessary
2. Place value squares if necessary
3. *Worksheet 28*

Activities:

1. Read **Lesson 52 Explanation** together. Complete the sample problems together and see if the students notice a pattern when multiplying multiples of 10.
2. The student should be able to complete **Lesson 52 Practice** independently.

He was delivered over to death for our sins
and was raised to life for our justification.
Romans 4:25

Lesson 53

Concepts:

Multiplication, multiplication by 10, 100, and 1,000, place value, expanded form, round to 100

Objectives:

1. The student will be able to multiply a two-digit number by a two-digit number using the regrouping process.
2. The student will be able to use mental math to find products of basic facts and multiples of 10, 100, or 1,000 when one or both of the factors are multiples of 10, 100, or 1,000.
3. The student will be able to multiply a three-digit number by a one-digit number using the regrouping (carrying) process.
4. The student will be able to identify a number written in standard form and write that same number in expanded form.
5. The student will be able to round a given number to the nearest 100s' place.

Teaching Tips:

When multiplying 2-digit numbers, or larger, it is a good idea to use graph paper or lined paper to keep each place value column straight.

Materials, Supplies, and Equipment:

1. Graph paper or lined paper
2. Place value chart if necessary

Activities.

1. Read **Lesson 53 Explanation** together. Write the sample problem on the graph paper placing only one number in each box. Label each place value column on the graph paper by drawing in heavy lines to indicate each column. Multiply the ones' column and write each answer digit in the appropriate box. Before multiplying the tens' column be sure to indicate to the students that they are now multiplying the tens' column and there fore their answer will have a zero on the end (refer to Lesson 52 on multiplying with multiples of 10). This is the reason for the "place holder" students are often instructed to place when multiplying larger numbers. (see below)

Thousands'	Hundreds'	Tens'	Ones'
		4	5
	X	3	1
		4	5
1	3	5	0
1	3	9	5

2. If students are having difficulty understanding, present the problem using the place value chart and the place value squares to give them a visual representation of each value.
3. Answer any questions that the students may have. Complete one or two more problems if necessary.

The student should be able to complete **Lesson 53 Practice** independently.

When the storm has swept by, the wicked are gone, but the righteous stand firm forever.
Proverbs 10:25

Lesson 54

Concepts:

Multiplication, multiplication by 10, 100, and 1,000, rounding 1,000, compare and order, multiplication properties

Objectives:

1. The student will be able to multiply a three-digit number by a two-digit number using the regrouping (carrying) process.
2. The student will be able to multiply a two-digit number by a two-digit number using the regrouping (carrying) process.
3. The student will be able to use mental math to find products of basic facts and multiples of 10, 100, or 1000 when one or both of the factors are multiples of 10, 100, or 1,000.
4. The student will be able to multiply a three-digit number by a one-digit number using the regrouping (carrying) process.
5. The student will be able to compare and order numbers through the hundred billions' place.
6. The student will be able to round numbers to the nearest 1,000.
7. The student will be able to write examples of given multiplication properties.

Teaching Tips:

Materials, Supplies, and Equipment:

1. Graph paper or lined paper
2. Place value chart if necessary
3. *Worksheet 29*

Activities:

1. Read **Lesson 54 Explanation** together. Divide the students into groups of two or three. Together work the sample problem explaining that these problems are worked exactly like the problems in **Lesson 53 Practice.**
2. Have the students work problems one and two on **Lesson 54 Practice** together. One student should write the problem, multiply the ones' column, and write the first portion of the answer (see below.)

$$\begin{array}{r} 128 \\ \times \underline{\ \ 23} \\ 384 \end{array}$$

   The second student should multiply the tens' column and write the second portion of the answer, and add the final answer (see below.)

$$\begin{array}{r} 128 \\ \times \underline{\ \ 23} \\ 384 \\ + \underline{2560} \\ 2,944 \end{array}$$

   After completing the problem, the students need to check each others work to verify that the answer is correct and verify that each student understands the multiplication process.
3. The students should be able to complete the rest of **Lesson 54 Practice** independently.

Cast your bread upon the waters, for after many days you will find it again.
Ecclesiastes 11:1

Lesson 55

Concepts:

Multiplication, compare and order, round to 1,000, multiplication terms

Objectives:

1. The student will be able to multiply a three-digit number by a multiple of 10, 100, or 1,000.
2. The student will be able to multiply a three-digit number by a two-digit number using the regrouping (carrying) process.
3. The student will be able to multiply a two-digit number by a two-digit number using the regrouping (carrying) process.
4. The student will be able to compare and order numbers through the hundred billions' place
5. The student will be able to round numbers to the 1000s' place.
6. The student will be able to identify the multiplication terms: multiplicand, multiplier, and product.

Teaching Tip:

You may wish to review **Lesson 52** on multiplication using multiples of 10 before beginning the lesson.

Materials, Supplies, and Equipment:

1. Place value chart if necessary

Activities:

1. Read **Lesson 55 Explanation** together. Have the students complete the sample problems.
2. For fun the students might enjoy multiplying problems with extremely large numbers once they have mastered the multiplication of multiples of 10, 100 and 1000. This could easily be turned into a game where one student creates a problem and another student works it.
3. The student should be able to complete **Lesson 55 Practice** independently.

Now faith is being sure of what we hope for and certain of what we do not see.
Hebrews 11:1

Lesson 56

Concepts:

Estimate products, multiplication, equations, missing numbers, definitions

Objectives:

1. The student will be able to estimate products by rounding each factor to the nearest 10 or 100.
2. The student will be able to multiply a three-digit number by 10, 100, or 1,000.
3. The student will be able to multiply a three-digit number by a two-digit number using the regrouping (carrying) process.
4. The student will be able to solve addition equations for the value n.
5. The student will be able to complete a word search containing various property names, terms, and place value names.
6. The student will be able to solve multiplication problems containing missing numbers within the product and the factors.

Teaching Tips:

Relate this activity to every day activities: going to the grocery store, calculating how many pieces of candy will be distributed to each child, etc.

Materials, Supplies, and Equipment:

1. One bag of candy

Activities:

1. Ask the students to count the total number of students in the classroom. Explain that you are going to distribute a treat to the students and that each student is to receive four pieces of candy. Explain that you have to purchase enough candy and therefore need to know about how much candy to buy. Ask the students how you could quickly complete a mathematical calculation which would give you an answer close enough to make this decision, but yet not have to calculate the exact answer. The answer is to estimate the problem. If there are 28 children in the room and each child is to receive 4 pieces of candy then we would multiply 30 X 4 (because 28 rounds to 30.) According to this equation we need about 120 pieces of candy. Wait to distribute the candy until the lesson is complete. Use it as a treat for completing the math lesson.
2. Read over **Lesson 56 Explanation** together and look at the sample problem. Answer any questions the students might have concerning the problem.
3. The student should be able to complete **Lesson 56 Practice** independently.
4. Distribute the candy appropriately.

The man who strays from the path of understanding comes to rest in the company of the dead.
Proverbs 21:26

Lesson 57

Concepts:

Equations, rounding, multiplication, equations, missing numbers, number properties

Objectives:

1. The student will be able to solve multiplication equations by solving for the value n.
2. The student will be able to estimate products by rounding each factor to the nearest 10 or 100.
3. The student will be able to multiply a three-digit number by 10, 100, or 1,000.
4. The student will be able to solve addition equations by solving for the value n.
5. The student will be able to match names of properties, terms, and place value with their corresponding examples.
6. The student will be able to solve multiplication problems containing missing numbers within the product and the factors.

Teaching Tips:

The students have done many equations and should not have any problem completing these simple subtraction equations.

Materials, Supplies, and Equipment:

1. *Worksheet 30*

Activities:

1. Read **Lesson 57 Explanation** together and complete the sample problem.
2. The student should be able to complete **Lesson 57 Practice** independently.

Store up for yourselves treasures in heaven, where thieves do not break in and steal.
For where your treasure is there your heart will be also.
Matthew 6:20-21

Lesson 58

Concepts:

Problem solving, equations, estimate, subtraction, equations, division terms

Objectives:

1. The student will be able to solve word problems using money when given a menu containing restaurant information.
2. The student will be able to solve multiplication equations by solving for the value N.
3. The student will be able to estimate products by rounding each factor to the nearest 10 or 100.
4. The student will be able to subtract a two-digit number from a two-digit number using the regrouping (borrowing) process if necessary.
5. The student will be able to solve subtraction equations by solving for the value *n*.
6. The student will be able to identify and label division terms when given an example problem.

Teaching Tips:

Many fun activities can be created using this lesson. Be as creative as you can using the resources that are available to you.

Materials, Supplies, and Equipment:

1. Takeout menus from a local restaurant
2. Calculators if needed
3. *Worksheet 31*

Activities:

1. Read **Lesson 58 Explanation** together. Complete the sample problems together.
2. Pass out menus form a local restaurant. Chose one or two students to place orders and then have the class calculate the cost of each order. Have several students come to the board and explain how they solved each problem. Pretend that the class is going to order pizza from this restaurant. Calculate how many pizzas would be needed, and then calculate the total order. Once this is done ask the students how to calculate the price each individual student would have to pay for their share or the pizza. These processes use many mathematical skills which are used everyday when ordering at a restaurant.
3. For enrichment divide the students into groups of three or four. Instruct the students to select one person to play waiter or waitress and write down the individual orders. Then each student is to calculate the cost of their order and how much the waitress/waiter should be tipped. This is a great opportunity to discuss how to calculate an appropriate tip when eating out. Have the groups swap orders and check each others calculations for accuracy.
4. The student should be able to complete **Lesson 58 Practice** independently.

Do not make friends with a hot-tempered man, do not associate with one easily angered or you may learn his ways.
Proverbs 22:24-25

Lesson 59

Concepts:

Problems solving, equations, multiplication, Roman numerals, geometric shapes, fractions

Objectives:

1. The student will be able to solve given word problems using the guess and check strategy of problem solving.
2. The student will be able to solve multiplication equations by solving for the missing value.
3. The student will be able to solve subtraction equations by solving for the value n.
4. The student will be able to identify and write the standard number when given its roman numeral equivalent.
5. The student will be able to identify and draw given geometric shapes.
6. The student will be able to identify and shade fractional pictures when given the standard fractional number.

Teaching Tips:

Some students don't understand whether a guess is reasonable or not. Stress that it is acceptable to guess in order to get started on some problems. Stress also that when guessing, try to think logically and make an educated guess, not just a guess.

Materials, Supplies, and Equipment:

1. Play money
2. Marbles

Activities:

1. Have 2 students come to the front of the classroom. Prior to the lesson, without allowing the rest of the class to see, give one student \$15.00 and one student \$14.00 worth of play money. Tell the class that student A has one more dollar than student B, and that the sum of the amounts is \$29.00. Then ask the students to guess how much money you have given each student.
2. Have 2 more students come to the front of the classroom. Prior to the lesson, without allowing the rest of the class to see, give one student 5 marbles and one student 7 marbles. Tell the class that student A has 2 more marbles than student B, and that the total number of marbles combined is 13. Then ask the class to guess how many marbles each student has. In both instances (activity 1 and 2) stress the importance of making the initial guess. Because some students are reluctant to guess, they need to understand the importance in making an initial **logical/rational** guess when solving some problems.
3. Go over the sample in **Lesson 59 Explanation** together and answer any questions.
4. The student should be able to complete **Lesson 59 Practice** independently.

Do not envy wicked men, do not desire their company;
for their hearts plot violence, and their lips talk about making trouble.
Proverbs 24:1-2

Lesson 60

Concepts:

Division, subtraction, equations, multiplication, multiplication tables

Objectives:

1. The student will be able to solve division problems with one-digit divisors and one-digit quotients.
2. The student will be able to subtract a four-digit number from a four-digit number across two or more zeros.
3. The student will be able to solve a multiplication equation.
4. The student will be able to round a two-digit number to the nearest ten and a three-digit number to the nearest hundred. The student will find the product of the estimated numbers.
5. The student will be able to find simple products and determine if the product is odd or even. The student will shade the even numbers to obtain a solution to a riddle.
6. The student will be able to find products given a three-digit multiplicand and a two-digit multiplier.

Teaching Tips:

If students have difficulty with division, these two strategies will be helpful. Take the student back to the manipulative stage to reinforce basic concepts. Help students see the relationship between multiplication and division as outlined in activity 5 and 6.

Materials, Supplies, and Equipment:

1. Multiplication Test (Worksheet pg. 32), and counters

Activities:

1. Have the students take the multiplication test.
2. Read the explanation in Lesson 60 with the students. Have a volunteer gather 81 counters. Have a student group the counters in even stacks of nine. How many counters are in each stack? **(9)**
3. Ask the students how one can check for accuracy. **(Multiply the quotient by the divisor.)**
4. Have the students orally solve the following problems: 14 ÷ 7 = ____
   24 ÷ 6 = ____   40 ÷ 8 = ____   25 ÷ 5 ____ **(Answers 2, 4, 5, 5)**
5. Tell the students that one can use multiplication to solve division problems.
   For instance, in the problem 14 ÷ 7 = ____, one might ask, _____ x 7 = 14.
   In the problem 24 ÷ 6 = ____ , one might ask, ______ x 6 = 24. **(Answers 2, 4)**
6. What might one ask for 40 ÷ 8 = ____ , and 25 ÷ 5 _____ ?
   (Answer ___ x 8 = 40 , ___ x 5 = 25)
7. The students should be able to complete **Lesson 60 Practice** independently.

Do not judge, or you too will be judged.
Matthew 7:1

Lesson 61

Concepts:

Division with remainders, multiplication, subtraction, prime numbers, mystery number

Objectives:

1. The student will be able to obtain a quotient with or without a remainder given a two-digit dividend and a one-digit divisor.
2. The student will be able to solve division problems with one-digit divisors and one-digit quotients.
3. The student will be able to round a two-digit number to the nearest ten and a three-digit number to the nearest hundred. The student will find the product of the estimated numbers.
4. The student will be able to subtract a four-digit number from a four-digit number across two or more zeros.
5. The student will be able to find the product of a three-digit multiplicand and a two-digit multiplier.
6. Given a set of numbers, students will be able to find the numbers that are prime. The student will be able to follow directions to construct a star.
7. Given clues, the student will be able to find a mystery number from a set of numbers.

Teaching Tips:

Allow the students time to practice simple division problems with and without remainders. This concept takes a lot of review and reinforcement. The game below, Stumper, was designed to meet that goal.

Materials, Supplies, and Equipment:

1. Counters, 1 die, 20 index cards, answer key, paper, and pencil
2. *Worksheet 33*

Activities:

1. Read the explanation in Lesson 61 with the students. Have a volunteer gather 38 markers. Have a student group the counters in even stacks of nine. How many counters are in each stack? **(4 with 2 left over, so the answer is 4 r 2)**
2. Ask the students how one can check for accuracy. **(Multiply the quotient by the divisor and add the remainder.)**
3. For division practice, allow the students to play the game **Stumper** (below).
4. The students should be able to complete **Lesson 61 Practice** independently.

<u>**STUMPER**</u> Two or three players can enjoy this game.

Materials: One die, 20 index cards, answer key, paper and pencil.

Getting Ready: Write one problem or statement on each index card, as follows:

1. $17 \div 3 =$ ____	2. $23 \div 7 =$ ____	3. $27 \div 4 =$ ____
4. $33 \div 8 =$ ____	5. $27 \div 5 =$ ____	6. $50 \div 7 =$ ____
7. $10 \div 3 =$ ____	8. $15 \div 4 =$ ____	9. $37 \div 6 =$ ____
10. $31 \div 6 =$ ____	11. $42 \div 6 =$ ____	12. $56 \div 8 =$ ____
13. $63 \div 9 =$ ____	14. $64 \div 8 =$ ____	15. $20 \div 5 =$ ____
16. $21 \div 7 =$ ____		

17. Draw again and double your points.
18. Add five points and draw again.
19. Subtract 2 points and draw again.
20. Add 10 points and draw again.

Procedure:

1. Decide who will go first.
2. Player One draws a card and solves the problem. If the answer is correct (Use the Answer Key), Player One may roll the die to see how many points he/she earned. If he/she rolls a 4, Player One gets 4 points. Record the score. If the answer is incorrect, no score is earned. It is the next player's turn.
3. Player Two draws a card and solves the problem. If the answer is correct, Player Two may roll the die to see how many points he/she earned. Record the score.
4. After each play, the number of points is added to the previous score. The player who reaches 25 first wins the game.

Answer Key for Stumper

1.	5 r 2	2.	3 r 2	3.	6 r 3	4.	4 r 1	5.	5 r 2	6.	7 r 1
7.	3 r 1	8.	3 r 3	9.	6 r 1	10.	5 r 1	11.	7	12.	7
13.	7	14.	8	15.	4	16.	3				

Some folks worry and putter, push and shove,
hunting little molehills to make big mountains of.
Author Unknown

Lesson 62

Concepts:

Division, word problems, odd and even, multiplication

Objectives:

1. The student will be able to find two-digit quotients with remainders when given a one-digit divisor and a three-digit dividend.
2. The student will be able to obtain a quotient with or without a remainder given a two-digit dividend and a one-digit divisor.
3. The student will be able to solve division problems with one-digit divisors and one-digit quotients.
4. The student will be able to solve division word problems with one-digit quotients and remainders.
5. The student will be able to find odd numbers in a set of numbers and solve a puzzle.
6. The student will be able to find the product of a three-digit multiplicand and a two-digit multiplier.

Teaching Tips:

Allow the students to refer to the division steps as needed. Turn a piece of lined paper sideways to maintain straight columns.

Materials, Supplies, and Equipment:

1. Posterboard and marker
2. *Worksheet 34*

Activities:

1. Read lesson **62 Explanation** with the students. Work through the example problem verbalizing each step.
2. Have the students make a poster with the division steps. Save this for future lessons.
3. Turn a piece of lined paper sideways and write the problems in **Lesson 62 Practice** in columns, as shown below. This will help the student maintain straight columns alleviating common errors.

		9	5	r 2
4	3	8	2	
	- 3	6		
		2	2	
		- 2	0	
			2	

4. Have the student work through the problems referring to their poster as needed. The student may need assistance in completing this exercise.

Commit to the Lord whatever you do, and your plans will succeed.
Proverbs 16:3

Lesson 63

Concepts:

Dividing money, division, odd and even, word problems, equations, missing numbers

Objectives:

1. The student will be able to solve a division money problem with two-digit quotients, one-digit divisors, and three-digit dividends.
2. The student will be able to find two-digit quotients with remainders when given a one-digit divisor and a three-digit dividend.
3. The student will be able to solve division problems with one-digit divisors and one-digit quotients. The student will shade the even quotients to solve a puzzle.
4. The student will be able to solve division word problems that involve money with one-digit divisors and two-digit quotients with remainders.
5. The student will be able to solve a multiplication equation.
6. Given a sequential set of numbers, the student will be able to determine the three numbers that come next.

Teaching Tips:

Allow the students time to practice simple division problems with and without remainders. This concept takes a lot of review and reinforcement.

Materials, Supplies, and Equipment:

1. Poster from **Lesson 62,** 20 index cards, and play money
2. *Worksheet 35*

Activities:

1. Review the division steps as outlined on the poster from **Lesson 62.**
2. Review the first problem in **Lesson 63** emphasizing that the decimal point in the quotient is directly above the decimal point in the dividend.
3. Review the second problem in **Lesson 63.** Explain the importance of placing the zero in the tenths' place.
4. Have the student write the following amounts in decimal form: 5¢ , 25¢ , 7¢ , 80¢ , 8¢ . **(Answers $.05, $.25, $.07, $.80, $.08)** Allow students to the play the game **Bust the Bank** (below) for reinforcement.
5. The students should be able to complete the problems in **Lesson 63 Practice** independently.

Bust the Bank

Materials: 20 index cards, play money

Getting Ready: Write the numbers given below on the index cards. The dollar amount should be written on one side, the corresponding amount in cents should be written on the other.

1.	30¢	$.30	2.	45¢	$.45	3.	7¢	$.07	4.	5¢	$.05
5.	1¢	$.01	6.	19¢	$.19	7.	26¢	$.26	8.	13¢	$.13
9.	11¢	$.11	10.	4¢	$.04	11.	6¢	$.06	12.	12¢	$.12
13.	21¢	$.21	14.	9¢	$.09	15.	33¢	$.33	16.	2¢	$.02
17.	8¢	$.08	18.	10¢	$.10	19.	18¢	$.18	20.	35¢	$.35

Procedures

1. Shuffle the cards. It does not matter which side is up.
2. Decide who goes first.

3. Player One draws a card. He/She reads the amount on the card and writes the corresponding amount that appears on the back of the card without looking at it. The player will turn the card over. If the answer is correct, the student will get play money to equal the amount on the card. If the answer is wrong, the student loses his turn, and the next player draws a card.
4. The first student to get $1.00 wins the game.

If ye have faith as a grain of mustard seed...nothing shall be impossible unto you.
Matthew 17:20

Lesson 64

Concepts:

Division, division with money, rounding, missing numbers

Objectives:

1. The student will be able to divide numbers with one-digit divisors and two-digit quotients with zeros.
2. The student will be able to solve a division money problem with two-digit quotients, one-digit divisors, and three-digit dividends.
3. The student will be able to find two-digit quotients with remainders when given a one-digit divisor and a three-digit dividend.
4. The student will be able to obtain a quotient with or without a remainder given a two-digit dividend and a one-digit divisor.
5. Given a set of numbers, the student will be able to circle numbers that round to the nearest ten. The student will be able to identify even, prime, and composite numbers.
6. Given a sequential set of numbers, the student will be able to determine the three numbers that come next.

Teaching Tips:

Students often leave out zeros in the quotient when dividing. Encourage them to work carefully and check their work using multiplication.

Materials, Supplies, and Equipment:

Poster from **Lesson 62**

Activities:

1. Review the division steps using the poster from **Lesson 62**.
2. Ask the students the following question. If they were buying 109 magazines at $3 a piece, how much would it cost? ($327)
3. Write the following problem on the board and have the students solve. Explain the division process at each stage.

```
     1 0 9
 3 )3 2 7
   -3
    0 2
   - 0
      2 7
     -2 7
        0
```

4. Ask the students what would happen if they did not write 0 in the quotient. **(The answer would be 19. This is incorrect 19 x 3 does not equal 327.)**
5. Advise the students to work the problems carefully in **Lesson 64 Practice.** It is easy to leave out a zero. Encourage them to check the first two problems using multiplication to make sure they are on track.

Behold the Lamb of God, which taketh away the sin of the world.
John 1:29

Lesson 65

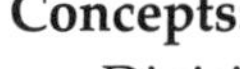

Concepts:

Division, dividing money, round to 10, missing numbers, definitions

Objectives:

1. The student will be able to divide numbers with one-digit divisors and four-digit quotients.
2. The student will be able to divide numbers with one-digit divisors and three-digit quotients. The student will be able to match the answer with the corresponding letter to spell a word.
3. The student will be able to solve division money problems with one-digit divisors and three-digit quotients.
4. The student will be able to shade numbers that round to 10.
5. The student will be able to look at a series of numbers and find a pattern. The student will be able to write the next three numbers to continue the pattern.
6. The student will be able to define: triangle, decagon, quadrilateral, octagon, hexagon, and pentagon.

Teaching Tips:

It is critical that students keep the columns straight when dividing larger numbers.

Materials, Supplies, and Equipment:

1. Poster from **Lesson 62**
2. *Worksheet 36*

Activities:

1. Review the division steps using the poster from **Lesson 62**.
2. Turn a piece of lined paper sideways and write the example problem in **Lesson 65 Explanation** in columns. This will help the student maintain straight columns alleviating common errors.
3. Have the students work through the problem explaining the division process at each stage.
4. Ask the students: **The first number in the quotient is above what number in the dividend? (4)**
5. Point out that the 4 in the divisor divides into the 4 in the dividend 1 time. Many of the problems they will encounter do not follow this pattern. Look at the problem in example 2.
6. Have the students work through problem 2 explaining the division process at each stage.
7. Ask the students: **The first number in the quotient is above what number in the dividend? (0)**
8. Point out that the 3 in the divisor does not divide into the one in the dividend, so we leave that space above the 1 blank. The 3 in the divisor divides into the 10 in the dividend 3 times. Thus, the 3 is placed above the 0 in the dividend.
9. Encourage the students to turn lined paper sideways and work the problems in **Lesson 65 Practice** carefully.

My presence shall go with thee, and I will give thee rest.
Exodus 33:14

Lesson 66

Concepts:

Divisibility, division, dividing money, equations, definitions

Objectives:

1. The student will be able to apply the divisibility rules for 2, 5, 10, and 3.
2. The student will be able to divide numbers with one-digit divisors and four-digit quotients.
3. The student will be able to divide numbers with one-digit divisors and three-digit quotients.
4. The student will be able to solve division money problems with one-digit divisors and four-digit quotients.
5. The student will be able to shade numbers that round to 80 and find their way through a maze.
6. The student will be able to solve addition equations.
7. The student will demonstrate an understanding of the following terms: multiplicand, divisor, minuend, quotient, dividend, addend, sum, product, difference, multiplier, subtrahend, and addend.

Teaching Tips:

Students enjoy learning the divisibility rules and applying the knowledge. Give them the opportunity to write the rules in language that they understand.

Materials, Supplies, and Equipment:

1. Manila Paper and Markers
2. *Worksheet 37*

Activities:

1. Read the divisibility rules aloud with the students answering any questions they might have.
2. Give each student a piece of manila paper and markers. Have them rewrite the rules in a manner that is easy for them to understand.
3. Work the problems in **Lesson 66 Practice** with the students using their rules as a guide.

The soul would have no rainbows if the eyes had no tears.
Author Unknown

Lesson 67

Concepts:

Average, divisibility, division, word problems, equations, addition, round to 100

Objectives:

1. Given three or four numbers, the student will be able to find the average.
2. The student will be able to shade a set of numbers that are divisible by three and find a mystery number.
3. The student will be able to divide numbers with one-digit divisors and four-digit quotients and solve a puzzle.
4. The student will be able to solve story problems that involve dividing one-digit divisors and three-digit dividends.
5. The student will be able to solve addition equations.
6. The student will be able to round numbers to the nearest hundred and solve a puzzle.

Teaching Tips:

Review the Order Property of Addition.

Materials, Supplies, and Equipment:

1. *Worksheet 12*

Activities:

1. Ask the students to give examples of when averages are used.(**Baseball averages, grades, average heights and weights...etc.)**
2. Read **Lesson 67 Explanation** with the students.
3. Ask the students **Can I put the addends in any easy to add order, or do I need to leave them as they are written? (The Order Property of Addition states that any order is acceptable)**
4. Ask the students **Why is 450 divided by the number 5? (You divide by the number of addends.)**
5. Work the first two examples in **Lesson 67 Practice** with the students. Allow them to complete the lesson independently.

I have learned silence from the talkative;
tolerance from the intolerant and kindness from the unkind.
I should not be ungrateful to those teachers.
Kahil Gibran

Lesson 68

Concepts:

Equations, average, divisibility, dividing money, missing numbers

Objectives:

1. The student will be able to solve division equations.
2. Given three or four numbers, the student will be able to find the average.
3. The student will be able to apply the divisibility rules for 2, 5, 10, and 3.
4. The student will be able to solve division money problems with one-digit divisors and four-digit quotients.
5. Given two three-digit addends and a sum with missing numbers, the student will be able to determine the value of the missing numbers.
6. The student will be able to solve subtraction equations.

Teaching Tips:

Help students who have difficulty by demonstrating the problem using counters. For instance, $n \div 7 = 2$. Allow the student to place 2 counters in each of seven groups. Add the counters to find that $n = 14$.

Materials, Supplies, and Equipment:

1. *Worksheet 38*

Activities:

1. Review the terms equation and variable.
2. Read the example problem in **Lesson 68 Explanation**.
3. Solve the problem verbalizing each step in the process.
4. Observe the students as they work the first two problems in **Lesson 68 Practice.** Allow them to complete the lesson independently.

The gift of God is eternal life through Jesus Christ our Lord.
Romans 6:23

Lesson 69

Concepts:

Problem solving, equations, averaging, divisibility, column addition, prime numbers

Objectives:

1. The student will be able to determine if the remainders in a division problem should be dropped or if the quotient should be rounded to the next higher number.
2. The student will be able to solve division equations.
3. Given three or four numbers the student will be able to find the average.
4. The student will be able to apply the divisibility rules for 2, 5, 10, and 3.
5. The student will be able to find the sum of four, two-digit numbers.
6. The student will be able to determine two consecutive numbers, or two consecutive odd numbers, or two consecutive even numbers that equal a given sum.

Teaching Tips:

Students readily grasp this concept given a visual representation.

Materials, Supplies, and Equipment:

29 counters, 5 sandwich bags

Activities:

1. Tell the students to place the 29 counters EVENLY in 4 bags. **(7 counters will go in each bag with one remaining)**
2. Point out that what is done with the left over counter depends on the question asked.
3. Ask the students **How many bags would be needed to hold 29 counters if only 7 counters could go in each bag? (The answer is 5. One bag would only have one.)**
4. Ask the students **How many bags can be filled with 7 counters each? (The answer is 4. The remaining counter can be discounted.**
5. Work the problems in **Lesson 69 Explanation** orally verbalizing each step in the process.
6. Guide the students as they solve the story problems in **Lesson 69 Practice.**

Other men's sins are before our eyes; our own are behind our backs.
Seneca

Lesson 70

Concepts:

Dividing by 10, equations, average, subtraction, multiplication, missing numbers

Objectives:

1. The student will be able to rewrite a division problem vertically and divide by two-digit divisors using divisors and dividends that are multiples of 10.
2. The student will be able to solve for the value n in division equations
3. The student will be able to calculate an average when given a specific set of numbers.
4. The student will be able to subtract two-digit numbers using the regrouping (borrowing) process.
5. The student will be able to multiply three-digit numbers by two-digit numbers using the regrouping (carrying) process.
6. The student will be able to identify and continue a specified number pattern when given examples of that pattern.

Teaching Tips:

Completing a division problem can be like completing an equation. You are solving for a missing value. Practicing a few basic division problems before the lesson might be good exercise for the students.

Materials, Supplies, and Equipment:

1. Multiplication chart if necessary
2. *Worksheet 39*

Activities:

1. Read **Lesson 70 Explanation** with the students. Look for a pattern in the sample problems and have the students complete the next step in the pattern. Remind the students that dividing by multiples of 10 has a pattern just like multiplying be multiples of 10 (refer to **Lessons 52 & 55**).
2. Have the students make up several division problems. Together work them on the board and create a pattern just like the sample in the lesson. Allow the students to use the multiplication chart only if necessary.
3. The student should be able to complete **Lesson 70 Practice** independently.

For it is by grace that you have been saved, through faith–and this not from yourselves, it is a gift of God–not by works, so that no one can boast.
Ephesians 2:8-9

Lesson 71

Concepts:

Division by multiples of 10, equations, subtraction, missing numbers, multiplication

Objectives:

1. The student will be able to complete division problems with two-digit divisors that are multiples of 10 and dividends that are two or three-digit numbers.
2. The student will be able to divide by two-digit divisors using divisors and dividends that are multiples of 10.
3. The student will be able to solve for the value n in division equations.
4. The student will be able to subtract two-digit numbers using the regrouping (borrowing) process.
5. The student will be able to multiply three-digit numbers by two-digit numbers using the regrouping (carrying) process.
6. The student will be able to identify and continue a specified number pattern when given examples of that pattern.

Teaching Tips:

A good way to have the students to remember the steps to a division problem is to develop an acronym with the first letters in each step of a division problem; <u>Step</u> <u>1</u>: **D**ivide; <u>Step</u> <u>2</u>: **M**ultiply; <u>Step</u> <u>3</u>: **S**ubtract; <u>Step</u> <u>4</u>: **C**heck and **B**ring down. An acronym sentence might be "**D**oes **M**cDonalds **S**ell **C**heese **B**urgers" (**D**ivide, **M**ultiply, **S**ubtract, **C**heck, **B**ring down.)

Materials, Supplies, and Equipment:

1. Multiplication sheet, or calculator, if needed

Activities:

1. Read **Lesson 71 Explanation** together. Have the students write down the sample problem and complete each step together labeling each step of the division problem (Divide, Multiply, Subtract, Check & Bring down.) Let the students know that a calculator can help them with the multiplication when doing a division problem, but if there is a remainder to the problem, most calculators <u>will not</u> state the remainder. Most calculators round the remainder into a decimal instead of indicating the actual numerical reminder. Allow them to divide the sample problem and compare the actual answer and remainder to the answer and remainder provided by the calculator. The actual answer is 7 Remainder 14; the calculator rounds the reminder to a decimal and shows an answer of 7.7. This will also help the students to understand that they must understand and demonstrate the mathematical process, as well as understand the operations of a calculator, before using a calculator to solve math equations.
2. Complete the first problem of **Lesson 71 Practice** together to insure the students understand the division process. Work with any students, individually, who may need additional assistance.
3. The student should be able to complete the rest of **Lesson 71 Practice** independently.

Blessed is the man who perseveres under trial, because when he has stood the test, he will receive the crown of life that God has promised to those who love him.
James 1:12

Lesson 72

Concepts:

Division, subtraction, word problems, equations

Objectives:

1. The student will be able to divide two-digit divisors into two- and three-digit dividends with one-digit quotients.
2. The student will be able to complete division problems with two-digit divisors that are multiples of 10 and dividends that are two- or three-digit numbers.
3. The student will be able to divide by two-digit divisors using divisors and dividends that are multiples of 10.
4. The student will be able to subtract three-digit numbers using the regrouping (borrowing) process if necessary.
5. The student will be able to read and interpret information concerning the position and value of ordinal numbers within the context of a story problem.
6. The student will be able to solve for the value n within a multiplication equation.

Teaching Tips:

Remind the students that sometimes <u>educated guessing</u> is acceptable when solving a problem. Refer to Lesson 59 if needed. A good explanation for educated guessing would be when a student tries an answer, or a problem solving method, because he/she has experienced success with that solving process/ answer, when solving a similar problem. This can aid a student when solving a large division problem.

Materials, Supplies, and Equipment:

1. Calculator (for multiplication steps and checking ONLY)
2. *Worksheet 40*

Activities:

1. Give the following example problem to start the lesson: 11 postmen have 627 letters to deliver. About how many letters will each man deliver? Estimating can help the student solve this problem for the exact answer.

```
      57
11 ) 627
   - 55
      77
    - 77
       0
```

Guessing (estimating):
11 rounds to 10 and 10 goes into 62 six times. Try 11 x 6.
11 x 6 = 66. That is close but is larger than 62. Try 11 x 5 = 55 .

Point out the steps of solving a division problem while working this sample problem (Divide, Multiply, Subtract, Check & Bring down.) This problem demonstrates how educated guessing can aid when solving for larger quotients. Read **Lesson 73 Explanation** together and solve the sample problems together. Multiplication table charts, or calculators, may be used, however, the student is still to show all his/her work. Remind them that using calculators on division problems with remainders will not yield the correct answer unless it is a specific type of calculator, and that they are to be used only for checking work.

2. The student should be able to complete **Lesson 73 Practice** independently.

Everyone should be quick to listen, slow to speak and slow to become angry, for man's anger does not bring about the righteous life that God desires.
James 1:19b-20

Lesson 73

Concepts:

Division, subtraction, money, mystery numbers

Objectives:

1. The student will be able to estimate answers to larger division problems and identify whether an estimate is reasonable or not when given and estimated problem.
2. The student will be able to divide two-digit divisors into two- and three-digit dividends with one-digit quotients.
3. The student will be able to complete division problems with two-digit divisors that are multiples of 10 and dividends that are two- or three-digit numbers.
4. The student will be able to complete subtraction problems which require regrouping (borrowing) across zeros.
5. The student will be able to calculate and count change which should be received after a given purchase transaction has occurred.
6. The student will be able to identify a mystery number by evaluating clues which describe the number's value.

Teaching Tips:

Remind the students that educated guessing, estimating, will aid in solving larger division problems. When solving larger division problems a calculator will probably be needed as an aid. Make sure they are always seen as a resource and not an easy way to solve a problem. The student should be calculating the work and showing all steps, not relying on the calculator. Monitor this carefully.

Materials, Supplies, and Equipment:

1. Calculator (for multiplication steps and checking ONLY)
2. *Worksheet 41*

Activities:

1. Read **Lesson 74 Explanation** together. Complete the sample problem together and notice each step carefully. If extra practice is needed, complete the following problems: 224 ÷ 21 and 584 ÷ 36.
2. The student should be able to complete **Lesson 74 Practice** independently. Please allow extra time for the students to work slowly and accurately. Stress accuracy, not speed. have the student check each problem manually by multiplying and then adding the remainder.

Every man will have to give account on the day of judgment
for every careless word they have spoken.
For by your words you will be acquitted,
and by your words you will be condemned.
Matthew 12:36-37

Lesson 74

Concepts:

Division, money, word problems

Objectives:

1. The student will be able to complete division problems with two-digit divisors, three and four-digit dividends, and two-digit quotients.
2. The student will be able to estimate answers to larger division problems and identify whether an estimate is reasonable or not when given and estimated problem.
3. The student will be able to divide two-digit divisors into two- and three-digit dividends with one-digit quotients.
4. The student will be able to complete division problems (on a division wheel) with two-digit divisors that are multiples of 10 and dividends that are two- or three-digit numbers.
5. The student will be able to calculate and count change which should be received after a given purchase transaction has occurred.
6. The student will be able to solve word problems which require formulating and completing a division equation or problem.

Teaching Tips:

Using graph paper, or lined paper like that used when multiplying large numbers, will be a tremendous aid if the students are having difficulty keeping the numbers and lines straight.

Materials, Supplies, and Equipment:

1. Graph paper, or lined paper.
2. Calculator (for multiplication steps and checking ONLY)
3. *Worksheet 42*

Activities:

1. Read **Lesson 74 Explanation** together. Have the students copy the sample problem onto their graph paper. Follow the sample directions and use the class acronym developed to remember the steps in the division process (see Lesson 71).
2. Allow the students to work in pairs and complete number one on **Lesson 74 Practice**. The paired students should take turns working different steps of the problem. For example: student 1 might complete steps 1 & 2 of the division process, while student 2 completes steps 3 & 4. Once the problem is completed, one set of paired students should swap problems with another set of paired students and check each others work. If one group has worked the problem incorrectly then their original problem is returned to them and they must find the error and correct it.
3. The student should be able to complete **Lesson 74 Practice** independently.

Do not testify against our neighbor without cause, or use your lips to deceive.
Proverbs 24:28

Lesson 75

Concepts:

Division, reasonable and not reasonable, correcting errors, money, geometric shapes

Objectives:

1. The student will be able to solve long division problems which contain a zero in the quotient.
2. The student will be able to complete division problems with two-digit divisors, three and four-digit dividends, and two-digit quotients.
3. The student will be able to estimate answers to larger division problems and identify whether an estimate is reasonable or not when given and estimated problem.
4. The student will be able to divide two-digit divisors into two- and three-digit dividends with one-digit quotients.
5. The student will be able to write a specified amount of money in dollar and cent notation when given a picture reference.
6. The student will be able to identify and label specific shapes, including a pentagon, hexagon, and octagon, when given a picture of that geometric shape.

Teaching Tips:

An interesting addition to Lesson 75 might be to discuss a scale of miles and practice finding actual mileage using real maps. You could then plan a pretend vacation and calculate how many miles need to be driven in a day to complete the vacation in a specified length of time.

Materials, Supplies, and Equipment:

1. Calculator if needed (to aid with multiplication and check ONLY)
2. Graph paper or lined paper

Activities:

1. Solve these problems with the entire class, reviewing the steps in the division process. Remind students how to round (estimate) the divisor in order to help solve for the quotient.

   189 ÷ 37   162 ÷ 51   192 ÷ 94   390 ÷ 61
2. Read **Lesson 75 Explanation** together. Complete and discuss the sample problem.
3. The student should be able to complete **Lesson 75 Practice** independently.

The prayer offered in faith will make the sick person well,
the Lord will raise him up.
If he has sinned, he will be forgiven.
James 5:15

Lesson 76

Concepts:

Dividing money, division, estimate division, geometric shapes, money

Objectives:

1. The student will be able to complete division problems containing dividends which are dollar amounts.
2. The student will be able to solve long division problems which contain a zero in the quotient.
3. The student will be able to complete division problems with two-digit divisors, three and four-digit dividends, and two-digit quotients.
4. The student will be able to estimate answers to larger division problems and identify whether an estimate is reasonable or not when given and estimated problem.
5. The student will be able to write a specified amount of money in dollar and cent notation when given a picture reference.
6. The student will be able to identify and match specific shapes, including a triangle, square and rectangle, when given a picture of that geometric shape.

Teaching Tips:

It might be useful to remind the students of the place value chart and how decimals are part of the place value chart as the "change" side. A good graphic is shown below:

Hundreds	Tens	Ones	Tenth	Hundredths
		$2	. 1	5
	$1	3	. 2	5
$3	9	6	. 0	0

Materials, Supplies, and Equipment:

1. Place value chart (for reference if needed)
2. Graph paper or lined paper (if needed)
3. *Worksheet 43*

Activities:

1. Write 125 cents on the chalkboard. Ask the students how many dollars and cents does 125 cents equal. Put a dollar sign and decimal point in when answered correctly. Write the following amounts on the board and complete each the same way:
   257 pennies = _____ dollars and ____ cents = $__.__
   975 pennies = _____ dollars and ____ cents = $__.__
   99 pennies = _____ dollars and ____ cents = $__.__
   1,357 pennies = _____ dollars and ____ cents = $__.__
   Review place value by asking question such as: "What digit tells how many dimes?" or "What digit tells how many dollar bills?"

2. Use a newspaper, catalogue, or sale advertisement and discuss specials such as 3 bars of soap for $3.75. Explain how division is used to calculate the individual prices in such deals and that by doing so you might discover some "deals" aren't actually "deals."

3. Go over **Lesson 76 Explanation** together. Work the sample problem together and discuss it. Allow the students to calculate the actual price of several items in the sale advertisements, catalogues, or newspaper aids, to practice dividing with money.
4. The student should be able to complete **Lesson 76 Practice** independently.

Confess your sins to each other and pray for each other so that you may be healed. The prayer of a righteous man is powerful and effective.
James 5:16

Lesson 77

Concepts:

Dividing money, correcting errors, money, telling time

Objectives:

1. The student will be able to estimate long division problems by rounding the divisor and the dividend.
2. The student will be able to complete division problems containing dividends which are dollar amounts.
3. The student will be able to solve long division problems which contain a zero in the quotient.
4. The student will be able to complete division problems with two-digit divisors, three and four-digit dividends, and two-digit quotients.
5. The student will be able to write a specified amount of money in dollar and cent notation when given a picture reference.
6. The student will be able to identify the indicated time, and passing of time, when presented with a clock face.

Teaching Tips:

A review of rounding might prove helpful before beginning the lesson.

Materials, Supplies, and Equipment:

1. Multiplication chart or calculator if necessary

Activities:

1. Read **Lesson 77 Explanation** together.
2. Discuss the sample problems and answer any questions.
3. The student should be able to complete **Lesson 77 Practice** independently.

Do not forget to entertain strangers in need,
for by doing so some people have entertained angels without knowing it.
James 13:2

Lesson 78

Concepts:

Dividing money, division and rounding, place value, equations

Objectives:

1. The student will be able to complete given problem solving situations which require the use of division.
2. The student will be able to estimate long division problems by rounding the divisor and the dividend.
3. The student will be able to complete division problems containing dividends which are dollar amounts.
4. The student will be able to solve long division problems which contain a zero in the quotient.
5. The student will be able to match given (indicated) numbers with their appropriate place value.
6. The student will be able to solve for a given value (n) in a subtraction equation.

Teaching Tips:

Most of the students should understand the division process very well. You might use this lesson as a way to incorporate various other skills with the division process.

Materials, Supplies, and Equipment:

1. Multiplication chart or calculator if necessary

Activities:

1. Read **Lesson 78 Explanation** together and discuss the sample problems. Remind the students of the steps involved in solving a division problem.
2. Divide the students into groups of three or four. Use mail order catalogues and have the students go shopping for a special occasion; Christmas, or someone's Birthday, etc. Tell them that the group is to find a nice present to give to someone for the special occasion, and the group is to divide the cost of the present evenly. After calculating the cost of the present, you might review how to write a check by having them write a check for the cost of the present
3. The student should be able to complete **Lesson 77 Practice** independently.

Therefore, since we are receiving a kingdom that cannot be shaken,
let us be thankful, and so worship God acceptable with reverence and awe,
for our "God is a consuming Fire."
Hebrews 12:28-29

Lesson 79

Concepts:

Problem solving, standard form, telling time, prime and composite, equations, geometric shapes

Objectives:

1. The student will be able to complete problem solving exercises by making an organized list.
2. The student will be able to match given (indicated) numbers with their appropriate place value.
3. The student will be able to identify the indicated time, and passing of time, when presented with a clock face.
4. The student will be able to identify prime and composite numbers.
5. The student will be able to solve for a given value (n) in a subtraction equation.
6. The student will be able to draw specific geometric shapes, including a triangle, square, rectangle, pentagon, hexagon, and octagon, when given the name of that geometric shape.

Teaching Tips:

Problem solving through the use of charts and diagrams to aid in the solution is a terrific skill to practice in conjunction with math. The students really love a good mental challenge if it is presented in a fun way. There are many resource books available that contain these type of problems which are great enrichment activities for students.

Materials, Supplies, and Equipment:

1. *Worksheet 44*

Activities:

1. Read **Lesson 79 Explanation** together and discuss the sample problem.
2. The student should be able to complete **Lesson 79 Practice**.

Make every effort to live in peace with all men and to be holy;
without holiness no one will see the Lord.
Hebrews 12:14

Lesson 80

Concepts:

Time definitions, equations, multiplication, division of money, expanded form, subtraction

Objectives:

1. The student will be able to identify time definitions.
2. The student will be able to solve subtraction and addition equations by finding a value *n*.
3. The student will be able to complete division problems containing dividends and quotients which are dollar amounts.
4. The student will be able to write a given number in standard form.
5. The student will be able to write a given number in expanded form.
6. The student will be able to subtract two-digit numbers and use the regrouping process as needed.
7. The student will be able to multiply two- and three-digit numbers and use the regrouping process as needed.

Teaching Tips:

Most of the students will not have any difficulty grasping this concept. For most of them it will be review. Try to make it as interesting as possible.

Materials, Supplies, and Equipment:

Activities:

1. Read **Lesson 80 Explanation** together and discuss it with the students.
2. The student should be able to complete **Lesson 80 Practice** independently.

For the Lord your God is a merciful God; He will not abandon or destroy you or forget the covenant with your forefathers, which he confirmed to them by oath.
Deuteronomy 4:31

Lesson 81

Concepts:

Telling time, equations, expanded form, subtraction, multiplication, time definitions

Objectives:

1. The student will be able to use a clock to determine time.
2. The student will be able to identify and define time definitions.
3. The student will be able to solve addition and subtraction equations for a value of *n*.
4. The student will be able to find a sum or difference using estimation.
5. The student will be able to write a given written number in standard form.
6. The student will be able to write a given standard number in expanded form.
7. The student will be able to subtract two-digit numbers using the regrouping process as needed.

Teaching Tips:

Materials, Supplies, and Equipment:

1. Demonstration clock
2. *Worksheet 45*

Activities:

1. Read **Lesson 81 Explanation** together and review the time equivalents posted in the box under Explanation.
2. Show the students the demonstration clock. Have them identify the hour, minute, and second hands. Then show the student the following times on the clock and have them read the times to you: 7:20. 4:15, 9:30, 1:45, 5:00, and 12:00. Have volunteers move the hands of the clock to show the following times: 3:30, 6:00, 2:45, 11:20.
3. Go over the explanation on **Lesson 81 Explanation** which details how and why the expression a "quarter after," "a quarter before," or "half after" is used. Use the demonstration clock to illustrate this point. Practice reading the following times on the demonstration clock: 5:45, 7:15, 3:30, 1:45, 6:45, 12:15.
4. The student should be able to complete **Lesson 81 Practice** independently.

Acknowledge and take to heart that the Lord is God in heaven above and on the earth below. There is no other. Keep His decrees and commands ... so that it may go well with you and your children after you, and that you may live long in the land the Lord your God gives you for all time.

Deuteronomy 4:39-40

Lesson 82

Concepts:

Telling time, time definitions, compare and order, subtraction, equations, division

Objectives:

1. The student will be able to use a clock to determine time and use the terms A.M. and P.M. correctly.
2. The student will be able to use a clock to determine time.
3. The student will be able to solve addition and subtraction equations for a value of *n*.
4. The student will be able to compare and order a given set of numbers from the largest to the smallest.
5. The student will be able to subtract three-digit numbers using the regrouping process as needed.
6. The student will be able to solve a multiplication equation for a value of *n*.
7. The student will be able to complete division problems containing a one-digit divisor, a one-digit dividend, and yield a one-digit quotient.

Teaching Tips:

The abbreviation A.M. stands for "ante meridian" which means between midnight and noon. The abbreviation P.M. means "post meridian" and means between noon and midnight.

Materials, Supplies, and Equipment:

1. Demonstration clock

Activities:

1. Read **Lesson 82 Explanation** together. Write the following times on the board: 2:00 P.M., 11:00 A.M., 9:45 P.M., and 6:25 A.M.. Have the students take turns reading the time and telling whether each is morning, afternoon or night. Have them show each time on the demonstration clock.
2. The student should be able to complete **Lesson 82 Practice** independently.

There will always be poor people in the land. Therefore I command you to be openhanded toward your brothers and toward the poor and needy in your land.

Deuteronomy 15:11

Lesson 83

Concepts:

Century, telling time, order numbers, subtraction, division, average

Objectives:

1. The student will be able to identify the present century and identify what century a given date is in.
2. The student will be able to use a clock to determine time and use the terms A.M. and P.M. correctly.
3. The student will be able to use a clock to determine time.
4. The student will be able to compare and order a given set of numbers from the smallest to the largest.
5. The student will be able to complete subtraction problems which require subtraction and regrouping across zeros.
6. The student will be able to complete division problems which contain a one-digit divisor, a one-digit dividend, and quotients which contain remainders.

Teaching Tips:

Most students will want to know why the century numbers do not match the beginning numbers of the year; for example why 1809 is not the 18th century. Direct them to **Lesson 83 Explanation** and remind them that because a time period of 100 years has to pass before it is called a century, the years 0–99 A.D. are considered the 1st century.

Materials, Supplies, and Equipment:

1. A timeline of historical events (can be obtained from any history book or encyclopedia)

Activities:

1. Read **Lesson 83 Explanation** together and look over the listing of century dates. Take the historical timelines and have the students pick 4 historical events (for example the American Revolution, World War II, The Civil War, and The Louisiana Purchase). Have the students name the date and century in which these major events occurred.
2. Most students will want to know why the century numbers do not match the beginning numbers of the year; for example why 1809 is not the 18th century. Direct them to **Lesson 83 Explanation** and remind them that because a time period of 100 years has to pass before it is called a century, the years 0–99 A.D. are considered the 1st century.
3. The student should be able to complete **Lesson 83 Practice** independently.

The grace of our Lord was poured out on me abundantly, along with the faith and love that are in Christ Jesus.
1 Timothy 1:14

Lesson 84

Concepts:

Time conversions, telling time, division, division by 10, problem solving

Objectives:

1. The student will be able to identify and write time equivalents.
2. The student will be able to identify the present century and identify what century a given date is in.
3. The student will be able to use a clock to determine time and use the terms A.M. and P.M. correctly.
4. The student will be able to use a clock to determine time.
5. The student will be able to complete division problems which contain a one-digit divisor, one-digit dividend, and yield a quotient of zero.
6. The student will be able to complete division problems which contain 2-digit divisors which are multiples of 10.

Teaching Tips:

Link time conversions and equivalents to everyday life. Always remember that relevancy to real world activities is necessary for the students to grasp the importance of all math concepts.

Materials, Supplies, and Equipment:

1. Several popular videos (age and content appropriate)
2. Demonstration clock
3. *Worksheet 46*

Activities:

1. Show the display clock and ask the students how many minutes are in an hour, how many minutes are in two hours, how many hours are in one day, and how many seconds are in two minutes. Call on students to answer individually and then have them come up and demonstrate the correct answer on the demonstration clock. This should get the students thinking in the correct direction.
2. Tell the students that you have planned to show a movie in class today. You only have 1 hour to show the movie, and the movie is 120 minutes long. Ask the students if the class will have enough time to see the entire movie in the 1 hour time slot. The answer, of course, is no. Ask the students who answer "no" how they arrived at that answer. The correct response would be that 120 minutes is 2 hours, and therefore the movie is longer than the allotted viewing period.
3. Read **Lesson 84 Explanation** together. Answer any questions that the students might have.
4. The student should be able to complete **Lesson 84 Practice** independently.

There are six things the Lord hates, seven that are detestable to him: haughty eyes, a lying tongue, hands that shed innocent blood, feet that are quick to rush into evil, a false witness who pours out lies, and a man who stirs up dissension among brothers.

Proverbs 6:16-19

Lesson 85

Concepts:

Elapsed time, time conversions, A.M., P.M., divisibility, division, money

Objectives:

1. The student will be able to use the relationships between units of time in order to identify or calculate elapsed time.
2. The student will be able to identify and write time equivalents.
3. The student will be able to identify the present century and identify what century a given date is in.
4. The student will be able to use a clock to determine time and use the terms A.M. and P.M. correctly.
5. The student will be able to identify numbers which are divisible by 2, 5, 10, and 3.
6. The student will be able to complete division problems which contain 2-digit divisors which are multiples of 10.
7. The student will be able to calculate and count the change due from a given purchase or transaction.

Teaching Tips:

Explain that estimating elapsed time and calculating elapsed time is extremely important in the work place. In order to schedule appointments, a salesman needs to be able to calculate elapsed travel time when arranging appointments and meeting customers. If a salesman did not have this skill he might have customers waiting on him, missing him, and consequently loosing business.

Materials, Supplies, and Equipment:

1. Demonstration clock
2. Daily planner sheets (taken from a business planner which a business person would use)
3. *Worksheet 47*

Activities:

1. Put the following appointments on the board:

   9:15 meeting with Pastor Kendall
   12:00 Lunch with Mr. Wallace
   1:30 meeting with Mr. Carmichael of APNC Industries
   3:00 pick up Caroline from school

   Instruct the students to write each event on their daily planner sheets by the appropriate time slot. Then instruct them to pretend that they are a businessman/woman and need to attend all of these appointments for the day. Travel time between each appointment is at least 30 minutes. Have the students calculate the maximum amount of time which can be spent at each appointment without being late for the next appointment. After the students have had time to work explain that this is an example of calculating elapsed time.
2. Read **Lesson 85 Explanation** together. Complete the sample problems. Answer any questions the students might have.
3. The student should be able to complete **Lesson 85 Practice** independently. Monitor the students in case further assistance is needed.

To everything there is a season, and a time to every purpose under the heaven:
A time to be born, and a time to die; a time to plant,
and a time to pluck up that which is planted...
Ecclesiastes 3: 1-2

Lesson 86

Concepts:

Calendar conversions, elapsed time, time conversions, century, division, change

Objectives:

1. The student will be able to read a calendar and use a calendar correctly.
2. The student will be able to use the relationships between units of time in order to identify or calculate elapsed time.
3. The student will be able to identify and write time equivalents.
4. The student will be able to identify the present century and identify what century a given date is in.
5. The student will be able to complete division problems which contain a two-digit divisor and a one-digit quotient.
6. The student will be able to calculate and count the change due from a given purchase or transaction.

Teaching Tips:

Have the students memorize the poem, if they do not already have it memorized.

Materials, Supplies, and Equipment:

1. A calendar for the entire year

Activities:

1. Take the calendar apart and place all the months on the board (in order) so that the students can see the entire year at once (see below).

January	February	March	April	May	June
July	August	September	October	November	December

   Check the number of days in each month to ensure that the poem is correct. Then have the students answer several questions using these monthly calendars. Ask questions like: How many days are between Thanksgiving and Christmas? How many weeks is that? or How many weeks are there between Easter and Halloween.

2. Have the students read **Lesson 86 Explanation**. Complete the sample questions together and discuss any questions together.
3. The student should be able to complete **Lesson 86 Practice** independently.

Whoever loves money never has money enough;
whoever loves wealth is never satisfied with his income.
This too is meaningless.
Ecclesiastes 5:19

Lesson 87

Concepts:

Time zones, calendar conversions, word problems, time conversions, place value, equations

Objectives:

1. The student will be able to identify time zones and compare time zone differences.
2. The student will be able to read a calendar and use a calendar correctly.
3. The student will be able to identify and write time equivalents.
4. The student will be able to identify place value through the hundred billions' place.
5. The student will be able to solve subtraction equations for a value of n.
6. The student will be able to complete division problems which contain a two-digit divisor and a one-digit quotient.
7. The student will be able to use the relationships between units of time in order to identify or calculate elapsed time.

Teaching Tips:

With satellite dishes easily available and affordable these days, some students have experienced time zone differences by watching news or sporting events on channels which are broadcast from cities in different time zones that their own.

Materials, Supplies, and Equipment:

1. Local television viewing guide (schedule)
2. Flashlight
3. Tennis ball (or some other small round ball)
4. 2 Push pins

Activities:

1. Have the students browse through the television viewing guides and pick out stations which broadcast the news (or favorite TV shows) at a different hour than the local channels (for example if living in Georgia where the news is broadcast at 12:00 P.M., 6:00 P.M., and 11:00 P.M., watching a channel in Chicago would show the news at 11:00 A.M., 5:00 P.M., and 10:00 P.M. Georgia time because of the time zone difference.) Discuss why the news in Chicago would be shown in Atlanta at 10:00 P.M. rather than 11:00 P.M..
2. Read **Lesson 87 Explanation** together. Work the sample problems together and answer any questions.
3. Illustrate how the rotation of the Earth results in the necessity for different time zones. Tell the students to imagine that the tennis ball is the Earth and the flashlight is the Sun. Push one push pin into the tennis ball and have it represent Atlanta. Push the second push pin into the ball at least 2 inches to the left of the first pin. This second pin will represent Los Angeles. While shining the light on the ball, rotate the ball to show that the Earth is constantly rotating. Discuss that fact that the rotation of the Earth as the Sun shines on cities in the East before shining on cities in the West. Point out that the sun shines on the push pin representing Atlanta before it shines on the pin representing Los Angeles. By the time the sun is shining on Los Angeles, the Atlanta push pin is in darkness. This illustrates why it is 10:00 in Atlanta, 9:00 in Chicago, 8:00 in Denver, 7:00 in Los Angeles and 5:00 in Hawaii. Remember to make sure the student understands that there are 24 time zones in all (24 hours in the day). This might be a good time to correlate Geography and Math by discussing the Prime Meridian and the International Date Line.

4. The student should be able to complete **Lesson 87 Practice** independently.

He was despised and rejected by men,
a man of sorrows, and familiar with suffering. Like one from whom men hide their faces he was despised and we esteemed him not.
Isaiah 53:3

Lesson 88

Concepts:

Logical reasoning, time zones, calendar conversions, elapsed time, place value, equations

Objectives:

1. The student will be able to solve a logic problem using two variables.
2. The student will be able to identify time zones and compare time zone differences.
3. The student will be able to read a calendar and use a calendar correctly.
4. The student will be able to use the relationships between units of time in order to identify or calculate elapsed time.
5. The student will be able to identify place value through the hundred billions' place.
6. The student will be able to identify and label prime and composite numbers.
7. The student will be able to solve subtraction equations for a value of n.

Teaching Tips:

If you have the students practice logic problems daily, or at least once a week they will greatly improve in this area. A variety of logic resources are available at teacher stores.

Materials, Supplies, and Equipment:

1. *Worksheet 48*

Activities:

1. Read **Lesson 88 Explanation** thoroughly. Discuss the strategies listed and ask the students if they have ever worked these type of problems another way. Remember, this example is just one strategy.
2. Have the student complete **Lesson 88 Practice** independently. After the students are finished complete the problem together and discuss the processes involved in solving the problem.

So then, just as you received Christ Jesus as Lord, continue to live in him, rooted and built up in him, strengthened in the faith as you were taught, and overflowing with thankfulness.

Colossians 2:6

Lesson 89

Concepts:

Word problems, standard form, expanded form, multiplication, fractions, comparing numbers

Objectives:

1. The student will be able to complete problem solving activities by using a strategy of working backwards to solve for an answer.
2. The student will be able to write a given number in standard form.
3. The student will be able to write a given standard number in expanded form.
4. The student will be able to solve multiplication problems which contain a three-digit muliplicand and a two-digit multiplier and requires use of the regrouping process.
5. The student will be able to complete addition of fractions with like denominators.
6. The student will be able to compare numbers through the hundred thousands' place value.

Teaching Tips:

Materials, Supplies, and Equipment:

1. *Worksheet 49*

Activities:

1. Read **Lesson 89 Explanation** together and discuss the sample problem.
2. Work the first problem in **Lesson 89 Practice** together. The student should be assigned to complete problem 2 independently.

Everyone should be quick to listen, slow to speak, and slow to become angry, for man's anger does not bring about the righteous life that God desires.
James 1:19-20

Lesson 90

Concepts:

Geometric terms, parallel and perpendicular, word problems, addition, time zones, calendar equivalence, expanded form

Objectives:

1. The student will be able to define, recognize in pictures, write in symbols, and verbalize the following geometric terms: point, line, line segment, ray, intersecting lines, parallel lines and perpendicular lines.
2. The student will be able to solve story problems using the reasoning skill of working backwards.
3. The student will be able to add two-digit numbers with carrying.
4. Given a time in one time zone, the student will be able to determine the time in the other time zones in the United States.
5. The student will be able to solve story problems involving elements of time: years in a century; years in a decade; days, months, and weeks in a year; days in a week.
6. The student will be able to write numbers in standard form given numbers in expanded forms.

Teaching Tips:

These concepts are not difficult to understand, but take repeated practice to memorize.

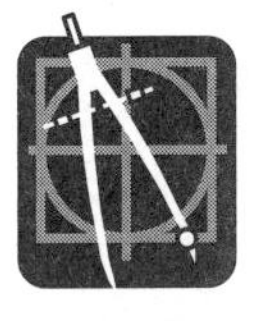

Materials, Supplies, and Equipment:

1. Manila paper
2. 9 index cards
3. *Worksheet 50*

Activities:

1. **Geometric terms:** Write each of the following terms on manila paper and ask the students to think of examples of each: point, line, line segment, ray, intersecting lines, parallel lines, perpendicular lines. For instance, a thumb tack might be an example of a point, the top and bottom of the chalkboard might be an example of parallel lines.
2. Students have little difficulty memorizing the definitions, but they need practice writing the geometric pictures, symbols, and words. To help with this skill, play Geometry Genius.
3. Have the student complete **Lesson 90 Practice** with the help of the chart in **Lesson 90 Explanation.**

<u>**Geometry Genius**</u>

Materials:

9 index cards and a chalkboard.

Getting Ready:

Write the following phrases on three index cards: Geometry in Pictures, Geometry in Symbols, Geometry in Words. Draw a game board on the chalkboard like the one on the next page.

Geometry Terms	Geometry in Pictures	Geometry in Symbols	Geometry in Words
Point			
Line			
Line Segment			
Ray			
Intersecting Lines			
Parallel Lines			
Perpendicular Lines			

Procedure:

a. Divide the class into two groups and decide who will go first. This may also be played with two players.

b. Place the index cards on a table word-side down.

c. Player One draws a card, reads it, and places it on the bottom of the deck. If he/she turns over **Geometry in Pictures**, the player will choose any of the lines under the column **Geometry in Pictures** and draw and label a picture. If the card is impossible to use because all the spaces are taken, draw again. Check the table in Lesson 90 for accuracy. The student may label the picture with letters of his choice. If the player's example is incorrect, he/she loses their turn and the example is erased. If it is correct, the drawing remains on the board.

d. Player Two follows the same procedure. If he/she draws a card for **Geometry in Symbols**, the player will choose any of the lines not completed under the column **Geometry in Symbols**. If the student chooses a row that already has a label, the same label must be used. For instance, if player two wants to place a letter under **Geometry in Symbols** in the row **Point** and a •K has already been placed under **Geometry in Pictures,** player two would need to use the label K.

e. **Strategy:** Points may be obtained by completing a row. For instance, if two of the columns have been completed under **Point**, the team to fill in the last column will score one point. They will also get to take another turn.

f. The team that gets the most points after the chart is completed wins the game.

Today I will make every attempt to see the good in all that I encounter.
Author Unknown

Lesson 91

Concepts:

Angles, geometric terms, word problems, time zones, multiplication, addition

Objectives:

1. Given an angle, the student will be able to define the rays and vertex.
2. The student will be able to label an angle in three different ways and will be able to determine if an angle is right, obtuse, or acute.
3. The student will be able to find pairs of lines that are perpendicular, parallel, or intersecting.
4. The student will be able to observe and name the following figures: point, line, line segment, and ray.
5. The student will be able to solve story problems using the reasoning skill of working backwards.
6. Given a time in one time zone, the student will be able to determine the time in the other given time zones in the United States.
7. The student will be able to find the product of a three-digit multiplicand and two-digit multiplier.
8. The student will be able to find the sum of two three-digit numbers that involve carrying.

Teaching Tips:

Students enjoy making tagboard strip angles and readily understand the concept.

Materials, Supplies, and Equipment:

1. Tagboard strips one inch wide and six inches long (2 per child), Punch a hole in one end of each strip
2. Metal brads (1 per child)

Activities:

1. Read **Lesson 91 Explanation** with the students. Emphasize that an angle is two rays that meet at a vertex. Explain that there are three names for any one angle.
2. Give each child two tagboard strips and a metal brad. Have them join the two pieces of tagboard together so the holes match. Place the brad through the hole and spread the ends of the brad.

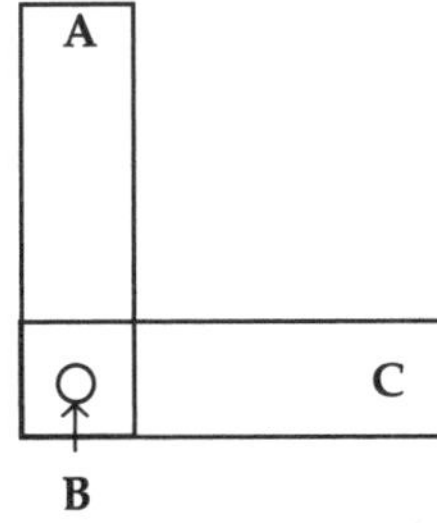

3. Have the students label their angle ∠**ABC**
4. Ask the students to name each ray. **($\overrightarrow{BA}$ and $\overrightarrow{BC}$)**
5. Ask the students to name the vertex. **(vertex B)**
6. Ask the students to name the three different ways to label this angle. **(∠ABC, ∠CBA, ∠B)**
7. Ask the students to move the tagboard so that their angle is acute. Obtuse. Right. Check each student's angle for accuracy.
8. Students should be able to complete **Lesson 91 Practice** independently.

Conversation is the laboratory and workshop of the student.
Ralph Waldo Emerson

Lesson 92

Concepts:

Polygons, average, angles, geometric terms, word problems, column addition

Objectives:

1. The students will be able to define and recognize the following: polygons, regular polygons, vertices, quadrilateral, triangle, pentagon, hexagon, and octagon.
2. The student will be able to label an angle in three different ways and determine if an angle is right, obtuse, or acute.
3. The student will be able to average numbers.
4. The student will be able to determine if an angle is right, obtuse, or acute.
5. The student will be able to match the following geometric terms with their picture: point, line, line segment, ray, intersecting lines, parallel lines, and perpendicular lines.
6. The student will be able to solve story problems using the reasoning skill of working backwards.
7. The student will be able to find the sum of four two-digit numbers.

Teaching Tips:

Students enjoy making tagboard strip polygons and readily learn the information.

Materials, Supplies, and Equipment:

1. 8 tagboard strips 1 inch wide and 5 inches long (per child), Punch a hole in each end
2. 2 tagboard strips 1 inch wide and 2 1/2 inches long (per child), Punch a hole in each end
3. 8 brads (per child)

Activities:

1. Read **Lesson 92 Explanation** orally with the students. Emphasize the definition of a polygon and the difference between a polygon and a regular polygon.
2. Pass out the tagboard and brads.
3. Tell the students to make one of the figures found in the lesson out of their tagboard and brads. They should be ready to tell the name of the polygon, number of sides, and number of vertices.
4. Allow the students to come to the front of the room and show their polygon. They should be able to tell the name of the polygon, number of sides, and number of vertices.
5. The students should be able to complete **Lesson 92 Practice** independently.

He that hath my commandments, and keepeth them, he it is that loveth me: and he that loveth me shall be loved of my father, and I will love him, and will manifest myself to him.

John 14:21

Lesson 93

Concepts:

Congruent and similar, polygons, geometric terms, subtraction, division

Objectives:

1. The student will be able to recognize and draw congruent and similar figures.
2. The student will be able to recognize the following polygons: quadrilateral, triangle, pentagon, hexagon, and octagon.
3. The student will be able to label an angle in three different ways and will be able to determine if an angle is right, obtuse, or acute.
4. The student will be able to draw and label the following geometric terms: point, line, line segment, ray, intersecting and parallel lines.
5. The student will be able to find the difference of two three-digit numbers that require borrowing.
6. The student will be able to find the quotient given a one-digit divisor and a two-digit dividend.
7. The student will be able to recognize the following polygons: quadrilateral, triangle, pentagon, hexagon, and octagon.

Teaching Tips:

The use of manipulatives enhances this lesson.

Materials, Supplies, and Equipment:

1. 10 tagboard strips 1 inch wide and 5 inches long (per child), Punch a hole in each end
2. 5 tagboard strips 1 inch wide and 2 1/2 inches long (per child), Punch a hole in each end.
3. 10 brads (per child)
4. *Worksheet 51*

Activities:

1. Read **Lesson 93 Explanation** orally with the students. Emphasize the definition of congruent and similar figures.
2. Pass out tagboard strips and brads.
3. Construct a square out of 4 large tagboard strips. Ask the students to construct a congruent figure.
4. Using the same tagboard square, have the students make a similar figure. **(It should be the same shape, but not the same size.)**
5. Continue to use the manipulatives until you feel the students have mastered the concepts.
6. The students should be able to complete **Lesson 93 Practice** independently.

Books are the treasured wealth of the world and
the fit inheritance of generations and nations.
Henry David Thoreau

Lesson 94

Concepts:

Symmetry, polygons, angles, congruent and similar, division, calendar equivalence, polygons

Objectives:

1. The student will be able to find lines of symmetry.
2. The student will be able to recognize the following polygons: decagon, quadrilateral, triangle, pentagon, hexagon, and octagon.
3. The student will be able to label an angle in three different ways and will be able to determine if an angle is right, obtuse, or acute.
4. The student will be able to recognize and draw congruent and similar figures.
5. The student will be able to find the quotient given a one-digit divisor and a two-digit dividend.
6. The student will be able to define the following words: A.M., P.M., 1st century, 21st century, 20th century, midnight, decade, millennium, and century.
7. The student will know and apply the following information: there are 7 days in a week, 24 hours in a day, and 60 minutes in an hour.
8. The student will be able to draw and label the following quadrilaterals: rhombus, rectangle, trapezoid, and parallelogram.

Teaching Tips:

Materials, Supplies, and Equipment:

1. 2 pieces of paper (per child)
2. 1 pair of scissors (per child)
3. *Worksheet 52*

Activities:

1. Read **Lesson 94 Explanation** orally with the students. Ask the students to point out objects in the room that are symmetrical.
2. Pass out paper and scissors.
3. Have the children fold one piece of paper in half. Tell them to cut a design out of the side of the paper that is not folded. Instruct the children to open the paper. What do they notice? **(It is symmetrical and the fold is the line of symmetry)**

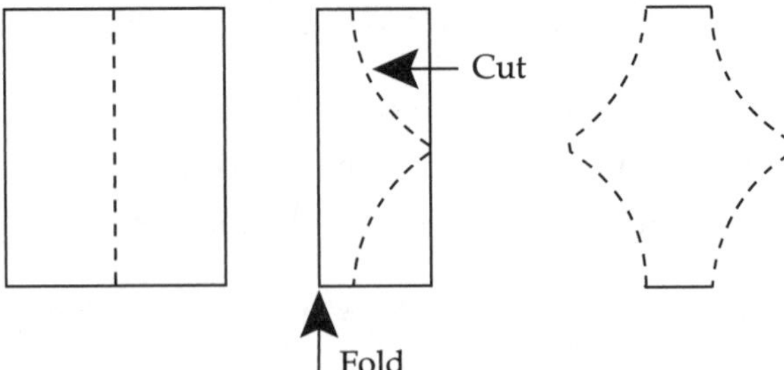

4. Have the children fold one piece of paper in half lengthwise. Instruct the children to fold it again across the width. (If opened, the paper would form a cross.) Cut the design out of the side of the paper not folded. Open the paper. What do they notice? **(It is symmetrical with two lines of symmetry along each fold.)**
5. The children should be able to complete **Lesson 94 Practice** independently.
6. JUST FOR FUN- Have the students design a symmetrical shape that they might want to use to wallpaper their room, or tile their floor.

Mathematics is the door and key to the sciences.
Roger Bacon

Lesson 95

Concepts:

Circles, symmetry, similar figures, geometric terms, polygons, division, time terms

Objectives:

1. The student will be able to identify the radius, diameter, and name of a circle.
2. Given a diameter, the student will determine the radius. Given a radius, the student will be able to determine the diameter.
3. The student will be able to determine if certain letters of the alphabet are symmetrical.
4. The student will be able to draw similar figures to ones given.
5. The student will be able to match the following terms with the pictures: acute, obtuse, right, perpendicular, parallel, and intersecting.
6. The student will be able to draw the following figures: octagon, pentagon, triangle, hexagon, and quadrilateral.
7. The student will be able to find the quotient given a one-digit divisor and a two-digit dividend.
8. The student will be able to define the following words: A.M., P.M., A.D., B.C., decade, century, and millennium.

Teaching Tips:

Allow plenty of time to learn to use a compass.

Materials, Supplies, and Equipment:

1. 1 compass (per child)
2. 1 ruler (per child)

Activities:

1. Read **Lesson 95 Explanation** orally with the students.
2. Ask the students to name things in the room that are circular.
3. Distribute a compass to each student and a ruler.
4. Demonstrate how to draw a circle using a compass. Point out the centerpoint and how each point on the circle is equidistant from that point. Label the circle using the diagram below.

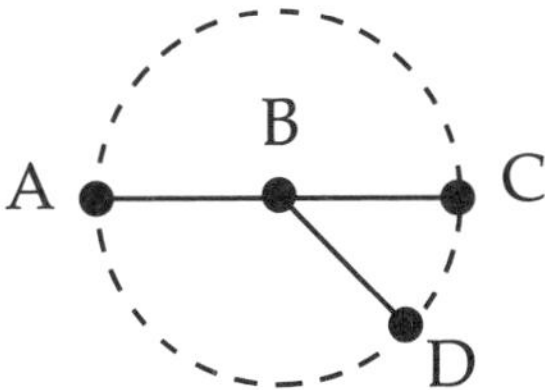

5. Have the students draw circles using their compass. Let them practice until they feel comfortable with the equipment.
6. Allow each child to draw a circle and label it. Tell them that you hope to get circles of different sizes.
7. Ask each child to measure the diameter and radius of their circle in centimeters.
8. Place a chart on the board and have the students come to the board and place the measurements from their circle.

Radius	Diameter

9. What did the students notice about the radius and diameter?
   (The radius x 2 equals the diameter)
10. Ask the students the following questions about their circle:
    Name the circle. **(Circle B)** Name the diameter. **($\overline{AC}$)**
    Name the three radii. **($\overline{AB}$,$\overline{BC}$,$\overline{BD}$** or **$\overline{BA}$,$\overline{CB}$,$\overline{DB}$** since the order of the letters can be reversed**)**
11. The students should be able to complete **Lesson 95 Practice** independently.

Be not deceived; God is not mocked: for whatsoever a man soweth, that shall he also reap.
Galatians 6:7

Lesson 96

Concepts:

Space figures, geometric shapes, circles, congruent and similar, round to 10, divisibility

Objectives:

1. The students will recognize five types of space figures: cones, cylinders, pyramids, spheres, and prisms.
2. The student will be able to give the number of edges, faces, and vertices of a space figure.
3. The student will be able to identify the radius, diameter, and name of a circle.
4. Given a diameter, the student will determine the radius. Given a radius, the student will be able to determine the diameter.
5. The student will recognize the following figures: triangle, rectangle, oval, hexagon, octagon, decagon, diamond, rhombus, square, and parallelogram.
6. The student will be able to draw similar and congruent figures.
7. The student will be able to round two-digit numbers to the nearest 10.
8. The student will be able to determine if a given number is divisible by 2, 3, 5, or 10.

Teaching Tips:

Leave the solid space figures in the room with the names on them. Review the names on a daily basis.

Materials, Supplies, and Equipment:

1. Solid space figures
2. *Worksheet 53*

Activities:

1. Read **Lesson 96 Explanation** orally with the students. Review the types of space figures.
2. Show the students the various solid space figures identifying them by name. Ask the students to find the number of faces, edges, and vertices on each figure.
3. The students should be able to complete **Lesson 96 Practice** independently.

It is not the IQ but the I will that is important in education.
Author Unknown

Lesson 97

Concepts:

Perimeter, space figures, symmetry, rounding, prime numbers, equations

Objectives:

1. Given the dimensions of a shape, the student will be able to find the perimeter.
2. The student will be able to give the number of edges, faces, and vertices of a space figure.
3. Given a diameter, the student will determine the radius. Given a radius, the student will be able to determine the diameter.
4. Given half of a shape, the student will be able to draw the other half.
5. The student will be able to round numbers to the nearest 100.
6. The student will be able to recognize prime numbers and find their way through a maze.
7. The student will be able to solve division equations.

Materials, Supplies, and Equipment:

1. 1 tape measure (per child)
2. *Worksheet 54*

Activities:

1. Read **Lesson 97 Explanation** orally with the students.
2. Review measuring with a tape measure.
3. Allow the students to work with partners and measure the perimeter of 4 objects in the room. They must include: a drawing of the object, the measurement of each side, and the perimeter of the object.
4. Have the children share one of their drawings with the class.
5. The students should be able to complete **Lesson 97 Practice** independently.

No one like you was ever born or ever will be.
Constance Foster

Lesson 98

Concepts:

Area, perimeter, space figures, circles, rounding, equations, division

Objectives:

1. The student will be able to find the area of a given figure.
2. The student will be able to find the perimeter of a given figure.
3. The student will be able to draw each type of space figure: cone, cylinder, pyramid, sphere, and prism.
4. The student will be able to identify the radius, diameter, and name of a circle.
5. Given a diameter, the student will determine the radius.
6. The student will be able to draw and label a point and parallel line.
7. The student will be able to round numbers to the nearest 100.
8. The student will be able to solve addition equations.
9. The student will be able to find the quotient given a two-digit divisor and three-digit dividend.

Teaching Tips:

Emphasize that when we label area, we use square units. (m^2, cm^2, mm^2)

Materials, Supplies, and Equipment:

1. Two pieces of grid paper (per student) (Worksheet 55)

Activities:

1. Read **Lesson 98 Explanation** orally with the students.
2. Distribute the grid paper. Have each child color a shape with the following dimensions: 15 square units long and 4 square units wide. Count the squares to compute the area. **(60 square units)**
3. Have the students use the formula to compute the area for the same figure. **(A = L x W, 60 = 15 x 4)**
4. Using the remaining grid paper, have the student draw and color a closed figure. Have them compute the perimeter and area and place the answers on the back.
5. Choose several pictures the students have created and have the class find the perimeter and area. Save the other students work for future use.
6. The students should be able to complete **Lesson 98 Practice** independently.

One may walk over the highest mountain one step at a time.
John Wanamaker

Lesson 99

Concepts:

Volume, area, perimeter, space figures, rounding, equations, average, division

Objectives:

1. The student will be able to find the volume of a given figure.
2. The student will be able to use the correct symbol for cubic units.
3. The student will be able to find the area of a given figure.
4. The student will be able to find the perimeter of a given figure.
5. The student will be able to find the missing length, width, perimeter, and/or area of several polygons.
6. The student will be able to give the number of edges, faces, and vertices of a space figure.
7. The student will be able to round numbers to the nearest 100.
8. The student will be able to solve addition equations.
9. The student will be able to find the quotient given a two-digit divisor and three-digit dividend.
10. The student will be able to average numbers.

Teaching Tips:

Emphasize that when we label volume, we use cubic units. (m^3, cm^3 , mm^3)

Materials, Supplies, and Equipment:

1. Centimeter cubes or sugar cubes
2. *Worksheet 56*

Activities:

1. Read **Lesson 99 Explanation** orally with the students. Demonstrate using centimeter cubes.
2. Have each student make a cube with 4 centimeter cubes on the bottom and 4 on the top. Have the students determine the volume by counting the blocks. **(8 cubic units)** Have the students compute the volume using the formula V = L x W x H. **(8 = 2 x 2 x 2)**
3. The students should be able to complete **Lesson 99 Practice** independently.

Let me look upward into the branches of the flowering oak and know that it grew great and strong because it grew slowly and well.
Wilfred A. Peterson

Lesson 100

Concepts:

Fractions, perimeter and area, place value, rounding, multiplication

Objectives

1. Given parts of an object evenly divided, the student will be able to find a fractional representation of those parts.
2. The student will be able to define: numerator, denominator, and fraction.
3. The student will be able to find the volume of a space figure given the height, width, and length.
4. The student will be able to find the area and perimeter of an object given the dimensions of the sides.
5. The student will be able to recognize place value to the hundred millions.
6. The student will be able to round numbers to the nearest hundred.
7. The student will be able to find the product given three-digit multiplicands and two-digit multipliers.

Teaching Tips:

Students can readily determine what fraction represents part of a whole. They often find fractions like 0/3 and 3/3 confusing. Give the students concrete examples of these fractions.

Materials, Supplies, and Equipment:

1. 4 paper plates, Draw lines on each paper plate dividing them as follows: thirds, fourths, sixths, and eighths
2. *Worksheet 57*

Activities:

1. Place the four paper plates in front of the children, and ask them which paper plate is divided into fourths.
2. After the correct plate has been chosen, ask a volunteer to color the plate so that 1/4 of the plate is colored.
3. Explain to the students that fractions have their own special names associated with them and that today they will learn those names.
4. Tell the students, **In the fraction 1/4, the number over the line is the numerator and the number under the line is the denominator.** Write the terms on the board.
5. Ask the students which paper plate is divided into thirds.
6. After the correct plate has been chosen, ask a volunteer to color the plate so that 2/3 of the plate is colored.
7. Write the fraction 2/3 on the board. Ask a student to identify the numerator and denominator.
8. Continue by asking which plate is divided into eighths. Have them color 8/8. Ask them to identify the numerator and denominator.
9. Continue by asking which plate is divided into sixths. Have them color 0/6. They will see that nothing would be colored to represent the fraction 0/6. Ask them to define the numerator and denominator.
10. Read **Lesson 100 Explanation** with the students.
11. The students should be able to complete **Lesson 100 Practice** independently.

His God doth instruct him to discretion, and doth teach him.
Isaiah 28:26

Lesson 101

Concepts:

Fractions, volume, mystery numbers, rounding, multiplication

Objectives

1. Given a fraction in numbers, the student will be able to write and say its name. Given a fractional name, the student will be able to write the fraction in numbers.
2. Given parts of an object evenly divided, the student will be able to find a fractional representation of those parts.
3. The student will be able to find the volume of a space figure given the height, width, and length.
4. The student will be able to recognize place value to the hundred billions.
5. The student will be able to round numbers to the nearest thousand.
6. The student will be able to find the product given three-digit multiplicands and two-digit multipliers

Teaching Tips:

Students have little difficulty with this concept.

Materials, Supplies, and Equipment:

1. 40 large index cards, On twenty of the index cards write a fraction in numbers (3/4 , 7/8, 1/3....), On the other twenty index cards write the corresponding word name (three-fourths, seven-eighths, one-third...)
2. *Worksheet 58*

Activities:

1. Read **Lesson 101 Explanation** with the students.
2. Divide the class into two equal teams. (This can also be played with two people.) Tell the students, **Today we are going to play <u>Fraction Matching</u>**. Show them the stack of index cards, and explain that each card has a match. Tell them**, The goal of this game is to see which team can get the most matches.** Place the cards in a neat stack face down.
3. Each team gets four cards to start. They should display the cards so that all of their team members can see the cards.
4. Decide which team will start. The first player goes to the front of the room and draws a card from the top of the pile of cards. He/She turns the card over and takes it back to their team. The player can either accept the card and discard one of their other cards or discard the card they just selected. They should return the card face-up, placing it beside the other stack of cards. At this time they may play any matches they have, displaying them before the class. They may draw cards from the pile to replace those cards that were a match. If any of the new cards match, they may not play them until their next turn.
5. Team number two follows the same procedure with one exception. The student may choose between taking the upturned card or the downturned card on the pile. Although the team may coach the player who is taking his/her turn, the final decisions rest with the participating student.
5. The winner of the game is announced after neither team can make another move. The team with the most matches wins.
6. The students should be able to complete **Lesson 101 Practice** independently.

Thy word is a lamp unto my feet, and a light unto my paths.
Psalms 119:105

Lesson 102

Concepts:

Fractions, place value, equations, expanded form

Objectives

1. Given a set of objects within a group, the student will be able to represent it in fractional terms.
2. Given a fraction in numbers, the student will be able to write and say its name. Given a fractional name, the student will be able to write the fraction in numbers.
3. Given parts of an object evenly divided, the student will be able to find a fractional representation of those parts.
4. The student will be able to recognize place value to the hundred billions and be able to complete a crossword puzzle with the information.
5. The student will be able to solve a multiplication equation.
6. The student will be able to write numbers in expanded form.

Teaching Tips:

Students should have little difficulty with this concept. It is an extension of Lesson 100.

Materials, Supplies, and Equipment:

1. *Worksheet 59*

Activities:

1. Read **Lesson 102 Explanation** with the students.
2. Review the terms numerator and denominator.
3. The students should be able to complete **Lesson 102 Practice** independently.

If any man do his will, he shall know of the doctrine,
whether it be of God, or whether I speak of myself.
John 7:17

Lesson 103

Concepts:

Equivalent fractions, writing fractions, place value, division

Objectives

1. Given a fraction, the student will be able to find an equivalent fraction.
2. Given a set of objects within a group, the student will be able to represent it in fractional terms.
3. Given a fraction in numbers, the student will be able to write and say its name. Given a fractional name, the student will be able to write the fraction in numbers.
4. The student will be able to define a numerator and denominator.
5. The student will be able to change a number from the following forms: expanded to standard, word to numerical. The student will solve a logic puzzle with these numbers.
6. The student will be able to find the quotient of a problem with a one-digit divisor and two-digit dividend.

Teaching Tips:

Students need lots of practice finding equivalent fractions and missing numerators. Use Worksheet 60.

Materials, Supplies, and Equipment:

1. Three sheets of paper per child
2. *Worksheet 60*

Activities:

1. Have the students fold a piece of paper in half. Set the paper aside.
2. Have the students fold a piece of paper in half, then in half again. The paper should be divided into fourths. Set the paper aside.
3. Have the students fold a piece of paper in half. Fold that rectangle into thirds. The paper should be divided into sixths. Set the paper aside.

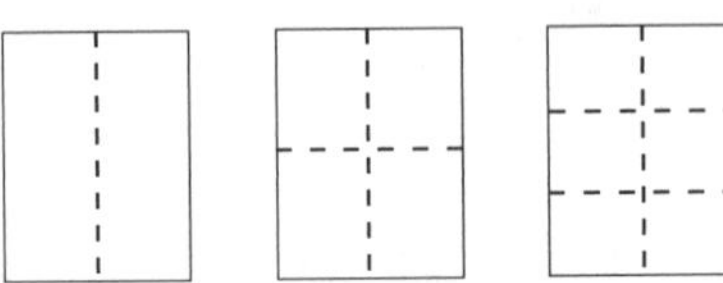

4. Have the students color 1/2 of the first piece of paper, 2/4 of the next piece of paper, and 3/6 of the last piece of paper. Ask the students: **If the shaded part was really your favorite kind of cake, which paper would you choose to eat?**
5. The students should declare that each piece would be equal.
6. Read **Lesson 103 Explanation** with the students.
7. Demonstrate how we can make equivalent fractions by multiplying the numerator and denominator by the same number. Use the examples:

   $\frac{1}{8} = \frac{1 \times 2}{8 \times 2} = \frac{2}{16}$ and $\frac{3}{4} = \frac{3 \times 7}{4 \times 7} = \frac{21}{28}$

8. Demonstrate how we find a missing numerator or denominator by applying the same principle. Use the examples: $\frac{1}{8} = \frac{?}{16}$

   Ask: **What did we multiply by 8 to get 16? (2)**
   If we multiply the denominator by 2 to get an equivalent fraction, we must multiply the numerator by 2, also. The numerator is 2, because 1 x 2 = 2.
9. Work the problems in **Lesson 103 Practice** with the students.

I will instruct thee and teach thee in the way which thou shalt go;
I will guide thee with mine eye.
Psalm 32:8

Lesson 104

Concepts:

Common factors, equivalent fractions, compare and order, subtraction, division

Objectives

1. Given two numbers, the student will be able to find the common factors and the greatest common factor.
2. Given a fraction, the student will be able to find an equivalent fraction.
3. Given a set of objects within a group, the student will be able to represent it in fractional terms.
4. The student will be able to match word fractions to number fractions.
5. The student will be able to order numbers from smallest to largest.
6. The student will be able to find the difference of two four-digit numbers with zeros in the minuend.
7. The student will be able to find the quotient of a problem with a one-digit divisor and two-digit dividend.

Teaching Tips:

Allow the students plenty of time to work these problems.

Materials, Supplies, and Equipment:

1. *Worksheet 61*

Activities:

1. Read **Lesson 104 Explanation** with the students.
2. Ask the students, **Give an example of two numbers that have a GCF (Greatest Common Factor) of 1. (Any two numbers that have no factors in common except one are correct answers. Some examples are 13 and 12, 4 and 7, 15 and 4.)**
3. Work the first two problems in **Lesson 104 Practice** orally with the students.
4. The students may need assistance as they work the remaining problems in **Lesson 104 Practice**.

The Lord is far from the wicked, but he heareth the prayer of the righteous.
Proverbs 15:29

Lesson 105

Concepts:

Greatest common factor, common factors, equivalent fractions, compare and order, division

Objectives

1. The student will be able to write fractions in lowest terms.
2. Given two numbers, the student will be able to find the common factors and the greatest common factor.
3. Given two equivalent fractions with a missing numerator or denominator, the student will be able to determine the missing number.
4. The student will be able to name a point on a number line with the appropriate fraction.
5. The student will be able to order numbers from greatest to least.
6. The student will be able to find the quotient of a problem with a one-digit divisor and two-digit dividend.

Teaching Tips:

Method One In **Lesson 105** is helpful in explaining the concept of renaming fractions. Most students prefer Method Two as they understand the concept and gain confidence. Use Worksheet 62 for additional practice.

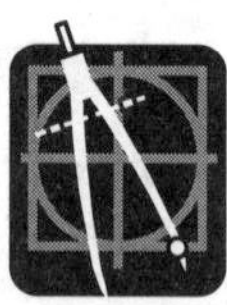

Materials, Supplies, and Equipment:

1. *Worksheet 62*

Activities:

1. Refer to the paper folding activities used in **Lesson 103**. Review the concept that all of these fractions are equivalent. Ask the students, **Which one of these fractions 1/2, 2/4, or 3/6 states the fraction in the lowest terms? (1/2)**

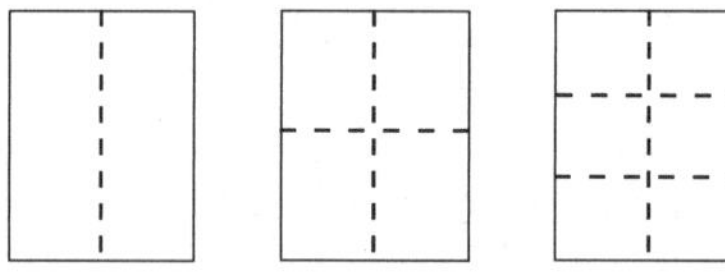

2. Explain to the students that lowest terms means the lowest numbers we can use to identify a fraction.
3. Read **Lesson 105 Explanation** with the students.
4. Work the first row of problems in **Lesson 105 Practice** with the students.
5. Students should be able to complete the remaining problems in the section with minimal intervention.

He led him about, he instructed him, he kept him as the apple of his eye.
Deuteronomy 32:10

Lesson 106

Concepts:

Compare and order fractions, lowest terms, common factors, equivalent fractions, prime numbers, divisibility, subtraction

Objectives

1. The student will be able to compare fractions with different denominators.
2. The student will be able to write fractions in lowest terms.
3. Given two numbers, the student will be able to find the common factors and the greatest common factor.
4. Given a fraction, the student will be able to find equivalent fractions out of a given set.
5. The student will be able to find prime numbers out of a given set.
6. The student will be able to determine if a number is divisible by 2, 5, 10, or 3.
7. The student will be able to find the difference of a three-digit minuend and three-digit subtrahend.

Teaching Tips:

Explanation of these concepts will be enhanced by the use of manipulatives.

Materials, Supplies, and Equipment:

1. Paper
2. *Worksheet 63*

Activities:

1. Take two pieces of paper folded into sixths. Ask the students, **Who can color this paper to show the fraction 4/6? (Four out of six shapes should be colored.)**
2. Ask the students, **Who can color the other sheet to show the fraction 2/6? (Two out of six shapes should be colored.)**
3. Ask the students, **What represents the larger fraction? (4/6)**
4. Take a piece of paper folded in half. Ask the students, **Who can color this paper to show the fraction 1/2? (One out of two shapes should be colored.)**
5. Take a piece of paper folded into fourths. Ask the students, **Who can color this paper to show the fraction 1/4? (One out of four shapes should be colored.)**
6. Ask the students, **These fractions have different denominators. Can you tell which fraction is larger? (1/2 is larger than 1/4)**
7. Tell the students that pictures can help us determine which fractions are larger, but as the numbers become larger this is very difficult. They will learn three other methods for comparing fractions today.
8. Read **Lesson 106 Explanation** with the students and answer questions.
9. Allow the students to complete the first row of problems in **Lesson 106 Practice** independently.
10. Assist the students as they complete the rest of the lesson.

The Comforter, which is the Holy Ghost, whom the Father will send in my name, he shall teach you all things, and bring all things to your remembrance, whatsoever I said unto you.

John 14:26

Lesson 107

Concepts:

Mixed numbers and improper fractions, compare fractions, reduce fractions, equivalent fractions, equations, geometric shapes

Objectives

1. Given whole objects and parts of the whole, the student will be able to name mixed fractions.
2. The student will be able to change a mixed number into an improper fraction.
3. The student will be able to compare fractions with different denominators.
4. Given a set of numbers, the student will be able to determine which numbers are in lowest terms.
5. Given two equivalent fractions with a missing numerator or denominator, the student will be able to determine the missing number.
6. The student will be able to solve addition equations.
7. The student will be able to solve division equations.
8. The student will be able to identify the following figures: square, pentagon, hexagon, rectangle, triangle, octagon, decagon, trapezoid, and rhombus.

Teaching Tips:

Explanation of these concepts will be enhanced by the use of manipulatives.

Materials, Supplies, and Equipment:

1. Paper
2. *Worksheet 64*

Activities:

1. Take two pieces of paper divided into sixths. Ask the students, **Who can color these pieces of paper to represent 1 1/6? (One whole sheet and 1/6 of the other sheet.)**
2. Take two pieces of paper divided into sixths. Ask the students, **Who can color these pieces of paper to represent 7/6? (One whole sheet and 1/6 of the other sheet.)**
3. The students can easily see that these two fractional representations are equal.
4. Read **Lesson 107 Explanation** with the students.
5. Allow the students to work the following problems on the board with guidance: Change each mixed fraction to an improper fraction: 1 1/2, 3 6/8, 4 2/7, 1 5/10, 1 6/6 **(3/2, 30/8, 30/7, 15/10, 2)**.
6. The students should be able to complete **Lesson 107 Practice** independently.

God, who commanded the light to shine out of darkness, hath shined in our hearts, to give the light of the knowledge of the glory of God in the face of Jesus Christ.
II Corinthians 4:6

Lesson 108

Concepts:

Improper and mixed numbers, compare fractions, reduce fractions, rounding, equations, averaging, geometric shapes

Objectives

1. The student will be able to change an improper fraction into a mixed number.
2. The student will be able to change a mixed number into an improper fraction.
3. Given a mixed fraction, the student will be able to draw a pictorial representation. The student will be able to change the mixed fraction into an improper fraction.
4. The student will be able to compare fractions with different denominators.
5. The student will be able to write fractions in lowest terms.
6. The student will be able to round numbers to the nearest hundred.
7. The student will be able to solve addition equations.
8. The student will be able to find the average of three or four numbers.
9. The student will be able to label drawings with one of the following definitions: rectangular pyramid, triangular prism, cone, sphere, cylinder, and hexagonal pyramid.

Teaching Tips:

Explanation of these concepts will be enhanced by the use of manipulatives.

Materials, Supplies, and Equipment:

1. Paper
2. *Worksheet 64*

Activities:

1. Ask the students, **Who remembers what mathematical concept we covered yesterday? (We changed mixed fractions to improper fractions.)**
2. Say, **Today we are going to do the opposite, we are going to change improper fractions to mixed numbers.**
3. Say, **Remember, we found that 1 1/6 equals 7/6.** Demonstrate using paper. **Can anyone tell us what mathematical operation we might use to change 7/6 to 1 1/6? (Division)**
4. Direct the students' attention to **Lesson 108 Explanation.** Read the lesson with the students answering questions.
5. Allow the students to work the following problems on the board with guidance: Change each improper fraction to a mixed fraction: 10/3, 7/2, 3/1, 8/5, 8/2, 3/3 (**3 r 1, 3 r 1, 3, 1 r 3, 4, 1**).
6. The students should be able to complete **Lesson 108 Practice** independently.

The heart of the wise teacheth his mouth, and addeth learning to his lips.
Proverbs 16:23

Lesson 109

Concepts:

Problem solving, improper to mixed fractions, compare fractions, symmetry, division

Objectives

1. The student will be able to solve story problems by applying the strategy, make it simpler.
2. The student will be able to change an improper fraction into a mixed number.
3. The student will be able to change a mixed number into an improper fraction.
4. The student will be able to compare fractions with different denominators.
5. The student will be able to draw lines of symmetry on a given object.
6. The student will be able to draw a figure that has no lines of symmetry and one that has two lines of symmetry.
7. The student will be able to find the quotient of a problem with a four-digit dividend and two-digit divisor.

Teaching Tips:

This lesson is especially helpful for students who can not decide what mathematical operation to use. The students will come up with many ways to write the problem in a simpler fashion. Accept all reasonable answers.

Materials, Supplies, and Equipment:

Activities:

1. Read **Lesson 109 Explanation** orally with the students.
2. Work problems one and two on **Lesson 109 Practice** orally.
3. Give the students assistance as they work the remaining problems in the lesson.

The meek will he guide in judgment: and the meek will he teach his ways.
Psalm 25:9

Lesson 110

Concepts:

Add fractions, word problems, improper to mixed fractions, division, symmetry

Objectives:

1. The student will be able to add fractions with common denominators.
2. The student will be able to use the problem solving strategy, solve a simpler problem, to find the answer to a story problem.
3. The student will be able to change an improper fraction to a mixed number.
4. The student will be able to change a mixed number to an improper fraction.
5. The student will be able to solve a division problem with a two-digit divisor and a four-digit dividend.
6. Given a figure, the student will be able to complete the other half to form a symmetrical figure.

Teaching Tips:

Students who work with fraction strips or other fraction manipulatives have a far better working knowledge of fractions than those who don't.

Materials, Supplies, and Equipment:

1. A set of fraction strips per student. (Worksheet 57)
2. *Worksheet 65*

Activities:

1. Write the following problem on the board: $\frac{1}{8} + \frac{4}{8}$
2. Ask the students to solve the problem using their fractional strips. Solution: **5/8**
3. Point out to the students that when you add fractions with like denominators, add the numerators and keep the denominator the same.
4. Ask the students to solve the following problems using fraction strips:

   $\frac{1}{6} + \frac{4}{6} = \mathbf{\frac{5}{6}}$ $\quad \frac{2}{12} + \frac{3}{12} = \mathbf{\frac{5}{12}}$ $\quad \frac{1}{4} + \frac{2}{4} = \mathbf{\frac{3}{4}}$

5. Read **Lesson 110 Explanation** with the students. Remind them that they must change all fractions to lowest terms.
6. Review reducing fractions with the following examples:

   $\frac{2}{4} = \mathbf{\frac{1}{2}}$ $\quad \frac{4}{6} = \mathbf{\frac{2}{3}}$ $\quad \frac{5}{15} = \mathbf{\frac{1}{3}}$

7. The students should be able to work problems in **Lesson 110 Practice** independently.

Better to remain silent and to be thought a fool than to speak out and remove doubt.
Abraham Lincoln

Lesson 111

Concepts:

Subtracting fractions, adding fractions, elapsed time, improper to mixed fractions, addition, multiplication congruent and similar figures

Objectives:

1. The student will be able to subtract fractions with common denominators.
2. The student will be able to add fractions with common denominators.
3. The student will be able to solve story problems by computing elapsed time.
4. The student will be able to find equations that are equivalent.
5. The student will be able to find the sum of two-digit numbers.
6. The student will be able to find the product of a three-digit multiplicand and a two-digit multiplier.
7. Given a closed figure, the student will be able to draw a similar and congruent figure.

Teaching Tips:

Students who work with fraction strips or other fraction manipulatives have a far better working knowledge of fractions than those who don't.

Materials, Supplies, and Equipment

1. A set of fraction strips per student (Worksheet 57)
2. *Worksheet 66*

Activities:

1. Write the following problem on the board: $\frac{7}{8} - \frac{4}{8}$
2. Ask the students to solve the problem using their fractional strips. Solution: **3/8**
3. Point out to the students that when subtracting fractions with like denominators, subtract the numerators and keep the denominator the same.
4. Ask the students to solve the following problems using fraction strips:

   $\frac{4}{6} - \frac{3}{6} = \mathbf{\frac{1}{6}}$ $\qquad \frac{5}{12} - \frac{3}{12} = \mathbf{\frac{2}{12}}$ $\qquad \frac{5}{8} - \frac{1}{8} = \mathbf{\frac{4}{8}} = \mathbf{\frac{1}{2}}$

5. Read **Lesson 111 Explanation** with the students. Remind them that they must change all fractions to lowest terms.
6. The students should be able to work problems in **Lesson 111 Practice** independently.

Wise men talk because they have something to say;
fools, because they have to say something.
Plato

Lesson 112

Concepts:

Add and subtract fractions, elapsed time, multiplication, division, congruent and similar figures

Objectives:

1. The student will be able to add and subtract fractions with common denominators.
2. The student will be able to add fractions with common denominators.
3. The student will be able to subtract fractions with common denominators.
4. The student will be able to solve story problems by computing elapsed time.
5. The student will be able to find the product of a three-digit multiplicand and a three-digit multiplier.
6. The student will be able to solve a division problem with a two-digit divisor and a three-digit dividend.
7. The student will draw a closed figure given grid lines. The student will be able to draw a similar and congruent figure.

Teaching Tips:

Students who are having difficulty with adding and subtracting fractions may benefit from using fraction strips.

Materials, Supplies, and Equipment

1. A set of fraction strips per student (*Worksheet 57*), if needed

Activities:

1. Read **Lesson 112 Explanation** with the students.
2. The students should be able to work problems in **Lesson 112 Practice** independently.

Wherefore, my beloved brethren,
let every man be swift to hear, slow to speak, slow to wrath......
James 1:19

Lesson 113

Concepts:

Addition with unlike denominators, subtract fractions, add fractions, column addition, subtraction, division, geometric symbols

Objectives:

1. With the aid of fraction strips or bars, the student will be able to add fractions with unlike denominators.
2. The student will be able to subtract fractions with common denominators.
3. The student will be able to add fractions with common denominators.
4. The student will be able to add four, three-digit numbers in a column.
5. The student will be able to subtract two, two-digit numbers that require borrowing.
6. The student will be able to find hidden division problems in a magic square. The problems will have two-digit dividends and one-digit divisors with one-digit quotients with remainders.
7. The student will be able to name a point, ray, line, and line segment.

Teaching Tips:

Allow the students to use the **Marked Fraction Strips** (*Worksheet 65*) to help them see the equivalent relationships.

Materials, Supplies, and Equipment:

1. Marked Fraction Strips (*Worksheet 57*)
2. *Worksheet 67*

Activities:

1. Ask the students: **Look at the Marked Fractions Strips. How many different ways can we express the fraction 1/3? (2/6, 4/12)** Remind that these fractions are equal and are called equivalent fractions.
2. Read **Lesson 113 Explanation** with the students. Tell the students: **In this lesson, we will be adding fractions with different denominators. We will need to change one of the fractions to an equivalent fraction, so that it has the same denominator as the other fraction.** Encourage the students to use the Marked Fraction Strips to see the equivalent relationships.
3. Complete the problems in **Lesson 113 Practice** as a group.

He that has the Son has life.
I John 5:12

Lesson 114

Concepts:

Subtract unlike fractions, add unlike fractions, add and subtract like fractions, round to 10, subtract, equations, geometric figures

Objectives:

1. With the aid of fraction strips or bars, the student will be able to subtract fractions with unlike denominators.
2. With the aid of fraction strips or bars, the student will be able to add fractions with unlike denominators.
3. The student will be able to add and subtract fractions with common denominators.
4. The student will be able to round numbers to the nearest 10.
5. The student will be able to find the difference of two, four-digit numbers that require borrowing.
6. The student will be able to solve a multiplication equation.
7. The student will be able to draw and label the following: point, line, line segment, and ray.

Teaching Tips:

Allow the students to use the **Marked Fraction Strips** (*Worksheet 65*) to help them see the equivalent relationships.

Materials, Supplies, and Equipment:

1. Marked Fraction Strips (*Worksheet 57*)
2. *Worksheet 68*

Activities:

1. Reinforce the concept of equivalent fractions by asking the students to look at their Marked Fraction Strips, and find all the fractions that equal the following: 1/2 (**2/4, 3/6, 4/8, 5/10, 6/12**) 1/5 (**2/10**) 2/3 (**4/6, 8/12**) 3/4 (**6/8, 9/12**).
2. Read **Lesson 114 Explanation** with the students. Complete the first two problems on **Lesson 114 Practice** with the students. They should be able to work the remaining problems independently.

You see things; and say "Why?"
But I dream things that never were and say, "Why not?"
George Bernard Shaw

Lesson 115

Concepts:

Add and subtract unlike fractions, word problems, rounding, division, prime numbers, geometric shapes

Objectives:

1. Given story problems with fractions, the student will be able to add and subtract fractions with unlike denominators.
2. With the aid of fraction strips or bars, the student will be able to subtract fractions with unlike denominators.
3. The student will be able to round numbers to the nearest 10.
4. The student will be able to divide a one-digit divisor by a two-digit dividend.
5. The student will be able to find the prime numbers between 1 and 50.
6. The student will be able to define the following: point, line, ray, parallel lines, intersecting lines, and perpendicular lines.

Teaching Tips:

Allow the students to use the **Marked Fraction Strips** (*Worksheet 65*) to help them see the equivalent relationships.

Materials, Supplies, and Equipment:

1. Marked Fraction Strips (*Worksheet 57*)

Activities:

1. Read **Lesson 115 Explanation** with the students.
2. Allow them to use the Marked Fraction Strips as they complete **Lesson 115 Practice** independently.

Faith cometh by hearing, and hearing by the word of God.
Romans 10:17

Lesson 116

Concepts:

Addition of mixed numbers, word problems, adding fractions, divisibility, A.M., P.M., geometric figures

Objectives:

1. The student will be able to find the sum of mixed numbers with common denominators.
2. Given story problems with fractions, the student will be able to add and subtract fractions with unlike denominators.
3. The students will be able to find fractions in a magic square with the sum of one.
4. The student will be able to find the sum and difference of fractions with common denominators.
5. The student will be able to determine if a number is divisible by 2, 3, 5 and or 10.
6. Given sentences that specify time, the student will be able to determine if the time is A.M. or P.M..
7. The students will be able to draw intersecting, parallel, and perpendicular lines.

Teaching Tips:

Have the students write the three steps in adding mixed numbers on chart paper. They may use this as a visual reference as they work the problems.

Materials, Supplies, and Equipment:

1. Chart paper
2. *Worksheet 69*

Activities:

1. Read **Lesson 116 Explanation** with the students. Have the students write the three steps in adding mixed numbers on chart paper. They may use this as a visual reference as they work the problems.
2. Remind students to reduce the answer to lowest terms.
3. The students should be able to work problems in **Lesson 116 Practice** independently.

If you believe what you like in the Gospel and reject what you do not like,
it is not the Gospel you believe, but yourself.
Author Unknown

Lesson 117

Concepts:

Subtract mixed fractions, add mixed fractions, reduce fractions, add and subtract unlike fractions, angles, equations, average

Objectives:

1. The student will be able to find the difference of mixed numbers with common denominators.
2. The student will be able to find the sum of mixed numbers with common denominators.
3. The students will answer questions regarding the states in the United States in fractional form.
4. The student will be able to find the sum and difference of fractions with common denominators.
5. The student will be able to draw and label a right, acute, and obtuse angle.
6. The student will be able to solve an equation involving two operations.
7. The student will be able to find the average of three numbers.

Teaching Tips:

Have the students write the three steps in subtracting mixed numbers on chart paper. They may use this as a visual reference as they work the problems.

Materials, Supplies, and Equipment:

1. Chart paper
2. *Worksheet 70*

Activities:

1. Read **Lesson 117 Explanation** with the students. Have the students write the three steps in subtracting mixed numbers on chart paper. They may use this as a visual reference as they work the problems.
2. Remind students to reduce the answer to lowest terms.
3. The students should be able to work problems in **Lesson 117 Practice** independently.

The joy of the Lord is your strength.
Nehemiah 8:10

Lesson 118

Concepts:

Add mixed fractions, subtract mixed fractions, equations, money, century, angles

Objectives:

1. The student will be able to find the sum of mixed numbers with common denominators. The student will be able to change the sum from an improper fraction to a mixed number.
2. The student will be able to complete a fraction pyramid.
3. The student will be able to find the difference of mixed fractions.
4. The student will be able to solve an equation where operations are required on both sides of the equal sign.
5. Given the price of an item and the amount paid, the student will be able to state the fewest coins and bills possible to make change.
6. Given years ranging from 7 AD to 2010 AD the students will be able to determine the century.
7. The student will be able to define a right, obtuse, and acute angle.

Teaching Tips:

Allow the students the opportunity to change improper fractions to mixed numbers before they begin this lesson.

Materials, Supplies, and Equipment

1. 2 sets of Marked Fraction Strips (*Worksheet 57*)
2. Scissors

Activities:

1. Pass out 2 sets of Marked Fraction Strips.
2. Allow the students to cut out the fraction strips that equal 1/4 on both sets.
3. Ask the students: **How many 1/4 strips are needed to equal 5/4?(5) 7/4?(7) 6/4?(6)**
4. Ask the students: **Can you change the improper fraction 5/4 to a mixed number?** Demonstrate by covering the one whole fraction strip with 4 of the 1/4 strips. Show that there is one left over to equal 1 1/4. 5/4 = 1 1/4. Ask them to use the fraction strips to change the remaining improper fractions to mixed numbers: **7/4?(1 3/4) 6/4?(1 2/4)**
5. Allow the students to cut out the fraction strips that equal 1/8 on both sets.
6. Ask the students: **How many 1/8 strips would I need to equal 10/8?(10) 13/8?(13)**
7. Ask the students: **Can you change these improper fractions to mixed numbers? 10/8? 1 2/8 = 1 1/4, 13/8? 1 5/8**
8. Read **Lesson 118 Explanation** with the students.
9. The students should be able to work problems in **Lesson 118 Practice** independently.

No man can think clearly when his fists are clenched.
George Jean Nathan

Lesson 119

Concepts:

Problem solving, money, calendar equivalence, circles, equivalent fractions, reduce fractions, compare fractions

Objectives:

1. The student will be able to use the problem solving strategy, logical reasoning, to find the answer to a story problem.
2. Given the price of an item and the amount paid, the student will be able to state the fewest coins and bills possible to make change.
3. The student will be able to match time equivalents.
4. The student will be able to define the name of a circle, radii, and diameter. Given the radius, the student will be able to determine the diameter.
5. Given equivalent fractions with a missing numerator, the student will be able to determine the numerator.
6. Given two fractions the student will be able to use the symbols >, <, or = to determine their relationship.

Teaching Tips: Allow the students to refer to the illustrations.

Materials, Supplies, and Equipment:

Activities:

1. Read **Lesson 119 Explanation** with the students.
2. The students should be able to work problems in **Lesson 119 Practice** independently.

He fills me with strength and protects me wherever I go.
Psalm 18:32

Lesson 120

Concepts:

Reading decimals, writing decimals, time equivalence, circles, equivalent fractions

Objectives:

1. The student will be able to identify place value through the tenths' place.
2. The student will be able to convert fractions to decimals and decimals to fractions.
3. The student will be able to add and subtract mixed numbers.
4. The student will be able to solve division problems containing two-digit dividends yielding a one-digit quotient.
5. The student will be able to identify time equivalents.
6. The student will be able to identify equivalent fractions.
7. The student will be able to draw and label the geometric parts of a circle.

Teaching Tips:

A review of place value through the hundred billions would be beneficial before beginning the lesson.
It is important to tell the students that fractions, percents, and decimals are all parts or whole numbers. They are different representations for the same concept.

Materials, Supplies, and Equipment:

1. 2 pieces of poster board, one green, the other white
2. Black magic marker
3. Flashcards with decimal numbers, as well as whole numbers through millions, written in standard form
4. King sized Kit Kat® Candy bar
5. Student place value charts

Activities:

1. Prior to the lesson make a place value chart using the 2 pieces of poster board listed under Materials, Supplies, and Equipment #1. The green poster board should be used to make a place value chart for the whole number side of the place value chart. The white poster board should be used to make a place value chart for the decimal part of the place value chart. (See diagram below)

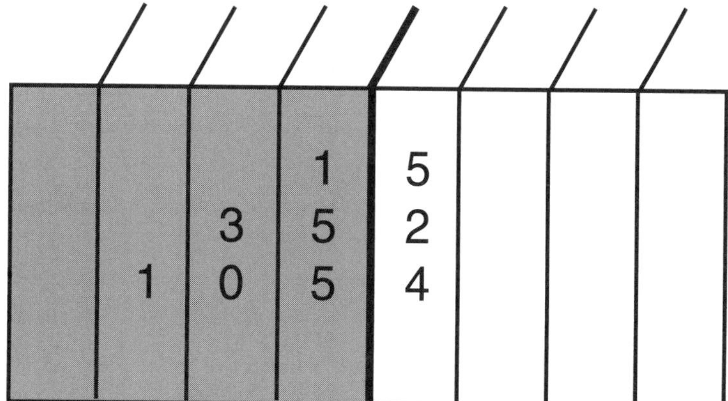

The bold line between the ones' and tenths' columns represents where the poster boards will be taped together AND the exact point where the decimal should be. A great way to illustrate this concept is with money. The whole number side would represent dollars ("green money"), the fractional side represents the "change side." The word "AND" in math should be used ONLY WHEN A DECIMAL IS PRESENT!

The problems shown in the chart on the previous page should be read "one **and** five tenths," "thirty-five **and** two tenths," and "one hundred five **and** four tenths." To mispronounce a number (for example *One Hundred and One Dalmatians*,) is to change the entire value of the number. This example, when written as pronounced, would actually be 100.1 **NOT** 101. Have the students add this portion of the decimal place value chart onto their existing place value charts (from Lessons 10 through higher lessons).

2. Read **Lesson 120 Explanation** together and discuss the example problem. Today's lesson will be dealing with the tenths' place.
3. Practice having the students read decimal numbers aloud by having a class competition between teams. Take turns reading decimal numbers off of pre-made flashcards. The key is to read the decimal as "AND," and not to read regular numbers with the word "AND."
4. Another good tactile example would be to use a Kit Kat™ candy bar. It is divided into strips which are easily broken apart. A king sized Kit Kat™ bar has 10 strips. Having the students break into groups and eat portions of each candy bar would be a good way to show what fractional portions of each candy bar had been eaten.
5. The student should be able to complete **Lesson 120 Practice** with little or no assistance.

For I will forgive their wickedness
and will remember their sins no more.
Jeremiah 31:34

Lesson 121

Concepts:

Reading and writing fractions as decimals, add and subtract fractions, subtraction, division, century, perimeter and area

Objectives:

1. The student will be able to identify place value through the hundredths' place and write a number in written form when given in standard decimal form.
2. The student will be able to convert fractions to decimals and decimals to fractions.
3. The student will be able to add and subtract mixed numbers.
4. The student will be able to complete three-digit subtraction problems and use the regrouping process if necessary.
5. The student will be able to solve division problems which contain two-digit divisors yielding a one-digit quotient.
6. The student will be able to identify and match given dates with the century in which they belong.
7. The student will be able to calculate the perimeter and area of a given figure.

Teaching Tips:

Review the place value chart again. Use the same poster board chart created for Lesson 120. It would be a good idea to laminate these posters for use with dry erase or overhead projector pens.

Materials, Supplies, and Equipment:

1. Poster board place value chart
2. Place value centimeter blocks or wooden place value blocks
3. Play money (bills and coins)
4. *Worksheet 71*

Activities:

1. Read **Lesson 121 Explanation** together and discuss. Use the poster board place value chart and place value blocks to illustrate the hundredths' place. Review the information from **Lesson 120** concerning the tenths' place. Also review the information concerning the proper pronunciation of each written number.
2. Have the students create several numbers and write them on the place value chart. Remind them that the tenths' place value column is like having dimes, and the hundredths' column is like having pennies ("change side of chart"- it takes 10 dimes to make $1.00 and 100 pennies to make $1.00.)
3. Have the students write the following numbers on their place value charts: 5.42, 5.12, and 2.89. Then have the students illustrate each number using the play money. This will reinforce the information given in Activities #2 stating that the decimal (or "change") side of the place value chart part of a whole, like dimes and pennies are to whole dollars or currency.
4. The student should be able to complete **Lesson 121 Practice** independently.

This is the day that the Lord hath made; let us rejoice and be glad in it.
Psalm 118:24

Lesson 122

Concepts:

Compare decimals, read decimals, missing fractions, subtraction, division, century, area and perimeter

Objectives:

1. The student will be able to compare decimals.
2. The student will be able to convert fractions to decimals and decimals to fractions.
3. The student will be able to add and subtract mixed numbers.
4. The student will be able to solve subtraction problems which require regrouping across zeros.
5. The student will be able to solve division problems which contain two-digit divisors and yield two-digit quotients.
6. The student will be able to calculate the perimeter and area of a given figure.

Teaching Tips:

Review place value and comparing whole numbers before beginning this lesson. Decimals are compared in the same way as whole numbers.

Materials, Supplies, and Equipment:

1. Place value chart
2. Play money
3. *Worksheet 72*

Activities:

1. Read **Lesson 122 Explanation** together. Look at the example numbers (Earned Run Averages) and have the student write them on the student place value chart. Go through the steps of comparing numbers.
2. Use the play money to illustrate the difference for students who do not seem to be comprehending the concept.
3. The student should be able to complete **Lesson 122 Practice** independently.

Open my eyes that I may see wonderful things in your law.
Psalm 119:18

Lesson 123

Concepts:

Order decimals, compare and order decimals, standard numbers, place value, equations, division, volume

Objectives:

1. The student will be able to order decimals.
2. The student will be able to compare decimals.
3. The student will be able to identify place value through the hundredths' and write a given decimal number in standard form.
4. The student will be able to convert fractions to decimals and decimals to fractions.
5. The student will be able to round given numbers to the nearest tens'.
6. The student will be able to complete subtraction equations by solving for a value of *n*.
7. The student will be able to solve division problems which contain a two-digit divisor and yield a two-digit quotient.
8. The student will be able to calculate the volume of a given figure.

Teaching Tips:

Review **Lesson 122** on comparing numbers before beginning **Lesson 123.** If the student understood the comparing concept in **Lesson 122**, then the ordering concept should be relatively easy.

Materials, Supplies, and Equipment:

Place value chart

Activities:

1. Read Lesson **123 Explanation** with the students. The information concerning Earned Run Averages is the same as **Lesson 122**. Have the student write these numbers in on their place value charts (or refer to them where they were written in from **Lesson 122** if still present and not erased). Remind the students that they are to order from the smallest to the largest. Go through each step of the explanation process written in **Lesson 123 Explanation** together using the student's place value chart.
2. The student should be able to complete **Lesson 123 Practice** independently.

And He will be called Wonderful Counselor, Mighty God,
Everlasting Father, Prince of Peace.
Isaiah 9:6b

Lesson 124

Concepts:

Round decimals, compare decimals, write decimals, rounding, equations, volume

Objectives:

1. The student will be able to round decimals to the nearest tenth and to the nearest whole number.
2. The student will be able to compare and order decimals.
3. The student will be able to write given standard number decimals in written form.
4. The student will be able to round given numbers to the nearest ten.
5. The student will be able to complete subtraction equations by solving for a value of *n*.
6. The student will be able to solve division problems containing two-digit divisors and yielding two-digit quotients.
7. The student will be able to calculate the volume of a given figure.

Teaching Tips:

Review the rounding of whole numbers before beginning **Lesson 124**.

Materials, Supplies, and Equipment:

1. Dry erase board or laminated poster board
2. Dry erase markers or Overhead markers
3. *Worksheet 73*

Activities:

1. Read **Lesson 124 Explanation** together. Have each student draw a number line on his/her paper. Draw a number line on the dry erase board (or laminated poster board) for the students to see. Remind them that when rounding numbers you are deciding whether a given number is closer to the number just above it or below it in numerical sequence. Have the students look at the example number line and the steps involved in the rounding process. Remind them that the magic number in rounding is 5. Anything below 5 rounds down. Anything above 5 rounds up. This should not be a difficult concept because the students have done this with whole numbers.
2. The student should be able to complete **Lesson 124 Practice** independently.

This is the message we have heard from him and declare to you:
God is light; in him there is no darkness at all.
1 John 1:5

Lesson 125

Concepts:

Add decimals, round decimals, order decimals, round to 100, average, time zones, add fractions

Objectives:

1. The student will be able to add decimals.
2. The student will be able to estimate decimals by rounding to the nearest tenth or whole number.
3. The student will be able to compare and order decimals.
4. The student will be able to round given numbers to the nearest hundred.
5. The student will be able to find the average of a given set of numbers.
6. The student will be able to identify different time zones and calculate the time differences between specified time zones.
7. The student will be able to add and subtract fractions with like denominators.

Teaching Tips:

Materials, Supplies, and Equipment:

1. Place value chart
2. Graph paper or lined paper
3. *Worksheet 74*

Activities:

1. Read **Lesson 125 Explanation** together. Have the student write the sample problem down on their place value chart or on the graph paper (lined paper). This will help them to keep the columns straight. Have them bring the decimal down first and then add or subtract the numbers.
2. The student should be able to complete **Lesson 125 Practice** independently.

The grace of our Lord was poured out on me abundantly,
along with the faith and love that are in Christ Jesus.
1 Timothy 1:14

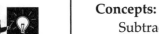

Lesson 126

Concepts:

Subtract decimals, add decimals, rounding decimals, order decimals, rounding, equations, time zones, add fractions

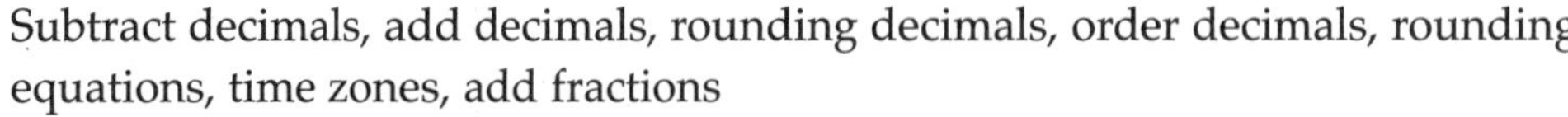

Objectives:

1. The student will be able to subtract decimals and use the regrouping process if necessary.
2. The student will be able to add decimals and use the regrouping process if necessary.
3. The student will be able to estimate decimals by rounding to the nearest tenth or whole number.
4. The student will be able to compare and order decimals.
5. The student will be able to round given numbers to the nearest hundred.
6. The student will be able to complete addition equations by solving for a value of n.
7. The student will be able to identify time zones and calculate the time differences in specified time zones.

Teaching Tips:

Review **Lesson 125** before beginning **Lesson 126.**

Materials, Supplies, and Equipment:

1. Place value chart (if necessary)
2. Graph paper or lined paper (if necessary)

Activities:

1. Read **Lesson 126 Explanation** together. Complete the example problem together by having the student write the problem on his/her graph paper or place value chart if necessary.
2. The student would be able to complete **Lesson 126 Practice** independently.

Behold, I stand at the door, and knock;
If any man hear my voice, and open the door,
I will come in to him, and will sup with him, and he with me.
Revelation 3:20

Lesson 127

Concepts:

Estimate addition of decimals, missing numbers, rounding decimals, century

Objectives:

1. The student will be able to estimate addition and subtraction problems containing decimals by rounding each number to the nearest whole number and then performing the required operation, using the regrouping process if necessary.
2. The student will be able to estimate decimals by rounding to the nearest tenths or whole number.
3. The student will be able to round given numbers to the nearest thousand.
4. The student will be able to complete addition equations by solving for a value of n.
5. The student will be able to identify and match time definitions.
6. The student will be able to covert fractions to decimals.

Teaching Tips:

Materials, Supplies, and Equipment:

Play money

Activities:

1. Read **Lesson 127 Explanation** with the students. This lesson should be a review due to the fact that various uses of estimating has been discusses in **Lessons 28, 37, and now 127.** Refer to these lessons if necessary. Most students will have this concept by now. Stress that estimating decimals is just like estimating money. Complete the example problems together. Use the play money, if necessary, to demonstrate why each number was rounded the way it was. Number lines may also be used, as in prior lessons, if more illustrations are needed.
2. The student should be able to complete **Lesson 127 Practice** independently.

Straight is the gate, and narrow is the way, which leadeth unto life, and few there be that find it.
Matthew 7:14

Lesson 128

Concepts:

Estimate money, rounding, math terms, A.M., P.M., place value

Objectives:

1. The student will be able to estimate with money by rounding to the nearest dollar and tenths' place.
2. The student will be able to add and subtract decimals using the regrouping process if necessary.
3. The student will be able to round given numbers to the nearest thousand.
4. The student will be able to define specific properties and mathematical terms, as well as identify place value from the hundred billions' through the hundredths' place.
5. The student will be able to tell time using a clock face and identify it as A.M. or P.M..
6. The student will be able to convert decimals to fractions.

Teaching Tips:

Materials, Supplies, and Equipment:

1. Play money
2. *Worksheet 75*

Activities:

1. Read **Lesson 128 Explanation** with the student. Go over the example problem together. Use the play money, if necessary, to demonstrate the rounding process.
2. The student should be able to complete **Lesson 128 Practice** independently.

Do not gloat when you enemy falls; when he stumbles,
do not let your heart rejoice, or the Lord will see and disapprove
and turn his wrath away from him.
Proverbs 24:17

Lesson 129

Concepts:

Problem solving, adding money, A.M., P.M., geometric terms, equivalent fractions, order fractions, add and subtract fractions

Objectives:

1. The student will be able to complete a given mathematical problem using the problem solving strategy of drawing a picture.
2. The student will be able to count back change from a given purchase or transaction.
3. The student will be able to tell time using a clock face and identify it as A.M. or P.M..
4. The student will be able to match specific geometric terms with their appropriate definition.
5. The student will be able to identify equivalent fractions.
6. The student will be able to reduce fractions.
7. The student will be able to compare and order fractions.
8. The student will be able to add and subtract fractions with unlike denominators.

Teaching Tips:

Explain to the students that "a picture is always worth a thousand words"! Drawing pictures on difficult problems can make things much clearer.

Materials, Supplies, and Equipment:

Paper and pencil

Activities:

1. Read **Lesson 129 Explanation** together. Discuss the different ways this problem may be solved. Look at both examples and explain why they arrive at the same answer by using different mathematical strategies based on a knowledge of mathematical rules and information.
2. Complete **Lesson 129 Practice #1** together and check the students' answers together. Assist any students that need further assistance.
3. The student should be able to complete the rest of **Lesson 129 Practice** independently.

Praise be to the name of God for ever and ever;
wisdom and power are his.
Daniel 2:19b

Lesson 130

Concepts:

Measure to the 1/4 inch, estimate money and add, subtract decimals, subtract, division, money, equivalent fractions

Objectives:

1. The student will be able to identify, measure, read, write, and label given items using Customary measurements of inches, half inches, and quarter inches.
2. The student will be able to use the regrouping process as needed to complete addition and subtraction problems which require the estimation of money to the nearest dollar.
3. The student will be able to add and subtract decimal numbers.
4. The student will be able to complete three-digit subtraction problems, using the regrouping process as needed.
5. The student will be able to complete division problems which contain two-digit divisors and yield a one-digit quotient.
6. The student will be able to calculate and count the change due from a given purchase or transaction.
7. The student will be able to write two equivalent fractions when given a fraction.

Teaching Tips:

The students have probably used portions of the Metric System and the Standard (Customary) System their whole lives and not realized that Metric and Standard (Customary) Units of measurement are <u>not</u> the same. Explain that Standard measurements were originally developed by an English King. For this reason the Customary system does not have a base unit (like the Metric System). A "foot" was the length of the King's foot. A "yard" is the distance from the King's nose to the tip of his outstretched arm. Needless to say, this would account for the random nature of this system.

Materials, Supplies, and Equipment:

1. 12 inch rulers (with 1/2 and 1/4 inch markings)

Activities:

1. Pass out the rulers so that every child, or at least every two children have a ruler. Read **Lesson 130 Explanation** together and have the students look at the drawn ruler examples. Remind the students that the diagrams in the book may not be drawn to scale. They are drawn for easy reference. Have the students measure several small items around the room. Pencils, paper clips, book widths, shoe lengths, and finger lengths are all handy items to have the students use. Explain the we sometimes refer to the 1/4 measurement as "quarter." This is because it is a quarter of the whole inch- just like in fractions 1/4 is a quarter of the whole shape.
2. Have the student complete **Lesson 130 Practice** independently. Again, remember that the pictures in the book may not be drawn to scale. Do not have the student use an actual ruler to measure the diagrammed nails, have them use the drawn ruler. Should you desire an extra exercise, having the students write the actual measurement of each drawing might be beneficial. This exercise is designed to assess the ability to read each measurement.

O Israel, put your hope in the Lord,
for with the Lord is unfailing love and with him is full redemption.
Psalm 130:7

Lesson 131

Concepts:

Linear measurement conversions, estimate money and add, subtract decimals, subtract, divide, century, reduce fractions

Objectives:

1. The student will be able to identify, measure, read, write, and label given items using Customary measurement units of feet, yards, and miles.
2. The student will be able to identify, measure, read, write, and label given items using Customary measurements of inches, half inches, and quarter inches.
3. The student will be able to use the regrouping process as needed to complete addition and subtraction problems which require the estimation of money to the nearest dollar.
4. The student will be able to add and subtract decimal numbers.
5. The student will be able to complete subtraction problems which require use of the regrouping process across zeros.
6. The student will be able to complete division problems which contain two-digit divisors and yield a one-digit quotient.
7. The student will be able to identify in which century a given event occurred.
8. The student will be able to reduce, or rename, a given fraction to its lowest terms.

Teaching Tips:

Review **Lesson 130** before beginning the new lesson.

Materials, Supplies, and Equipment:

1. 12 inch ruler
2. Yard stick
3. *Worksheet 76*

Activities:

1. Read **Lesson 131 Explanation** together. Discuss the size of the Ark and Noah's ability to build and measure such a large boat in his day. have the student measure several items around the room with the ruler- a student desk, the door height, or the teacher's desk. Then have the students measure the size of the classroom with the 12 inch (foot) ruler and the yard stick. Explain that the yard stick equals 3 feet and therefore is easier to measure larger distances with. After measuring the classroom, you might go outside and have the students measure the length and width of the Ark. This gives a vivid example of the Ark's size.
2. Ask the students how to measure the distance from the school to their house. Would this be a measurement done in yards or feet? Obviously not. Discuss the mile measurement and instances where this measurement would be used. Look at the conversion chart listed in **Lessons 131 Explanation**. Complete a few conversions together by rereading the example problems. You may wish to make up a few other examples from the measurements taken within your room.
3. The student should be able to complete **Lesson 131 Practice** independently.

Unless the Lord builds the house, its builders labor in vain.
Unless the Lord watches over the city, the watchmen stand guard in vain.
Psalm 126:1

Lesson 132

Concepts:

Weight conversions, linear measurement conversions, estimate decimals to add and subtract, equations, division, century, reduce fractions

Objectives:

1. The student will be able to identify, measure, read, write, write, and label given items using Customary measurement units of ounces, pounds, and tons.
2. The student will be able to identify, measure, read, write, and label given items using Customary measurement units of feet, yards, and miles.
3. The student will be able to identify, measure, read, write, and label given items using Customary measurements of inches, half inches, and quarter inches.
4. The student will be able to use the regrouping process as needed to complete addition and subtraction problems which require the estimation of money to the nearest dollar.
5. The student will be able to complete subtraction equations by solving for a value of *n*.
6. The student will be able to complete division problems which have a two-digit divisor and yield a two-digit quotient.
7. The student will be able to identify in which century a given event occurred.
8. The student will be able to reduce, or rename, a given fraction to its lowest terms.

Teaching Tips:

Review **Lesson 131** before beginning the lesson.

Materials, Supplies, and Equipment:

1. Measuring cups (dry and liquid)
2. Various boxes, cans, and bottles of grocery items which weigh varied amounts
3. Scales
4. Ounce and pound weights
5. *Worksheet 77*

Activities:

1. Explain that the students are going to study the units of weight in the Customary System. Have them look over the measuring cups, scales, and weights. It would be a good idea to have uncooked rice, dry beans, uncooked popcorn, or some other dry product to use for measurement. Allow the students to see the different amounts of weight using different dry products. It would also be a good idea to set this up at different centers and allow the students several minutes at each center to experiment with each of the items. Ask them to measure out one pound of one substance and one once of the same substance. Compare the two amounts.
2. Read **Lesson 132 Explanation** together and discuss the example problems. Discuss the difference between each measurement unit.
3. Use the various boxes, bottles, and grocery items to compare their weights.
4. The students should be able to complete **Lesson 132 Practice** independently.

Blessed are all who fear the Lord, who walk in his ways.
Psalm 128:1

Lesson 133

Concepts:

Liquid measure, linear measure, equations, division, addition and subtraction of fractions

Objectives:

1. The student will be able to identify, measure, read, write, write, and label given items using Customary measurement units of cups, pints, quarts, and gallons.
2. The student will be able to identify, measure, read, write, write, and label given items using Customary measurement units of ounces, pounds, and tons.
3. The student will be able to identify, measure, read, write, and label given items using Customary measurement units of feet, yards, and miles.
4. The student will be able to identify, measure, read, write, and label given items using Customary measurements of inches, half inches, and quarter inches.
5. The student will be able to complete subtraction equations by solving for a value of n.
6. The student will be able to complete division problems which have a two-digit divisor and yield a two-digit quotient.
7. The student will be able to add and subtract fractions with unlike denominators.

Teaching Tips:

Materials, Supplies, and Equipment:

1. Containers in the following sizes: cups, pints, quarts, and gallons
2. Access to water, or some non-staining liquid

Activities:

1. Read **Lesson 133 Explanation** together. Discuss the different measuring containers and allow the students to compare them. Demonstrate how 4 quarts is the same amount of liquid as 1 gallon by using a quart container to fill up a gallon container. Have four students come up one at a time and each one pour a quart container of water into the gallon container. After the 4th student has done this, the gallon container should be full. Complete the example problems in **Lesson 133 Explanation** by using the measuring containers to prove they are correct.
2. If space and equipment allows, have the students divide into groups and demonstrate how many pints are needed to fill 1 quart, how many cups are needed to fill one pint and how many cups are needed to fill 1 quart. If time, space, or equipment do not allow this activity, conduct it as a whole class demonstration with as much student participation as possible.
3. The students should be able to complete **Lesson 133 Practice** independently.

Blessed are those whose ways are blameless,
who walk according to the law of the Lord.
Blessed are they who keep his statutes
and seek him with all their heart.
Psalm 119:1-2

Lesson 134

Concepts:

Temperature, weight, linear measure, addition, average, add and subtract fractions

Objectives:

1. The student will be able to identify, read, and write temperatures given in Fahrenheit degrees.
2. The student will be able to identify, measure, read, write, write, and label given items using Customary measurement units of cups, pints, quarts, and gallons.
3. The student will be able to identify, measure, read, write, and label given items using Customary measurement units of ounces, pounds, and tons.
4. The student will be able to identify, measure, read, write, and label given items using Customary measurement units of feet, yards, and miles.
5. The student will be able to complete two-digit addition problems and use the regrouping process if necessary.
6. The student will be able to average a given set of numbers.
7. The student will be able to add and subtract mixed numbers with like denominators.

Teaching Tips:

Most of the students will have no difficulty reading a thermometer using Fahrenheit degrees.

Materials, Supplies, and Equipment:

1. Weather sections of the local newspaper from the past 4 or 5 days
2. Glass of ice water, a cup of hot coffee, and a lamp
3. Several thermometers (which read Fahrenheit)

Activities:

1. Read **Lesson 134 Explanation** together. Discuss the temperature ranges and at what temperature things would begin to get cold, or hot. Have the students break up into small groups. Each group will need a thermometer. Give one group the ice water, one group the hot coffee (monitor this group carefully to avoid any accidents), one group a lamp which has been burning for only about 1 min., the last two groups will need no additional equipment besides the thermometer. Have the groups with the ice water and the coffee place their thermometer in the liquid and monitor the temperature. Have the group with the lamp measure the temperature of the bulb. Have one group measure the room temperature and the last group measure the temperature of one of the students in the room. Allow enough time for the students to monitor these temperatures. Then come back together and discuss the data collected. You might even want to graph this information on the board to track the temperature differences tomorrow in order to compare Fahrenheit and Celsius.
2. If an extra activity is needed, have the student look over the weather sections of several papers. Ask them to notice the actual temperatures and forecast temperatures for the past several days. Then check and see if the temperatures which were forecast match to the actual temperature that was recorded. You might make this an ongoing activity where the students monitor the temperatures and record the changes. This could be easily correlated with a science unit.
3. The students should be able to complete **Lesson 134 Practice** independently.

How can a young man keep his way pure? By living according to God's word.
Psalm 119:9

Lesson 135

Concepts:

Temperature, liquid and linear measure, addition, decimals

Objectives:

1. The student will be able to identify, read, and write temperatures given in Celsius degrees.
2. The student will be able to identify, read, and write temperatures given in Fahrenheit degrees.
3. The student will be able to identify, measure, read, write, and label given items using Customary measurement units of cups, pints, quarts, and gallons.
4. The student will be able to identify, measure, read, write, and label given items using Customary measurement units of ounces, pounds, and tons.
5. The student will be able to complete three-digit addition problems and use the regrouping process if necessary.
6. The student will be able to identify place value through the tenths' place.
7. The student will be able to add and subtract mixed numbers with like denominators.

Teaching Tips:

Review **Lesson 134** before beginning the lesson.

Materials, Supplies, and Equipment:

1. Several Celsius thermometers
2. Glass of ice water, a cup of hot coffee, and a lamp

Activities:

1. Remind the students that the Fahrenheit scale is used in Customary (Standard) measurement. Today's lesson will cover the Metric temperature measurement of Celsius degrees. Have the students conduct the same exercises that they did in **Lesson 134, Activity #1**. This time use the Celsius thermometers. After the students have measured the temperatures and you have discussed them as a class, graph the temperature differences between the Fahrenheit readings taken yesterday and the Celsius readings taken today of the same items.
2. The students should be able to complete **Lesson 135 Practice** independently.

Clap your hands all you nations; shout to God with cries of joy.
How awesome is the Lord Most High, the great King over all the earth!
Psalm 47:1-2

Lesson 136

Concepts:

Metric, liquid measure, column addition, decimals, comparing decimals

Objectives:

1. The student will be able to identify, measure, read, write, write, and label given items using Metric measurement units of centimeter and millimeter.
2. The student will be able to identify, read, and write temperatures given in Celsius degrees.
3. The student will be able to identify, read, and write temperatures given in Fahrenheit degrees.
4. The student will be able to identify, measure, write, write, and label given items using Customary measurement units of cups, pints, quarts, and gallons.
5. The student will be able to add a column one and two-digit numbers.
6. The student will be able to identify place value through the tenths' place.
7. The student will be able to compare decimals.

Teaching Tips:

Remind the students that you will be discussing and using measurements from the Metric System, not the Customary (Standard) System.

Materials, Supplies, and Equipment:

1. Centimeter ruler with millimeter markings
2. Meter stick with centimeter markings and millimeter markings
3. *Worksheet 78*

Activities:

1. Read **Lesson 136 Explanation** together. Have enough rulers for each student to have one. Begin by having the students measure something personal they have, i.e. their desk top, the length of their shoe, or the length of the chair leg. Discuss that these items cam be measured in either centimeters or millimeters. Give examples of items which would be better measured in millimeters and which items it would be better to measure in centimeters. Try to involve the students as much as possible. The more involvement, the more likely the students are to understand and remember the concept. Practice measuring items which require use of centimeters and millimeters (2 cm 3 mm).
2. The students should be able to complete **Lesson 136 Practice** independently.

God is our refuge and strength, an ever-present help in trouble.
Therefore we will not fear, though the earth give way
and the mountains fall into the heart of the sea,
though its waters roar and foam
and the mountains quake with their surging.
Psalm 46:1-3

Lesson 137

Concepts:

Metric, temp, equations, angles, order fractions

Objectives:

1. The student will be able to identify, measure, read, write, and label given items using Metric measurement units of decimeters, meters, and Kilometers.
2. The student will be able to identify, measure, read, write, write, and label given items using Metric measurement units of centimeter and millimeter.
3. The student will be able to identify, read, and write temperatures given in Celsius degrees.
4. The student will be able to identify, read, and write temperatures given in Fahrenheit degrees.
5. The student will be able to complete addition equations by solving for a value of n.
6. The student will be able to identify and match geometric terms.
7. The student will be able to compare and order given fractions from the largest to the smallest.

Teaching Tips:

Before beginning the lesson remind the students of the differences between the Standard (Customary) System of measurement and the Metric System of measurement. Have a large chart made from laminated covered posterboard which matches the conversion chart shown on **Lesson 137 Explanation**. Covering the chart with lamination will allow you to write on the board with a dry erase marker or overhead marker which can be erased with paper towels and water. It will make the chart reusable.

Materials, Supplies, and Equipment:

1. Large Metric conversion chart
2. Overhead markers
3. 5 in x 2 in rectangles of posterboard

Activities:

1. Read **Lesson 137 Explanation** together. Discuss the conversion chart by using the large instructional conversion chart and overhead markers. Discuss the prefix names (Kilo, Hecto, Deka, deci, centi, and milli). You might want to make up a class acronym to help the students remember the order of the prefix columns. Practice several conversions as a class, using the large conversion chart. Allow the students to complete some example problems by using the large chart and overhead markers. Have the students make their own copy of the conversion chart. They can simply copy the chart onto a piece of notebook paper. If you wish to have an additional activity, have the students make individual conversion charts out of small pieces of posterboard approximately 5 in x 2 in. They can keep these for use whenever necessary.
2. Complete all the example problems, except the last one, using the large instructional conversion chart. Have the students complete the last example on their own charts and check their answer with the book.
3. The students should be able to complete **Lesson 137 Practice** independently. If any students still need extra assistance, work with them on the practice problems.

O Lord, my soul yearns for you in the night;
in the morning my spirit longs for you.
Isaiah 26:9

Lesson 138

Concepts:

Metric, temperature, equations, geometry, order fractions

Objectives:

1. The student will be able to identify, measure, read, and write, and label given items using Metric measurement units of liter and milliliter.
2. The student will be able to identify, measure, read, write, and label given items using Metric measurement units of decimeters, meters, and Kilometers.
3. The student will be able to identify, measure, read, write, write, and label given items using Metric measurement units of centimeter and millimeter.
4. The student will be able to identify, read, and write temperatures given in Celsius degrees.
5. The student will be able to complete addition equations by solving for a value of *n*.
6. The student will be able to identify and match geometric terms.
7. The student will be able to compare and order given fractions from the largest to the smallest.

Teaching Tips:

The students will be familiar with the use of a metric meter measurement. They will not, however, probably be as familiar with the liquid (liter) measurement and weight (gram) measurement. They will need examples of various weights and liquid amounts.

Materials, Supplies, and Equipment:

1. Large instructional Metric conversion chart from **Lesson 136**
2. Individual student Metric conversion charts
3. Metric liquid containers, Metric measuring rulers and sticks, and Metric weights and scales, if possible
4. *Worksheet 79*

Activities:

1. Review **Lesson 136** by going over the conversion chart. Discuss the three different basic units of the Metric system (grams, liters, and meters). Use the liquid containers, the rulers to demonstrate the differences if necessary. Give examples of various liquid amounts and measurements. You might want to allow the students to break into groups and "play" with these items. Read **Lesson 138 Explanation** together. Complete the example problems.
2. The students should be able to complete **Lesson 138 Practice** independently.

Who is a God like you, who pardons sin
and forgives the transgressions of the remnant of his inheritance.
You do not stay angry forever but delight to show mercy.
Micah 7:18

Lesson 139

Concepts:

Metric, multiply and compare decimals, add decimals

Objectives:

1. The student will be able to identify, measure, read, write, and label given items using Metric measurements units of grams and Kilograms.
2. The student will be able to identify, measure, read, and write, and label given items using Metric measurement units of liter and milliliter.
3. The student will be able to identify, measure, read, write, and label given items using Metric measurement units of decimeters, meters, and Kilometers.
4. The student will be able to identify, measure, read, write, write, and label given items using Metric measurement units of centimeter and millimeter.
5. The student will be able to complete multiplication problems containing a three-digit multiplicand, and two-digit multiplier, using the regrouping process when needed.
6. The student will be able to compare given decimals using <, >, and =.
7. The student will be able to add decimals and use the regrouping process as needed.

Teaching Tips:

Materials, Supplies, and Equipment:

1. Large instructional Metric conversion chart from **Lesson 136**
2. Individual student Metric conversion charts
3. Metric liquid containers, Metric measuring rulers and sticks, and Metric weights & scales, if possible

Activities:

1. Review **Lesson 136** and **137** by going over the Metric conversion chart. Discuss the three different basic units of the Metric system (grams, liters, and meters). Use the Metric weights, liquid measurements, and rulers to reiterate and demonstrate the differences, if necessary. Give examples of various gram amounts (1 g is about the weight of a paper clip, etc.) and measurements by weighing items in the classroom like a paper clip, a book, or a child (if you have the proper type of Metric scale). You might want to allow the students to break into groups and "play" with items which weigh various weights in order to "feel" the different weights. Read **Lesson 138 Explanation** together. Complete the example problems.
2. The students should be able to complete **Lesson 138 Practice** independently.

Though the fig tree does not bud and there are no grapes on the vines,
though the olive crop fails and the fields produce no food,
though there are no sheep in the pen and no cattle in the stalls,
yet I will rejoice in the Lord, I will be joyful in God my Savior.
Habakkuk 3:17

Lesson 140

Concepts:

Bar graph, weight, metric, metric conversion, subtraction, equations, multiplication

Objectives:

1. The student will be able to read and interpret information using both vertical and horizontal bar graphs.
2. The student will be able to convert given measurements using Metric measurement units of grams and Kilograms.
3. The student will be able to convert given measurements using Metric measurement units of Liters, milliliters, decimeters, Meters, and Kilometers.
4. The student will be able to complete three-digit subtraction problems using the regrouping process as needed.
5. The student will be able to complete subtraction equations by solving for a value of n.
6. The student will be able to complete multiplication problems which contain a 3-digit multiplicand, a two-digit multiplier and require use of the regrouping process.

Teaching Tips:

The next 9 lessons are all on constructing and interpreting graphs. This can be a very exciting unit of study for the students if you use a little creativity. Taking surveys either within the classroom, or by visiting other classrooms can make activities more fun. Try to be creative for your students!

Materials, Supplies, and Equipment:

1. Rulers
2. Colored pencils or crayons
3. Paper (lined notebook paper is fine)
4. *Worksheet 80*

Activities:

1. **Lesson 140 Explanation** together. Go over the first graph. Discuss the parts of the graph: the dollar amounts on the side of the graph, the times listed on the bottom of the graph and the corresponding bar lines. Discuss the proper way to read a graph: for example: the bar for pony rides is half way between the $250 and the $300 line. Half way between $250 and $300 is $275. This means that the total amount made on pony rides is $275.
2. Conduct a survey within the classroom. Survey the students on their favorite food. Give them 4 or 5 choices and vote on each choice. Once this data is compiled, ask the students to make two bar graphs to show this information; one horizontal bar graph and one vertical bar graph. The students need to use rulers to draw all lines straight. They also need to neatly color the bars.
3. The students should be able to complete **Lesson 140 Practice** independently.

The Lord is the keeper; the Lord is the shade upon they right hand.
Psalm 121:5

Lesson 141

Concepts:

Line graph, bar graph, weight, metric conversion, subtraction, equations, rename fractions

Objectives:

1. The student will be able to read and interpret information presented in a line graph.
2. The student will be able to read and interpret information using both vertical and horizontal bar graphs.
3. The student will be able to convert and add given measurements using Metric units of grams and Kilograms.
4. The student will be able to convert given measurements using Metric units of liters and milliliters.
5. The student will be able to complete subtraction problems which require use of the regrouping process across zeros.
6. The student will be able to complete subtraction equations by solving for a value of n.
7. The student will be able to rename, or reduce, given fractions to their lowest terms.

Teaching Tips:

Materials, Supplies, and Equipment:

1. Rulers
2. 1 centimeter graph paper
3. Colored pencils or crayons
4. *Worksheet 80*

Activities:

1. Read **Lesson 141 Explanation** together. Discuss the fact that line graphs are good at showing changes over a period of time.
2. Chose one subject area where you can give the students several test scores or daily homework grades. Have the students make a line graph, using the 1 centimeter graph paper, to show this information. This makes each graph personalized for each student. If you would rather have each child create the same graph, give the students a set of grades and have them create a graph. The student needs to use the rulers and colored pencils to create a neat graph.
3. The student should be able to complete **Lesson 141 Practice** independently.

For as much as ye know that ye were not redeemed with corruptible things... but with the precious blood of Christ, as of a lamb without blemish and with out spot.

1 Peter 1:18a & 19

Lesson 142

Concepts:

Pictographs, line graphs, bar graphs, metric conversions, prime and composite, equations, reduce fractions

Objectives:

1. The student will be able to read and interpret information presented in a pictograph.
2. The student will be able to read and interpret information contained in a line graph.
3. The student will be able to read and interpret information using both vertical and horizontal bar graphs.
4. The student will be able to convert and add given measurements using Metric units of grams and Kilograms.
5. The student will be able to identify prime and composite numbers.
6. The student will be able to complete multiplication equations by solving for a value of *n*.
7. The student will be able to reduce, or rename, given fractions to their lowest terms.

Teaching Tips:

Pictographs can be great fun. Try to think of different pictures to use for the graphic on the pictograph. Most students will enjoy drawing these pictures.

Materials, Supplies, and Equipment:

1. Colored pencils or crayons
2. Rulers
3. *Worksheet 55*
4. *Worksheet 80*

Activities:

1. Read **Lesson 142 Explanation** together. Answer the example problems together. Create a class pictograph which shows the number of girls and the number of boys in your class. Have the students use 1 stick person to represent 2 students. Have the student use the rulers and colored pencils/crayons to create a neatly colored and straight graph. Stress that pictographs, and all graphs, need to be neat so that there is no difficulty interpreting the information contained in the graph.
2. The students should be able to complete **Lesson 142 Practice** independently.

The God of our fathers raised up Jesus, whom ye slew and hanged on a tree. Him hath God exalted with his right hand to be a Prince and a Savior, for to give repentance to Israel, and forgiveness of sins.
Acts 5:30-31

Lesson 143

Concepts:

Circle graph, line graph, pictograph, bar graph, average, divide, equations

Objectives:

1. The student will be able to read and interpret circle or pie graphs.
2. The student will be able to read and interpret information contained in a pictograph.
3. The student will be able to read and interpret information presented in a bar graph.
4. The student will be able to read and interpret information presented in a line graph.
5. The student will be able to average a given set of numbers.
6. The student will be able to complete division problems which contain a two-digit divisor and yield a one-digit quotient.
7. The student will be able to add and subtract fractions with like denominators.

Teaching Tips:

Pie, or circle, graphs can be show either with numbers in each slice of the pie or as percentages in the slices of the pie. Make sure the students understand that all the sections of the graph must add up to 100 if using actual numbers, or 100% if using percentages. Remind them that there should never be a percentage total more than 100%. Also remember that pie graphs can show breakdowns on numbers which are larger than 100 or smaller than 100, but they must be converted to percentages of the whole first. This concept will probably be too difficult for most children this age to comprehend. Try to stick to basic surveys of 100 people or items.

Materials, Supplies, and Equipment:

1. Compass
2. Ruler
3. Colored pencils or crayons
4. *Worksheet 80*

Activities:

1. Read **Lesson 143 Explanation** together. Discuss the proportions of the pie graph and how each "pie slice" size needs to be accurate to the number proportions of the pie. For example: The pie graphs below show an incorrect number/slice proportion and a correct number/slice proportion.

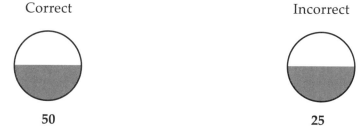

If the pie graph is supposed to total to 100 then half of the pie graph should total to 50 not 25.

2. Have the students draw a circle using their compasses. Instruct the students to make a circle graph which shows the following information:
Title: Favorite Ice cream Flavors of 100 students

Data: Chocolate - 25, Oreo™ Cookie - 25, Banana-Strawberry - 12, Chocolate Almond - 13, Vanilla - 12, Strawberry - 13. Remind the students that each pie slice should be proportioned according to the number in the slice. The finished graph should look similar to the one below.

Favorite Ice Cream Flavors of 100 Students

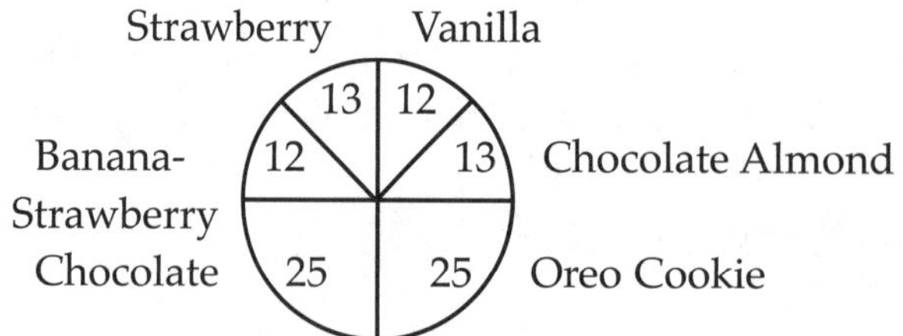

Have the students neatly color each pie slice a different color.

3. The student should be able to complete **Lesson 143 Practice** independently.

What good will it be for a man if he gains the whole world, yet forfeits his soul?
Or what can a man give in exchange for his soul?
Matthew 16:26

Lesson 144

Concepts:

Coordinate graphs, circle graphs, pictographs, line graphs, equations, division, place value, fractions

Objectives:

1. The student will be able to read and interpret information presented in a coordinate graph.
2. The student will be able to read and interpret information presented in a circle or pie graph.
3. The student will be able to read and interpret information presented in a pictograph.
4. The student will be able to read and interpret information presented in a line graph.
5. The student will be able to complete addition equations by solving for a value of n.
6. The student will be able to complete division problems which contain a two-digit divisor and yield a one-digit quotient.
7. The student will be able to identify numbers which are in the tenths place on the place value chart.
8. The student will be able to add and subtract fractions with like denominators.

Teaching Tips:

Many fun coordinate picture books may be found at your local teacher store. The students will enjoy plotting coordinates to reveal various pictures. Many teacher magazines also offer these type of activities.

Materials, Supplies, and Equipment:

1. 1 centimeter graph paper from
2. *Worksheet 80*

Activities:

1. Read **Lesson 144 Explanation** together. Have the students use the centimeter graph paper to plot the following coordinates: (4,1) (5,5) (2,5). Connect the coordinates in the order they were given. Ask the students what shape is made by connecting these coordinates? It should reveal a triangle.
2. The students should be able to complete **Lesson 144 Practice** independently.
3. Have the students create their own coordinate picture on a piece of graph paper and write down the coordinates on an index card. Collect these and use them as a student center in the room during your study of graphs. The students will love doing these during their spare time.

Blessed is the man who trust in the Lord, whose confidence is in him.
Jeremiah 17:7

Lesson 145

Concepts:

Ratio, coordinate graphs, circle graphs, pictographs, equations, change, order fractions

Objectives:

1. The student will be able to define and write a ratio.
2. The student will be able to read and interpret information presented in a coordinate graph.
3. The student will be able to read and interpret information presented in a circle or pie graph.
4. The student will be able to read and interpret information presented in a pictograph.
5. The student will be able to complete addition equations by solving for a value of *n*.
6. The student will be able to count change due from a given transaction, or purchase, using the fewest bills and coins possible.
7. The student will be able to identify numbers which are in the tenths place on the place value chart.

Teaching Tips:

Materials, Supplies, and Equipment:

Activities:

1. Pick 5 students from the room. Chose 2 that have some article of clothing that is the same color. Chose another 3 which have the same article of clothing but in a different color: 2 with blue shirts and 3 with red shirts. Ask the rest of the class to tell you what 3 of these student have in common. Then ask what the other 2 have in common. Once they have figured out that you chose the students based on a certain criteria, like shirt color, explain that the ratio of red shirts to blue shirts is 2 to 3. 2 to 3, 2/3.
   Read **Lessons 145 Explanation** together. Go over each example carefully. Chose a few more examples from the room if additional explanation is needed.
2. The student should be able to complete **Lesson 145 Practice** independently.

Therefore I will give him a portion among the great,
and he will divide the spoils with the strong,
because he poured out his life unto death,
and was numbered with the transgressors.
Isaiah 53:12

Lesson 146

Concepts:

Ratio, coordinate graphs, circle graphs, division, change, fractions

Objectives:

1. The student will be able to write a simple ratio as a fraction.
2. The student will be able to define and write a ratio.
3. The student will be able to read and interpret information contained in a coordinate graph.
4. The student will be able to read and interpret information contained in a circle or pie graph.
5. The student will be able to complete division problems which contain a two-digit divisor and yield a two-digit quotient.
6. The student will be able to count change from a given transaction, or purchase, using the fewest bills and coins possible.
7. The student will be able to compare and order fractions.

Teaching Tips:

Try to make this lesson more interesting by involving the students in a cooking project which involves converting information through the use of ratios.

Materials, Supplies, and Equipment:

Activities:

1. Review **Lesson 145** before beginning this lesson. Read **Lesson 146 Explanation** together. Most of the students will not have a problem with this activity since it is mainly pattern recognition and multiplication.
2. The student should be able to complete **Lesson 146 Practice** independently.

Be imitators of God, therefore, as dearly loved children and live a life of love, just as Christ loved us and gave himself up for us as a fragrant offering and sacrifice to God.
Ephesians 5:1

Lesson 147

Concepts:

Ratio, coordinate graphs, division, geometric terms, fractions

Objectives:

1. The student will be able to multiply ratios in order to find an equal ratio.
2. The student will be able to write a simple ratio as a fraction.
3. The student will be able to define and write a ratio.
4. The student will be able to read and interpret information presented in a coordinate graph.
5. The student will be able to complete division problems which contain a two-digit divisor and yield a two-digit quotient.
6. The student will be able to identify and label geometric terms with the appropriate picture or definition..
7. The student will be able to compare and order fractions.

Teaching Tips:

It might be useful to review equivalent fractions before beginning the lesson.

Materials, Supplies, and Equipment:

Activities:

1. Read **Lesson 147 Explanation** together. Tell the students that finding equal ratios is just like finding equivalent fractions.
2. The student should be able to complete **Lesson 147 Practice** independently.

Be very careful how you live—not as unwise but as wise,
making the most of every opportunity, because the days are evil.
Therefore do not be foolish, but understand what the Lord's will is.
Ephesians 5:15 - 17

Lesson 148

Concepts:

Ratio, multiplication, geometric terms, equivalent fractions

Objectives:

1. The student will be able to divide ratios to find equal ratios.
2. The student will be able to multiply ratios to find equal ratios.
3. The student will be able to write a simple ratio as a fraction.
4. The student will be able to define and write a ratio.
5. The student will be able to complete multiplication problems which contain a three-digit multiplicand, a two-digit multiplier, and require use of the regrouping process.
6. The student will be able to match geometric terms with their appropriate definition.
7. The student will be able to write an equivalent fraction from a given fraction.

Teaching Tips:

Materials, Supplies, and Equipment:

Activities:

1. Review **Lesson 147** on equal ratios before beginning the lesson. Read **Lesson 148 Explanation** together and complete the example problem together. Remind the students that equal ratios are just like equivalent fractions. In order to get an equal ratio or equivalent fraction one must complete the same mathematical function to the top and the bottom of the fraction or ratio. This lesson is dividing to find smaller equal ratios rather than multiplying to find larger equal ratios as in **Lesson 147**.
2. The student should be able to complete **Lesson 148 Practice** independently.

Sing and make music in your heart to the Lord,
always giving thanks to God the Father for everything,
in the name of our Lord Jesus Christ.
Ephesians 5:19b-20

Lesson 149

Concepts:

Bar graphs, ratio, equations, multiplication

Objectives:

1. The student will be able to complete problem solve questions by using information contained in a graph.
2. The student will be able to divide ratios to find equal ratios.
3. The student will be able to multiply ratios to find equal ratios.
4. The student will be able to write a simple ratio as a fraction.
5. The student will be able to complete subtraction equations by solving for a value of n.
6. The student will be able to complete multiplication problems which contain a three-digit multiplicand, a two-digit multiplier, and require use of the regrouping process.
7. The student will be able to write an equivalent fraction from a given fraction.

Teaching Tips:

Materials, Supplies, and Equipment:

Activities:

1. Read **Lesson 149 Explanation** together. Discuss the graph and the graph key. Explain that this graph is a way of comparing information which is about the same topic. The different colored bars represent two different dollar earnings for the two different years that the same activity took place. Answer the example questions together and answer any questions which the students might have.
2. The students should be able to complete **Lesson 149 Practice** independently.

Praise and glory and wisdom and thanks and honor and power
and strength be to our God for ever and ever.
Revelation 7:12

Lesson 150

Concepts:

Ratios, subtraction, reduce fractions, add and subtract fractions

Objectives:

1. The student will be able to write a ratio.
2. The student will be able to complete a table to equivalent ratios.
3. The student will be able to divide to find equal ratios.
4. The student will be able to subtract two, three-digit numbers.
5. The student will be able to reduce fractions to lowest terms.
6. The student will be able to find the sum or difference of fractions that do not have common denominators.

Teaching Tips:

Allow the students to make their own ratio of objects to reinforce the concept of ratio.

Materials, Supplies, and Equipment:

1. Beans, corn, chalk, pencils, or any classroom objects

Activities:

1. Allow students to make their own ratios using classroom objects. For instance: 1/10; 1 bean to 10 pieces of corn.
2. The students should be able to complete these review activities independently.

Our soul waits for the Lord; he is our help and shield.
Psalm 33:20

Lesson 151

Concepts:

Prime numbers, A.M., P.M., equations, reduce fractions, ratios, add and subtract decimals, add and subtract fractions

Objectives:

1. The student will be able determine if a number is prime or composite.
2. The student will be able to tell the difference between A.M. and P.M..
3. The student will be able to solve equations that require one operation on one side and two operations on the other.
4. The student will be able to reduce fractions to lowest terms.
5. The student will be able to complete a table of equivalent ratios.
6. The student will be able to add and subtract decimals to solve a crossword puzzle.
7. The student will be able to find the sum or difference of fractions that do not have common denominators.

Teaching Tips:

Materials, Supplies, and Equipment:

1. Paper, markers, crayons, etc.

Activities:

1. The students will memorize the prime numbers if they are given the opportunity to work with them. Ask them to complete one or several of the following activities:
   a. Make a winter scene using nothing but prime numbers.
   b. Make a board game using prime numbers.
   c. Create a card game using prime numbers.
   d. Create a playground on paper. All of the equipment must be made of prime numbers.
   e. Write a poem about prime numbers.
   f. Work with a friend and memorize the prime numbers.
2. The students should be able to complete these review activities independently.

If you think you can, you can. And if you think you can't, you're right.
Mary Kay Ash

Lesson 152

Concepts:

A.M., P.M., add and subtract fractions, average, division, add and subtract decimals, temperature

Objectives:

1. Given 4-6 numbers the student will be able to find the average.
2. The student will be able to find the quotient of a two-digit dividend and a one-digit divisor.
3. The student will be able to add and subtract decimals.
4. The student will be able to read and record the temperature on a thermometer.
5. Starting at 12:00 A.M. the student will be able to follow the incremental times through a maze passing through 12:00 P.M. and ending at 6:00 A.M..
6. The student will be able to find the sum or difference of two fractions with common denominators.

Teaching Tips:

Students often enjoy averaging their own grades.

Materials, Supplies, and Equipment:

Activities:

1. The students should be able to complete these review activities independently.

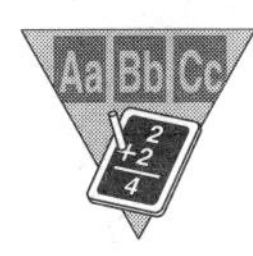

You will never "find" time for anything. If you want time you must make it.
Charles Buxton

Lesson 153

Concepts:

Fractions to decimals, temperature, equations, century, add and subtract fractions, division, linear measure

Objectives:

1. The student will be able to write fractions in decimal form.
2. The student will be able to read and record the temperature on a thermometer.
3. The student will be able to solve equations that require one operation on one side and two operations on the other.
4. Given dates, the student will be able to determine the century.
5. The student will be able to find the sum or difference of fractions with common denominators.
6. The student will be able to find the quotient of a two-digit dividend and a two-digit divisor.
7. The student will be able to find the standard measure of an object to the nearest one quarter inch.

Teaching Tips:

Give the students many opportunities to read and write decimals.

Materials, Supplies, and Equipment:

Activities:

1. The students should be able to complete these review activities independently.

If at first you don't succeed; try, try again.
Author unknown

Lesson 154

Concepts:

Decimals to fractions, century, linear conversions, division, change, equations

Objectives:

1. The student will be able to read and write decimals as fractions.
2. Given dates, the student will be able to determine the century.
3. The student will be able to convert inches to feet, feet to yards, and yards to miles.
4. The student will be able to find the quotient of a 2-digit divisor and 3-digit dividend.
5. Given the cost of one item and the number of items to be purchased, the student will be able to find the product. Given the amount of money the customer paid, the student will be able to compute the exact change the customer will receive.
6. The student will be able to solve equations that require one operation on one side and two operations on the other.

Teaching Tips:

Give the students many opportunities to read and write decimals.

Materials, Supplies, and Equipment:

Activities:

1. The students should be able to complete these review activities independently.

Life hardly ever lives up to our anxieties.
Paul Monash

Lesson 155

Concepts:

Weight, change, add and subtract fractions, compare fractions, division, mathematical terms

Objectives:

1. The student will be able to convert ounces into pounds, and pounds into tons.
2. Given the cost of one item and the number of items to be purchased, the student will be able to find the product. Given the amount of money the customer paid, the student will be able to compute the exact change the customer will receive.
3. The student will be able to find the sum or difference of mixed numbers.
4. The student will be able to compare two fractions.
5. The student will be able to find the quotient of a 2-digit divisor and 3-digit dividend.
6. The student will be able to place the following terms next to the appropriate problem: multiplicand, divisor, minuend, quotient, dividend, addend, sum, product, difference, multiplier, subtrahend, numerator, and denominator.

Teaching Tips:

Allow children to weigh objects around the room.

Materials, Supplies, and Equipment:

Activities:

1. Have the students gather objects from around the room and guess how much they weigh. Then, allow them to actually weigh the objects. How close were their predictions?
2. Try the activity again using different objects. The results should be more accurate.
3. The students should be able to complete these review activities independently.

The Lord has done great things for us; we are glad.
Psalms 126:3

Lesson 156

Concepts:

Compare fractions, weight, linear measure, liquid measure, add and subtract fractions, add and subtract decimals

Objectives:

1. The student will be able to compare two fractions.
2. The student will be able to convert grams to kilograms and kilograms to grams.
3. The student will be able to express metric measurements in three ways: centimeters and millimeters, millimeters, and centimeters.
4. The student will be able to convert gallons to quarts, quarts to pints, and pints to cups.
5. The student will be able to find the sum or difference of fractions that do not have common denominators.
6. The student will be able to find the sum or difference of decimals.

Teaching Tips:

Materials, Supplies, and Equipment:

Activities:

1. The students should be able to complete these review activities independently.

Words are the most powerful drug used by mankind.
Rudyard Kipling

Lesson 157

Concepts:

Linear measure, geometry, metric, fractions, addition, multiplication, ratios

Objectives:

1. The student will be able to express metric measurements in three ways: centimeters and millimeters, millimeters, and centimeters.
2. The student will be able to match a picture to the following terms: point, parallel lines, intersecting lines, perpendicular lines, line, and ray.
3. The student will be able to convert centimeters to millimeters and millimeters to centimeters.
4. The student will be able to find fractions that are equivalent.
5. The student will be able to find the sum of two, two-digit numbers.
6. The student will be able to find the product of a three-digit multiplicand and a two-digit multiplier.
7. The student will be able to complete a ratio table.

Teaching Tips:

Give the students a tape measure and allow them to measure objects in the room.

Materials, Supplies, and Equipment:

1. Tape measure

Activities:

1. Children enjoy measuring objects in their environment. Give them a tape measure and ask them to record the data they collect.
2. Help the students express their measurements in the three ways discussed in **Lesson 157.**
3. The students should be able to complete these review activities independently.

A blow with a word strikes deeper than the blow with a sword.
Robert Burton

Lesson 158

Concepts:

Ratios, angles, equivalent fractions, multiplication, even numbers, addition

Objectives:

1. Given several ratios, the student will be able to determine which ratio does not belong.
2. The student will be able to name the following figures: right angle, obtuse angle, acute angle.
3. The student will be able to find the vertex and sides of an angle.
4. The student will be able to solve for n given equivalent fractions.
5. The student will be able to find the product of a three-digit multiplicand and a two-digit multiplier.
6. The student will be able to find even numbers in a maze.
7. The student will be able to find the sum of two, three-digit numbers.

Teaching Tips:

Materials, Supplies, and Equipment:

Activities:

1. The students should be able to complete these review activities independently.

Leisure is a beautiful garment, but it will not do for constant wear.
Anonymous

Lesson 159

Concepts:

Column addition, equations, mystery numbers, temperature, time, metric, reduce fractions

Objectives:

1. The student will be able to find the sum of a column of five numbers.
2. The student will be able to solve equations that require one operation on one side and two operations on the other.
3. Given number clues, the student will be able to determine the number.
4. The student will be able to match Fahrenheit and Celsius readings to the following: boiling point, freezing point, room temperature, freezer, and body temperature.
5. The student will be able to define the terms: century, millennium, BC, AD, decade, 21st century, and 20th century.
6. The student will be able to match grams, liters, and meters to liquid, linear, or weight.
7. The student will be able to reduce fractions to the lowest terms.

Teaching Tips:

Materials, Supplies, and Equipment:

Activities:

1. The students should be able to complete these review activities independently.

A wise man will make more opportunities than he finds.
Francis Bacon

Lesson 160

Concepts:

Decimals to fractions, subtraction, equivalent fractions, equations, add and subtract fractions, ratios

Objectives:

1. The student will be able to match word numbers with decimals and fractions.
2. The student will be able to find the difference of two, three-digit numbers that require borrowing.
3. The student will be able to match equivalent fractions.
4. The student will be able to solve equations that require one operation on one side and two operations on the other.
5. The student will be able to find the sum or difference of two fractions without common denominators.
6. The student will be able to write the product of a unit fraction and a multiple of the denominator.

Teaching Tips:

Give the students many opportunities to read and write decimals.

Materials, Supplies, and Equipment:

Activities:

1. Try one of these activities to reinforce the understanding of reading and writing decimals.
   a. Make flashcards with the decimal name on the front and the mixed number on the back. Work through them daily with your students.
   b. Make flashcards with the decimal name on the front and the decimal number on the back. Work through them daily with your students.
   c. Have two students work together to learn decimals. One student says a decimal, the other student writes the decimal. Change roles.
   d. Have two students play HIGH, LOW. Begin by making a stack of ten cards. Five of the cards should read, high. Five of the cards should read, low. Each child writes a secret number with four digits on a piece of paper. The decimal point may go wherever the student chooses. Each student must read the number they have written correctly to the other student. If they can not read the number correctly, they lose. Then, either person may draw one card and read it. The winner is the person who has the high number, if the card says, high. The winner is the person who has the low number, if the card says, low. Continue playing until one player has 5 wins.
2. The students should be able to complete these review activities independently.

"The Lord is my helper, I will not be afraid; what can man do to me?"
Hebrews 13:6

Answer Key

Lesson 1

1. a. addend, addend, sum, 73
   b. addend, addend, sum, 98
   c. addend, addend, sum, 57

2. $6.75; $3.53; $1.57; $2.65; $4.44

3. 97,630; 97,211; 97,321; 99,972; 84,310

4. 1/8; 3/8; 5/8; 7/8

5. MATH IS A BLAST

6. BUCKLE YOUR SEAT BELT

7. TAKE OFF

Lesson 2

1. a. 2. Grouping Property of Addition
   b. 3. Order Property of Addition
   c. 1. Zero Property of Addition

2. addend, addend, sum, 129
   addend, addend, sum, 89
   addend, addend, sum, 97

3. ROCKING HORSE

4. 11,358; 34,567; 12,336; 11,456; 12,889

5. 12

6. 3; 5; 7; 1

7.

6 + 0	8 + 0	9 + 0
0 + 6	0 + 8	0 + 9
1 + 5	1 + 7	1 + 8
5 + 1	7 + 1	8 + 1
4 + 2	6 + 2	7 + 2
2 + 4	2 + 6	2 + 7
3 + 3	5 + 3	6 + 3
	3 + 5	3 + 6
	4 + 4	5 + 4
		4 + 5

8. The rocket would get bigger.

9.

<	<	>	<
>	<	>	<
<	<	<	<

Lesson 3

1.

11;	9;	10;	11;	9;	6
11;	9;	10;	11;	9;	6
11;	8;	10;	14;	17;	15
11;	8;	10;	14;	17;	15
10;	13;	19;	17		
10;	13;	19;	17		

2.

Across	Down
15	10
12	15
18	12
17	18
16	17
14	16
13	14

3.

30	180	1,270	100
90	120	5,090	300
30	790	8,260	3,100
20	450	7,890	
10	290	4,380	

4. Teacher check

5.

0	1	0	1
1	2	1	4
1	1	0	1
1	1	1	0
2	2	2	1
0	0	0	1
2	4	0	2

Lesson 4

1. 1. minuend, subtrahend, difference, 5
   2. minuend, subtrahend, difference, 9
   3. minuend, subtrahend, difference, 6

2.

37; 12; 25	44; **12**; 32	68; **24**; 44
20; 7; **13**	24; 12; 12	**27**; 3; **24**
17; **5**; **12**	**20**; **0**; **20**	41; 21; **20**

3. 1. addend, addend, sum
   2. minuend, subtrahend, difference

4. 1/4 — one-fourth
2/9 — two-ninths
3/8 — three-eighths
1/8 — one-eighth
2/6 — two-sixths
3/11 — three-elevenths
3/4 — three-fourths
6/12 — six-twelfths

5.

2 quarters	14 nickels
2 dimes	3 pennies
3 pennies	
5 quarters	25 nickels
4 pennies	4 pennies

6.

2/4 = 4/8	2/6 = 1/3
1/2 = 2/4	4/8 = 1/2

7. THE LAMB CHOP

8. 1. 11 students
2. 47 students

Lesson 5

1. 9; 0; 12; 0

8; 9
7; 8

2.

7; 4; 5	6; 8; 1	7; 9; 2
3; **6; 7**	**2; 4**; 9	**3; 8**; 7
6; 6; 4	7; **3**; 5	8; 1; **9**
sum = 16	sum = 15	sum = 18

3.

triangle	cube
circle	hexagon
cylinder	oval
square	rectangular pyramid
diamond	pentagon
sphere	cone

4.

439;	479;	889;	798;	996
899;	809;	915;	899;	759

5.

961	798	614	598
320	371	12	138

Lesson 6

1. 0; 2; 8; 10;
7; 2; 9; 0; 9;
6; 5; 4; 0; 5;

2. 1. 9 + 6 = 15
2. 3 + 7 = 10
3. 6 + 6 = 12
4. 8 – 4 = 4
5. 8 – 4 = 4
6. 11 – 6 = 5
7. 3 + 10 = 13
8. 9 – 0 = 9

3.

8:20;	9:45;	10:55;	12:00;	2:35
6:02;	1:39;	8:12;	5:44;	3:29

4. THEN IT WOULD BE A FOOT

5. 18; 21; 21; 18; 19; 14

6. 3; 6; 9; 12; 15; 18; 21; 24; 27
2; 4; 6; 8; 10; 12; 14; 16; 18
4; 8; 12; 16; 20; 24; 28; 32; 36
5; 10; 15; 20; 25; 30; 35; 40; 45;

Lesson 7

1.

9;	6;	9
9;	6;	9
7;	5;	6
2;	1;	3

2.

4;	6;	4
3;	5;	8
11;	7;	14

3. JESUS

4. 73¢; 47¢; 82¢; 78¢; $1.32

5.

	minuend			
	subtrahend			
127	difference,	140;	259;	65
119;	324;	234;	224;	217

6.

X; 2; 3	X; 1; 2	X; 4; 5
4; **8; 12**	5; **5; 10**	3; **12; 15**
2; **4; 6**	4; **4; 8**	2; **8; 10**
3; **6; 9**	2; **2; 4**	4; **16; 20**

7. 4; 4; 2; 4; 5
   1; 4; 4; 2; 5
8. parallelogram; trapezoid
   rhombus; triangular prism

Lesson 8

1. odd even even even odd
   odd even even odd odd
   even odd odd odd odd

2. Teacher check

3. 1 – penny; 1 – dime; 1 – quarter;
   2 – one dollar bills = $2.36

   2 – pennies; 3 – quarters;1 – one dollar bill = $1.77

   4 – pennies; 2 – dimes; 1 – one dollar bill = $1.24

4. 12; 11; 11; 8
   12; 8; 6; 8
   3; 8; 5; 2
   9; 8; 5; 8

5. Clockwise starting from the top:
   1. 20; 45; 30; 15; 40; 25; 10; 35
   2. 36; 20; 32; 8; 24; 16; 28; 12

6. 1. 28; even; yes
   2. 49; odd; no;
   (Odd numbers cannot be evenly paired)

Lesson 9

1. 1. $6.50
   2. 13 cookies
   3. $58.00
   4. $2.00 left over
   5. 7 cupcakes

2. odd
   odd
   even
   odd
   even
   odd

   examples may vary

3. Clockwise starting from the top:
   12; 11; 10; 13; 7; 9; 5; 8

   2; 4; 8; 0; 10; 12; 6; 14

4. 10; 12; 11
   4; 7; 3
   6; 5; 8
   4; 7; 3

5. $n = 7$; $n = 8$; $n = 7$
   $n = 6$; $n = 12$; $n = 13$; $n = 5$

6. 36; 63; 18; 81; 72
   9; 54; 0; 45; 90

7. 3:27; 8:04; 12:30; 7:56; 11:17

Lesson 10

1. 100 thousand; ones; thousands; thousands; tens
   52; 408,030; 2,304; 2,073; 60,092

2. Be not hasty to be angry.

3. 15; 5; 1; 3; 21; 27; 11

4. 95; 83; 156; 143; 61; 39

5. 20; 33; 12; 61; 10; 8

6. 2; 6; 1; 7; 3

7. triangle oval
   rectangle square
   sphere cone
   diamond cylinder
   pentagon hexagon

8. 3/6; 4/6; 10/12; 6/8; 2/4

Lesson 11

1. 384,000,000
   267,000,000
   419,200,000
   874,354,000
   525,000,020

2. 4
   7
   1
   3
   6
   2
   5

3. odd
odd
odd
even
odd
even

4. 4
8
9
5
7
6

5. 4
2
2
8
16
16

6. =; =; ≠;
= =

Lesson 12

1.

5	5
9	6
2	8
0	2

2. Teacher check

3. Clockwise starting from the top:
2; 11; 12; 6; 9; 3; 7; 4
7; 3; 5; 6; 2; 4; 11; 8
11; 2; 8; 5; 9; 3; 6; 4

4. yd; 24
ft; 12

5. 1 2/4; 3 1/2
1 3/4; 3 6/8

6.

16;	20;	24;	28;	32;	36
20;	25;	30;	35;	40;	45
24;	30;	36;	42;	48;	54
28;	35;	42;	49;	56;	63
32;	40;	48;	56;	64;	72

Lesson 13

1. 800 + 50 + 7
3,000 + 200 + 30 + 5
20,000 + 9,000 + 300 + 0 + 7
40 + 2
300,000 + 70,000 + 9,000 + 600 + 0 + 2
800,000 + 20,000 + 0 + 900 + 50 + 4

2. Answers may vary:
Order Property: 5 + 4 = 9; 4 + 5 = 9
Zero Property: 3 + 0 = 3
Grouping Property: 5 + 2 + 1 = 8;
2 + 1 + 5 = 8, 1 + 2 + 5 = 8

3.

DOWN	ACROSS
1. eight	1. six
2. seven	2. sixteen
3. five	3. four
4. zero	4. eight
	5. three
	6. nine
	7. one

4. 2/4 + **1/4** = 3/4; 2/4 + **2/4** = 4/4
4/12 + **3/12** = 7/12
1/5 + **3/5** = 4/5; 4/10 + **3/10** = 7/10

5. 4; 8; 12; 16; 20; 24; 28; 32; 36; 40
5; 10; 15; 20; 25; 30; 35; 40; 45; 50
6; 12; 18; 24; 30; 36; 42; 48; 54; 60
7; 14; 21; 28; 35; 42; 49; 56; 63; 70

6. $1.61; $14.77
$37.23; $52.14

Lesson 14

1.

XI;	XIX;	XXIV;	XXX
XIV;	X;	VI;	XVII

2. 40,000 + 2,000 + 200 + 70 + 5 = 42,275
200,000,000 + 50,000,000 + 600,000 + 40,000 + 2,000 + 100 + 60 + 2 = 250,642,162
6,000,000,000 + 700,000,000 + 10
= 6,700,000,010
900 + 50 + 1 =951

3. 4/6; 7/20
15/25; 2/9

4. a. $73.50
b. Teacher check

5.

18	22
3	2
7	4
11	6
14	8
19	12
23	15
27	24
1	26
5	21
9	10
16	13
17	20
25	

6. 7; 14; 21; 28; 35; 42; 49
8; 16; 24; 32; 40; 48; 56
9; 18; 27; 36; 45; 54; 63
10; 20; 30; 40; 50; 60; 70

Lesson 15

1. 758; 6,039; 34,221
369,734; 10,000; 420
5.6 billion

2. 1,010; 989; 946

5,961; 5,691; 5,463; 5,436

29,110; 29,035; 28,887; 28,788

386,324; 328,834; 324,396

3. 50,000 + 4,000 + 200 + 70 + 1
80,000 + 6,000 + 300 + 4
300,000 + 60,000 + 7,000 + 900 + 30 +2
20,000 + 7,000 + 3

4. 1/2 + 1/2 = 2/2 = 1; 3/4 – 2/4 = 1/4
10/20 – 10/20 = 0/20 = 0

5/15 + 3/15 = 8/15; 8/22 – 4/22 = 4/22
15/50 + 10/50 = 25/50

5.

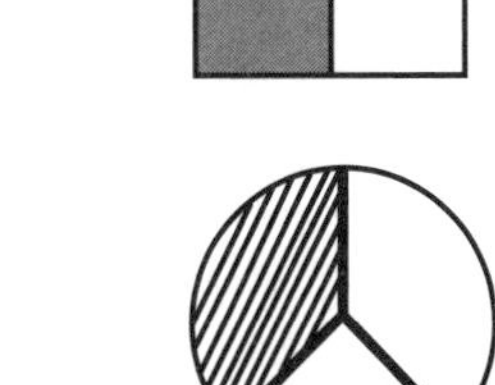

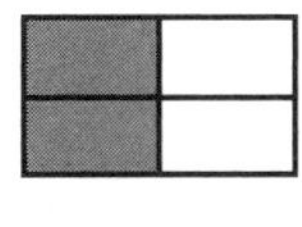

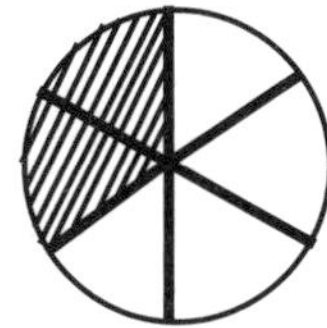

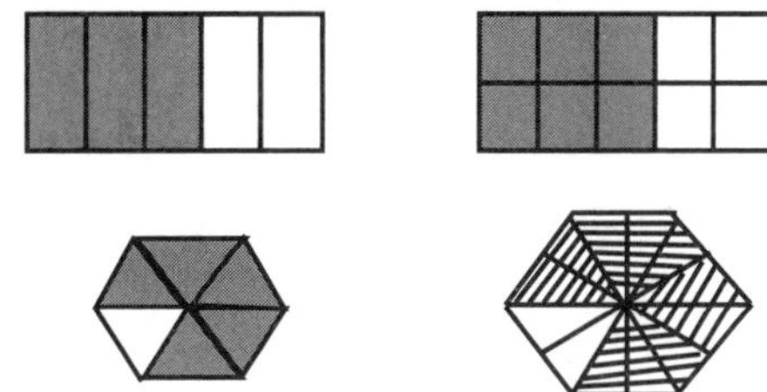

6. BEHIND THE PLATE

Lesson 16

1. =; ≠; ≠; =; ≠

2. 452,963; 463,259; 492,364; 546,253

32,593; 52,369; 93,256; 98,325

25,362,253; 35,259,125; 51,253,352;
53,253,853

798; 879; 897; 987

3. a. 30,000 + 2,000 + 70 + 6
b. 30,000 + 200 + 70 + 6
c. 30,000 + 2,000 + 700 + 6
d. 30,000 + 2,000 + 700 + 60

4. MATTHEW = 6,166,856
RUTH = 9,868
SAMUEL = 716,852
EZEKIEL = 5,559,952
ISAIAH = 971,918
HAGGAI = 817,719
MATTHEW

5. 6 + **9** = 15; 6 + 7 = **13**; 6 + **6** = 12; 6 + 3 = **9**
6 + 2 = **8**

5 + 3 = **8**; 5 + **5** = 10; 5 + **2** = 7; 5 + **15** = 20
5 + 4 = **9**

9 + 2 = **11**; 9 + **3** = 12; 9 + 9 = **18**;
9 + 1 = **10**; 9 + **11** = **20**;

6. 5/8; 3/9; 9/10
12/15; 25/25 = 1

Lesson 17

1. <; <
<; <
<; <
>; <

2. 2/12; 2/10; 2/8; 2/4; 2/3

3.

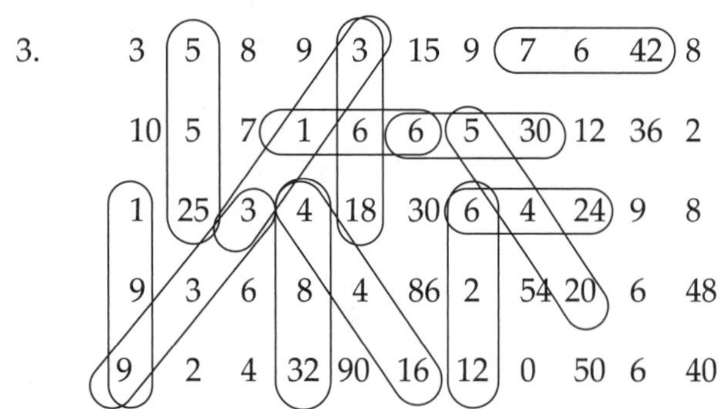

3 5 8 9 3 15 9 7 6 42 8
10 5 7 1 6 6 5 30 12 36 2
1 25 3 4 18 30 6 4 24 9 8
9 3 6 8 4 86 2 54 20 6 48
9 2 4 32 90 16 12 0 50 6 40

4. 950
71

5. hexagon; trapezoid; rectangular pyramid
parallelogram; rhombus; cube
square; triangle; sphere

6. 100; 10; 1
1,000; 100; 10; 1
1,000; 100; 10; 1
1,000; 100; 10; 1
10,000; 1,000; 100; 10; 1
100,000; 10,000; 100; 10; 1

Lesson 18

1. 90
350
The missing number is 5,800
5,793 rounds to 5,790

2. 60
80
40
60

3. 40 = 40; 3,620 = 3,620

530 > 520; 9,870 > 9,850

4. $6.24; $15.39

$27.57 $98.46

5. 7:35; 11:20; 3:13; 5:57

6. 4
5
7
13

7. 17; 9; 13; 7; 9; 5
9; 2; 10; 4; 9; 8; 10
5; 14; 7; 9; 3; 4; 16
14; 21; 12; 20; 14; 9; 0

Lesson 19

1. yes
no
yes
yes
no

2. Answers may vary:
How much would 3 CD's cost?
Answer: $39.00

How many more miles did Karen run on Wednesday and Friday than on Monday?
Answer: 2 miles

How much money does Sarah earn if she works on Monday, Tuesday, and Saturday?
Answer: $119.00

How much commission did Tom make?
Answer: $210.00

3. 1,020 miles
545 miles
Craig to Burton
1,565 miles

4.

40	100		
80	20	2,200	56,970
+50	+40	+3,150	+42,770
170	160	5,350	99,740

5. 1,235 2,579
1,226 1,234

6. Twenty four thousand, five hundred – 24,500
Seven hundred sixty-two thousand, fourteen – 762,014
Sixteen million, two thousand – 16,002,000
Five hundred seventeen – 517

Lesson 20

1. 2,570; 6,980; 350; 2,190
3,300; 1,000; 700; 9,700
4,000; 7,000; 4,000; 8,000

2. 1. odd; 5. odd; 9. odd
2. even; 6. odd; 10. odd
3. odd; 7. odd; 11. even
4. even; 8. odd; 12. odd

3. 2; 5; 10; 50
   3; 15; 75
   4; 10; 20; 100
   12; 24; 120

4. 5/8; 4/6; 7/10; 3/7; 5/9

5. X; 5; 6 | X; 3; 4 | X; 7; 8
   4; **20; 24** | 4; **12; 16** | 4; **28; 32**
   5; **25; 30** | 5; **15; 20** | 5; **35; 40**
   6; **30; 36** | 6; **18;24** | 6; **42; 48**

6. <; =; >
   <; <; =
   <; >; >

7. yes
   no
   yes
   yes
   no

Lesson 21

1. 45; 30; 41; 32; 41; 31
2. 12,000; 897,000; 934,000
   79,000; 46,000; 49,000
   144,000; 68,000; 547,000

3. 10; 50; 110
   20; 60; 200
   30; 80; 330
   Puzzle: Teacher check

4. 9; 12 ; 15; 18 ; 21; 24 ; 27; 30
   Every other number is even.

5. 15; 20 ; 25; 30 ; 35; 40 ; 45; 50
   Every other number is even.

6. 12; 15; 16; 11; 15; 14 7; 10;
   12; 13; 18; 14 8; 4; 6; 12;
   10; 9 12; 12; 14; 11; 12; 8
   9; 5; 16; 10; 10; 9 11; 9

7. 1. 7,585,331
   2. 50,427; 987,321
   3. 2,553,782; 7,585,331
   4. 50,427
   5. 438; 88
   6. 987,321; 7,585,331
   7. 770; 2,553,782
   8. 3,567; 873,911; 2,553,782

   1. 7,500
   2. 98,100
   3. 400
   4. 5,900
   5. 8,100
   BOARD

Lesson 22

1. 416; 832; 794; 849; 822

2. 88; 108; 63; 86; 70

3. 1. 14 | 6. 50,400
   2. 18 | 7. 61,576
   3. 76 | 8. 61,578
   4. 5,404 | 9. 62,002
   5. 16,412 | 10. 111,608

4. 1. 6,024
   2. 1,312,002
   3. 400,001
   4. 2,033,000,005
   5. 5,502
   6. 49,000,005,000
   7. 13,234
   8. 19,000,000,000

5. 48,000 | 1,229,000 | 10,214,000
   47,000 | 3,000 | 2,000
   721,000 | 2,224,000 | 23,000
   1,000
   Path answers:
   1,000; 2,224,000; 721,000; 47,000; 10,214,000; 3,000; 23,000; 1,229,000; 2,000; 48,000

6. 24, 16
   24, 39 score: 63
   16, 17 score: 33
   24
   24, 16; 23, 17

Lesson 23

1. 72; 76; 88; 92
   105; 88; 147; 155

2. 24,000; 346,000; 700,000
   44,000; 587,000; 324,000
   31,000; 910,000; 812,000

3.
1. 78
2. 30, 25, 27 score: 82
3. 6, 3
4. 72
5. 46
6. 19, 6; 25

4. 194; 166; 134; 158; 180
111; 120; 94; 100; 62

5. =
≠
=
≠
≠

6. 300,000 + 90,000 + 1,000 + 200 + 70 + 4
1,000,000 + 600,000 + 20,000 + 1,000 + 200 + 90 + 9

7. GOD IS MY ROCK

Lesson 24

1. 80; 60; 80; 50; 80

2. 8/8; 7/12; 5/9
4/16; 5/6; 5/8

3.

1, 2 **1** 3	4, 6 **4** 8	1, 6 4 **2**	**2**, 4 2 7
4, 2 5 9	4, **2** 6 0	3, **4** 5 7	3, 5 **2** 1
5, 4 7 2	**8**, 9 0 8	5, 0 **9** 9	5, 9 4 8

4. 120; 210; 160; 170
120; 240; 190; 190; 140

5. 3,000,008
1,236,514
4,913
1,616
6,500
160
500
box: Teacher check

6.

Across	Down
1. 774	1. 79
2. 1551	2. 1160
3. 1230	3. 124
4. 486	4. 1330
5. 206	5. 48
	6. 1256
	7. 671
	8. 688

Lesson 25

1. 2,839; 7,008; 2,492; 17,319
6,099; 9,860; 7,717; 6,797

2. 170; 750; 380; 1,050; 900

3.
1. 58
2. 24
3. 652
4. 5498

4. 134; 170; 188; 204; 94;
169; 112; 82

5. 71; 160; 14
90; 23; 52
30; 109; 300

6.
a. Montpelier – 8,247
b. Helena – 24,569
c. Santa Fe – 55,859
d. Salem – 107,786
e. Salt Lake City – 159,936
f. Lincoln – 191,972
g. Jackson – 196,637
h. Richmond – 203,056
i. Columbus – 632,910

Lesson 26

1. $n = 38$; $n = 21$; $n = 29$
$n = 17$; $n = 53$; $n = 13$

2. 8,700
4,800
14,400
5,700
14,500
2,400
400
11,200
12,600

3.
1. Mount Whitney
2. Mount Elbert
3. Humphries Peak
4. Mount Hood
5. Guadalupe Peak
6. Mount Rodgers
7. Brasstown Bald
8. Mount Frissell
9. New Castle City

4. 161; 192; 316; 284; 114; 219

5. 290,684; 508,757; 390,930; 588,982

6. Shape should be a star

7. 1. 78
   2. 61

Lesson 27

1. \$419.29; \$513.70; \$1,489.93; \$699.54

2. \$2.41; \$3.10; \$2.90; \$2.28; \$1.19; \$0.16

3. 271,976; 668,999; 592,959; 729,428

4. Teacher check

5. 2,000
   261,900
   121,400
   96,000
   43,600
   81,800
   30,900
   79,600
   7,400

6. 1. Texas
   2. Delaware
   3. Oregon, New Mexico, Texas
   4. Louisiana, Maine, New Jersey, Delaware
   5. Oregon

7. 245,731; 679,311; 5,798; 490; 21,099

8. $n = 22$; $n = 36$

Lesson 28

1. \$9.00; \$17.00; \$9.00; \$52.00; \$13.00
   900; 1000; 700; 1,000; 300

2. $n = 19$; $n = 46$

3. 80; 68; 146; 83
   45; 96; 100; 146; 88; 178

4. AT LAUNCH TIME

5. Teacher check

6. 23; 1,023; 2,023; 3,023; 4,023; 5,023; 6,023; 7,023; 8,023; 9,023; 10,023; 11,023 12,023; 13,023; 14,023;15,023; 16,023; 17,023 18,023; 19,023

7. 369,813; 1,198,107; 609,702; 1,134,000

Lesson 29

1. 1. 1
   2. 36
   3. 2
   4. 23

2. $n = 50$; $n = 62$

3. \$2.35; \$2.85; \$2.00; \$12.25; \$24.50; \$49.00

4. 9; 7; 5; 21

5. HAD MORE CENTS

6. \$361.17; \$748.27; \$97.09; \$417.18

Lesson 30

1. 22 31 24 21 31

2. \$7.00; \$8.00 \$7.00
   \$29.00; \$30.00 \$29.00
   \$9.00; \$10.00 \$10.00
   \$2.00; \$3.00 \$2.00
   \$17.00; \$18.00 \$18.00

3. 7 – Billions; 9 – 10 Thousands; 9 – 100 Billions; 6 – Hundreds; 8 – Tens; 1 – 10 Millions

7 – Billions		6 – Hundreds
9 – 10 Thousands		8 – Tens
9 – 100 Billions		1 – 10 Millions

4. 4,700; 569,800; 68,500
   400; 700; 5,100

5. 181,790 people
   3,568,473 people

6. $n = 7$; $n = 14$; $n = 6$
   $n = 8$; $n = 6$; $n = 31$

Lesson 31

1. 141; 166; 236; 771
   99; 321; 48; 142

2. 38; 47; 41; 69

3. \$10.15; \$7.67; \$31.03;
   \$107.23; \$400.61; \$730.43

4. Shape should form a cross.

5. 5,130; 3,540
8,280; 8,280

6. 9; 2; 8
6; 4; 3
1; 7

7. 2,000
1,000
10,000
7,000

8. 315; 69

Lesson 32

1. 79; 75; 240; 44; 103; 11

2. 48; 3; 219; 421
6; 11; 233; 408

3. 9; 8; 35
63; 57; 50
34; 16; 60
MOSES

4. $6.00
$13.00
$9.00
$136.00

5. 603,418
600,000 + 3,000 + 400 + 10 + 8
125,732
100,000 + 20,000 + 5,000 + 700 + 30 + 2
457,385
400,000 + 50,000 + 7,000 + 300 + 80 + 5
572,906
500,000 + 70,000 + 2,000 + 900 + 6

6. $13.49
$375.00

Lesson 33

1. 30; 40; 70
300; 800; 1,200
6,000; 6,000; 1,000

2. 64; 1,987; 83,562
281; 461; 6,634

3. 12; 49; 375; 671
418; 41; 296; 53

4. 6,020
6,386
6,492
600,150

5. 3 x 1,000; 1 x 100; 9 x 10; 7 x 1;
7 x 1,000; 2 x 100; 9 x 10; 8 x 1
2 x 10,000; 6 x 1,000; 9 x 100; 7 x 10; 8 x 1
1 x 100,000; 2 x 10,000; 6 x 1,000; 9 x 100
0 x 10; 8 x 1
5 x 100,000,000; 6 x 10,000,000
7 x 1,000,000; 2 x 100,000; 9 x 10,000;
8 x 1,000; 6 x 100; 5 x 10; 4 x 1

6. 7,000 – H
5,000 – E
22,000 – A
5,000 – V
79,000 – E
32,000 – N
HEAVEN

Lesson 34

1. 439; 408; 781; 3,289
6,163; 6,607; 41,049; 4,680

2. 7,000 – 2,000 = 5,000
9,000 – 5,000 = 4,000
3,000 – 1,000 = 2,000

3. 1,239; 639; 273; 476
4,693; 1,238; 778; 163

4. 12,345; 6,789
1,468; 12,578
1,468; 6,789; 12,345; 12,578

5. Actual: $2.09 + 3.95 + 3.95 = $9.99
Estimated: $ 2.00 + 4.00 + 4.00 = $10.00
Actual: $12.95 + 5.25 = $18.20
Estimated: $13.00 + 5.00 = $18.00
Actual: $46.75 + 125.00 + 15.76 = $187.51
Estimated: $47.00 + 125.00 + 16.00 = $188.00

6. (cd) – 1-$10; 2-$1; 3-25¢; 1-1¢
(watch) – 4-$10; 2-$1; 3-25¢; 2-10¢; 4-1¢
(solder gun) – 1-$10; 3-25¢; 2-10¢; 4-1¢

Lesson 35

1. 9; 18; 19
27; 17; 8

2. 1,464; 2,142; 7,745; 4,742
2,297; 1,188; 1,448; 3,137

3. 24,830; 23,840; 23,486; 23,480
59,701; 57,910; 51,970; 51,790

4. $32.00 + 19.00 + 28.00 = $79.00
$29.00 - 16.00 = $13.00
$14.00 + 39.00 + 27.00 = 80.00
$39.00 - 27.00 = $12.00
$24.00 + 57.00 + 6.00 = 87.00
$90.00 - 43.00 = $47.00

5.

4	**9**	13	5	**5**	10	**1**	8	**9**
8	10	**18**	**4**	**2**	**6**	5	**8**	13
12	**19**	**31**	**9**	7	16	6	**16**	**22**

6. cone; triangular pyramid; octagon
oval; cylinder; square
cube; parallelogram

Lesson 36

1. $18.12; $24.97; $35.03; $241.26

2. 40; 60; 30
6; 39; 58

3. 58; 60; 56
8; 67; 46

4. 3,221; 2,970; 2,993; 3,172; 4,221

5. 8

6. 240; 3,588; 4,247
6,191; 12,539; 26,077

7. 3,000 – 1,000 = 2,000
5,000 – 4,000 = 1,000
86,000 – 9,000 = 77,000
2,000 – 1,000 = 1,000
8,000 – 1,000 = 7,000

8. Monday $7.00 x 7 = $49.00
Wednesday $6.00 x 5 = $30.00
She earns more money on Monday

Lesson 37

1. $12.00; $3.00; $24.00
$4.00; $91.00; $49.00

2. $8.59; $48.73; $64.50
$27.75; $42.85; $180.00

3. 12; 33; 19
14; 26; 49

4. $n = 5$
$n = 3$; $n = 5$

5. 134
778
5986
7557
4456

6. 39,522; 19,759; 11,209

Lesson 38

1. 1-penny; 1-quarter; 1-1 dollar bill = $1.26
1-penny; 2-dimes; 2-quarters; 1-1 dollar bill = $1.71
4-pennies; 1-dime; 2-quarters; 3-1 dollar bills 1-5 five dollar bill = $8.64
1-dime; 3-quarters; 2-1 dollar bills; 1-5 dollar bill; 1-10 dollar bill = $17.85
1-penny; 1- nickel; 3-quarters; 2-1 dollar bills = $2.81
2-quarters; 4-1 dollar bills; 1-10 dollar bill = $14.50

2. $11.23; $5.10; $3.25
$231.85; $46.08; $34.58

3. $n = 135$; $n = 70$; $n = 35$
$n = 25$; $n = 102$; $n = 11$

4. 4,786; 5,556; 3,432; 2,693

5. $n = 4$; $n = 7$
$n = 1$; $n = 2$

6. 3,494; 23,725; 176,382; 5,605

7. 1. D
   2. B
   3 H
   4. G
   5. A
   6. F
   7. E
   8. C

Lesson 39

1. no
   no
   no
   yes
   no

2. $.15 1-dime; 1-nickel
   $2.41 1-penny; 1-nickel; 1-dime; 1-quarter
   2-1 dollar bills
   $17.05 1-nickel; 2-1 dollar bills; 1-5 dollar bill; 1-10 dollar bill
   $11.35 1- dime; 1- quarter; 1-1 dollar bill
   1-10 dollar bill

3. $9.00
   $35.00
   $10.00
   $471.00
   $18.00

4. $64.43; $12.91; $49.00; $46.39; $3.45

5. $n = 30$; $n = 100$; $n = 33$
   $n = 51$; $n = 75$; $n = 36$

6. 1. 60,164
   2. 5,357; 45,612; 765,137
   3. 572,301
   4. 392; 45,612
   5. 380,659

Lesson 40

1. Multiplicand
   Multiplier
   15 Product
   14; 9; 20; 10; 16; 16; 12

2. 11¢; 1 penny; 1 dime
   41¢; 1 penny; 1 nickel; 1 dime; 1 quarter,
   75¢; 3 quarters
   64¢; 4 pennies; 1 dime; 2 quarters
   22¢; 2 pennies; 2 dimes

3. no, yes

4. WHEN IT IS IN A JAM

5. 236,501,213,111

6. 1; 2; 3; 2; 5; 3
   2; 1; 3; 2; 9; 8; 3

7.

93,482	84,715	17,697
-61,421	-21,395	-14,289
32,061	63,320	3,408

Lesson 41

1. 1. a
   2. c
   3. d
   4. b

2. multiplicand multiplicand multiplicand
   multiplier multiplier multiplier
   10 product 24 product 27 product

3. 24¢, 76¢, 3 quarters, 1 penny
   40¢, 10¢, 1 dime
   72¢, 28¢, 1 quarter, 3 pennies
   54¢, 46¢, 1 quarter, 2 dimes, 1 penny

4. Teacher check

5. 1.00
   2.00
   1.00
   3.00
   2.00
   2.00
   1.00
   $12.00

6. 391,511,739,111

7.

94,889	98,708	65,897
-61,421	-21,387	-64,289
33,468	77,321	1,608

Lesson 42

1. 16; 16; 24; 24
   63; 63; 28; 28

   0; 0; 7; 8; 0; 8
   20; 20; 56; 56; 36; 36

2. muliplicand
multiplier
72 product 6; 27; 28; 18; 7
49; 21; 63; 24; 42; 9
14; 35; 9; 15; 56; 21

3. 13

4. END ↓

5[illegible]¢	5¢	1¢	5¢	1¢	10¢
[illegible]¢	25¢	25¢	5¢	25¢	10¢
5[illegible]¢	5¢	1¢	1¢	1¢	5¢
[illegible]¢	25¢	5¢	25¢	25¢	1¢
5[illegible]	[illegible]¢	2¢	5¢	10¢	10¢
25¢	[illegible]	[illegible]¢	5¢	25¢	10¢
5¢	5¢	5[illegible]¢	25¢	5¢	10¢
5¢	10¢	1[illegible]	[illegible]	5¢	25¢
50¢	1¢	5¢	1[illegible]	5¢	5¢
10¢	10¢	25¢	10[illegible]	2¢	25¢

↑ BEGIN

$4.10

5. 3,915; 142,003; 2,347,022; 14,025,319,000; 5,000,000,000; 16,009,000,033; 100,030,052,104; 92,000,013,000

6. 27; 45; 54; 2; 18,no; $27.00

7. 3,085; 633; 16,003; 6,910

Lesson 43

1. Teacher check

2. 2,4,6,8,10,12,14,16,18,20
5,10,15,20,25,30,35,40,45,50
9 x 4; 2 x 7; 9 x 7
10; 42; 32

3. 50; 21; 27

4. muliplicand muliplicand muliplicand
multiplier multiplier multiplier
12 product 27 product 36 product

5. answers may vary

6. 36; 21; 32; 30; 12
24; 9; 81; 36; 28
C A T

Lesson 44

1. 13 x 1; 2 x 6 3 x 4; 5 x 5
2 x 2 x 3 3 x 2 x 2

2. F O R K R O A D
1 2 3 4 5 6 7 8

3. multiplicand
multiplier
72 product; 27; 49; 16; 10; 28; 45; 42
9; 24; 6; 2; 4; 7; 9; 5; 2; 1

4. ≠; =; =; ≠; =; ≠; ≠; =

5. 96; 137; 129; 145; 102

6. $48.00 + $45.00 + $15.00 = $108.00
$130 - $108.00 = $22.00
$15.00 + $6.00 + 2.00 = $23.00
$25.00 - $23.00 = $2.00

Lesson 45

1. OK

2. 4; 17; 36; 23; 16; 21; 31; 18; 29; 20; 12; 5
GREAT JOB

3. 15; 20; 18; 25; 14; 36; 2; 81; 6
8; 9; 10; 45; 5; 30; 12; 35; 16
72; 10; 40; 18; 27; 4; 54; 63; 9

4. HE SHALL LIFT YOU UP

5. 106; 95; 88; 163; 143

6. 81

Lesson 46

1. quotient, divisor, dividend
9; 8; 4; 4

2. SUN

3. 3 x 3 x 3; 5 x 7; 2 x 2 x 2 x 5;
2 x 3 x 7

4. 8; 14; 16; 18 9; 6; 27; 21
24; 42; 48; 54 15; 10; 45; 35
20; 35; 40; 45 12; 8; 36; 28

5. 1,198; 1,129; 1,075; 1,181; 1,051
674; 1,127; 1,138; 224; 1,325

6. = >
= >
< <
< =

7. SUMMER

Lesson 47

1. b; a; c; d

2.

5 quotient livisor)5 25 dividend 5x5=25	4)6 24 4x6=24	4)4 16 4x4=16	4)5 20 4x5=20	3)9 27 3x9=27
3)4 12 3x4=12	1)7 7 1x7=7	8)4 32 8x4=32	4)9 36 4x9=36	7)7 49 7x7=49
3)2 6 3x2=6	2)5 10 2x5=10	7)4 28 7x4=28	3)6 18 3x6=18	6)5 30 6x5=30

3. 7; 4; 6; 12; 2
   2; 3; 5; 2; 49

4. CHOO CHOO TRAIN

5. 79; 56; 56; 61
   45; 56; 59; 51

6. n = 13; n = 8; n = 10

7. 719; 2,870; 3,168; 1,729; 549

Lesson 48

1. 6; 6; 6; 6
   5; 5; 5; 5
   1; 8; 1; 12; 0
   1; 5; 1; 10; 0
   division by zero

2. quotient
   divisor dividend
   3; 9; 1; 3; 2
   5; 9; 9; 4; 9
   9; 3; 1; 5; 7

3. 3; 4; 9; 6; 64
   7; 4; 2; 15; 3
   RIGHT

4. n = 12; n = 4; n = 13

5. MILLIONAIRE

6. 1. 20
   2. 10
   3. 28
   4. 26
   a. David
   b. Susan
   c. 30
   d. 3
   e. 2, 4, 6
   f. 2

Lesson 49

1. 1. He purchased a race car for $3.50 while he was at the mall.
      $ 2.25
   2. $ 4.20
   3. He bought his mother a gallon of milk on the way home.
      2 x 75¢ = $ 1.50; $ 1.50 + $ 1.85 + 75¢ = $ 4.10
   4. Gary bought a race car for $1.75 before lunch.
      $ 2.00

2. 7; 9; 6; 4; 4
   1; 5; 2; 5; 4
   3; 5; 2; 6; 4

3. 9; 11; 40; 6; 9

4. n = 37; n = 15; n = 20

5. YES

6. 1. a
   2. b
   3. d
   4. b

Lesson 50

1. 1,005; 1,296; 1,839; 884; 1,082

2. 7; 6; 3; 7
   6; 6; 6; 9

3. 45 odd; 29 odd; 20 even; 47 odd
   115 odd; 72 even; 76 even; 75 odd

4. 1; 7
8; 0
6; 4
3; 5
2; 9
METHUSELAH

5. 5,490; 34,220; 4,770
170; 980; 72,970

6. 485; 245; 328; 565
288; 17; 61; 86

7. 1. Dividend – The number to be divided in a division operation.
2. Divisor – The number by which a number is divided.
3. Quotient – The answer to a division operation.

Lesson 51

1. 1,560; 4,152; 2,352; 732
812; 1,706; 2,064; 4,236

2. 696; 226; 802; 2,096

3. 6; 9; 9; 7
7; 8; 5; 6

4. Teacher check

5. 2,504 hours
90 sheep
540 minutes

6. 1. 3,795,421
2. 496,017
3. 138,404,693,016
4. 213,072,496
5. 5,692,013,069
6. 9,217,236
7. 321,097,651,833

7. 280; 3,140; 460; 8,630; 2,100; 5,000

8. 561; 5,256; 1,811; 2,227; 61; 361

Lesson 52

1. 900; 2,500; 4,900; 1,600; 1,200; 160,000
180,000; 36,000

2. 328; 1,590; 5,075; 7,929; 1,038
286; 693; 826

3. 2; 9; 9; 8
6; 5

4. 1. 3,000 + 400 + 90 + 6
2. 300,000 + 60,000 + 900 + 40
3. 30,000 + 9,000 + 400 + 60
4. 3,000 + 600 + 40

5. 500; 300; 400; 200; 700; 200

6. Shape should be a cross and a Bible

Lesson 53

1. 1,998; 2,886; 2,905; 1,653; 460; 132

2. 3,000; 7,000; 60,000; 50,000; 200,000
400,000

3. 1,001; 3,920; 3,395; 1,512
3,336; 1,614; 1,950; 3,738

4. 98,752,431
92,875,431
98,754,231
98,754,321
98,275,431
98,754,312

5. 200,000 + 60,000 + 3,000 + 900 + 40 + 5
6,000 + 0 + 40 + 5
100,000,000 + 90,000,000 + 8,000,000 + 200,000 + 40,000 + 5,000 + 300 + 20 + 1
900 + 20 + 5

6. 8,200; 55,200; 300; 5,200
1,600; 985,100; 6,200; 44,300

Lesson 54

1. 2,944; 12,787; 5,250
8,288; 27,729; 13,156

2. Across
   1. 1,197
   2. 5,625
   3. 572

   Down
   1. 1,855
   4. 2,925
   5. 725

3. 2,000; 8,000; 40,000; 30,000; 600,000
   400,000

4. 984; 4,620; 3,285; 2,086
   1,000; 5,000; 3,000; 2,000
   3,615; 1,320; 2,862; 1,359
   4,000; 1,000; 3,000; 1,000

5. 60,271,532,104; 65,432,110; 65,432,101;
   65,324,100

   865,120,326; 865,021,345; 189,256,326
   108,513,064

6. Teacher check (Answers will vary)

Lesson 55

1. 2,470; 8,950; 49,000; 32,700; 602,000
   474,000

2. 5,964; 24,264; 10,586; 33,435; 26,928; 5,434

3. 1,608; 3,741; 1,836; 1,748; 3,927
   FAITH

4. 314,220,156,203; 7,190,045,978 2,741,285,101;
   367,008,200

5. 43 – Multiplicand
   2 – Multiplier
   86 – Product

6. 5,000; 6,000; 11,000; 12,000

Lesson 56

1. 450; 150; 720; 490
   1,200; 1,600; 1,200; 1,000

2. 5,240; 8,950; 92,500; 41,500; 225,000

3. 9,821; 7,488; 29,304; 17,496; 22,181; 56,658

4. $n = 50$; $n = 8$; $n = 16$
   $n = 7$; $n = 11$; $n = 4$

5. 9; 7; 6; 2; 0; 3
   6; 3

6. Teacher check

Lesson 57

1. $n = 5$; $n = 9$; $n = 9$; $n = 7$
   $n = 10$; $n = 8$

2. 120; 5,600; 42,000
   12,000; 360

3. 868,000; 750,000; 7,880; 119,200

4. $n = 12$; $n = 25$; $n = 36$; $n = 51$
   $n = 30$; $n = 21$

5. 1, 9; 9, 1
   8, 6; 5, 4

6.
   1. $5 + 4 = 9; 9 - 4 = 5$
   2. A letter that stands for a number.
   3. A number sentence containing an equal (=) sign.
   4. $(4 \times 5) \times 2 = 4 \times (5 \times 2)$
   5. $8 - 0 = 0; 8 - 8 = 0$
   6. $1 \times 8 = 8$

Lesson 58

1.
   1. $18.90
   2. $1.70
   3. 27,196 sandwiches
   4. 17,577 customers

2. $n = 6$; $n = 9$; $n = 7$; $n = 6$

3. 360; 1,200; 7,200; 56,000

4. 43; 48; 5; 9; 12; 17

5. $n = 36$; $n = 80$; $n = 420$; $n = 222$

6. Quotient
   Divisor
   Dividend

Lesson 59

1. 1. Through Tinytown & Bankston
   2. Tinytown
   3. Through Tinytown , Bankston & Williamsport

2. $n = 14$; $n = 15$; $n = 34$; $n = 36$
   $n = 15$; $n = 20$; $n = 19$; $n = 37$

3. 4; 2; 5; 8

4. 54; 590; 20
   347; 12; 1,911

5. Teacher check

6. 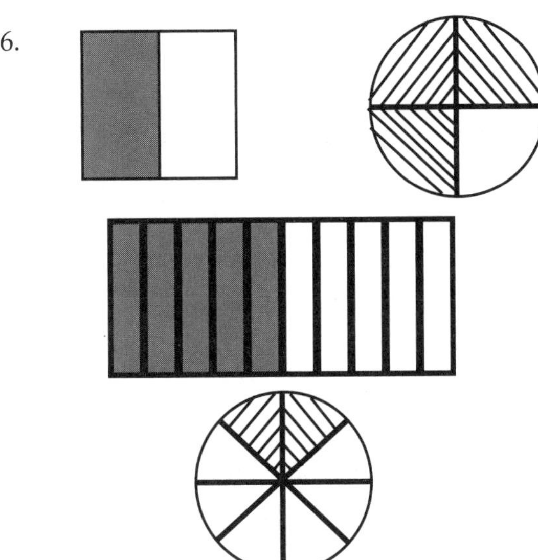

Lesson 60

1. 7; 4 ; 5; 9; 6
   5; 5; 4; 4; 3

2. 1,223; 5,728; 3,329; 1,109

3. ÷ 6, ÷ 6, $n = 6$; 6 x 6 = 36
   ÷ 8, ÷ 8, $n = 4$; 4 x 8 = 32
   ÷ 4, ÷ 4, $n = 6$; 4 x 6 = 24

4. 360; 90; 640
   1,800; 3,500; 2,000
   12,000; 560,000; 120,000

5. CAR

6. 5,236; 30,288; 34,609; 35,518; 41,356

7. 3; 9; 6; 5; 9; 9

Lesson 61

1. 4 r 1; 6 r 2; 8 r 1; 6 r 2; 4 r 1
   3 r 2; 4 r 2; 2 r 2; 5 r 2; 9 r 1

2. 4; 5; 8; 7; 3
   1; 2; 6; 9
   SPECTACULAR

3. 1,200; 12,000; 200,000; 90,000

4. 16; 1,031; 168; 509; 1,156

5. 18,970; 38,012; 43,344; 53,436; 8,804

6. Shape should be a star

7. 43
   74

Lesson 62

1. 16; 14 r 2; 27; 15 r 1
   75 r 1; 22 r 5; 96 r 2; 91 r 6

2. SUPER

3. 6; 8; 1; 2; 4
   5; 7; 9
   ARCHEOLOGY

4. 3 cookies
   9 boxes with 2 bars left over

5. The letter *X* should appear

6. 4,524; 36,950; 33,642; 58,433; 18,970

Lesson 63

1. \$.09; \$.83; \$.43; \$.32
2. 32 r 2; 42 r 1; 73; 91 r 2

3. The letter *T* should appear

4. \$.09
   \$.95

5. 9, 6 x 9 = 54; 5, 5 x 7 = 35
   8, 4 x 8 = 32

6. 1. 7; 8; 9
   2. 16; 32; 64;
   3. 16; 19; 22
   answers will vary

Lesson 64

1. 40 r 3; 50 r 6; 30; 105
   50 r 4; 150; 110 r 1; 102

2. $.35
   $.51
   $.10
   $.32
   LAMB

3. 73; 58 r 2; 96 r 3; 91 r 8; 87

4. 9 r 2; 4 r 2; 8 r 1; 5 r 1; 6 r 3

5. 78
   92
   47
   33; 32

6. 1. 45; 40; 35
   2. 16; 19; 22
   3. 13; 21; 34
   4. 256; 8,192

Lesson 65

1. 1,237 r 1; 492 r 1; 316 r 2; 251; 1,050 r 1

2. 201; **D** 310; **I** 102; **V**
   805; **I** 908; **D** 450; **E**

3. $1.24; $5.45; $9.60; $.93; $6.40

4. The number 10 should appear

5. 1. 10; 12; 14;
   2. 7; 7; 7
   3. 16; 15; 18
   4. 50; 40; 30

6. 1. 3
   2. 10
   3. 4
   4. 8
   5. 6
   6. 5

Lesson 66

1. 2; 5; 10; 3
   2
   2; 3
   3

2. 317 r 3; 471 r 2; 1,935 r 1; 546 r 5; 601

3. 51; 305; 170; 102; 109

4. $32.06; $25.04; $13.70; $29.20

5. Teacher check

6. 5; 28; 18

7. 1. multiplicand–3; multiplier–6
      product–18
   2. divisor–2; dividend–28; quotient–14
   3. addend–13; addend–21; sum–34
   4. minuend–76; subtrahend–23
      difference–53

Lesson 67

1. 24; 30
   5; 21
   30; 8

2. The mystery number is 31

3. 985; 1,597;1,070
   1,570;600; 995
   476; 1,946;950
   GENIUS

4. 1. 109 bottle caps
   2. 67 loops

5. 24; 46; 20

6. 135; 104; 105; 110; 110

7. 1. 2,400 2. 88,500
   3. 800 4. 243,900
   5. 5,300 6. 5,100
   BEST IN YOU

Lesson 68

1. x 3, x 3, $n = 12$; $12 \div 3 = 4$
   x 5, x 5, $n = 15$; $15 \div 5 = 3$
   x 7, x 7, $n = 21$; $21 \div 7 = 3$
   x 9, x 9, $n = 81$; $81 \div 9 = 9$
   x 5, x 5, $n = 45$; $45 \div 5 = 9$
   x 5, x 5, $n = 20$; $20 \div 5 = 4$

2. 30; 40
   80; 25

3. 3
   2; 5; 10; 3
   2
   2; 5; 10; 3
   3

4. \$3.92; \$6.51; \$46.42; \$4.28

5.

451	619	924	830	737
+139	+699	+210	+399	+421
590	1318	1134	1229	1158

6. + 632, + 632, $n = 663$; $663 - 632 = 31$
   + 264, + 264, $n = 376$; $376 - 264 = 112$
   + 29, + 29, $n = 36$; $36 - 29 = 7$

Lesson 69

1. 1. 10 days 3. 4 boxes
   2. 8 tables 4. 2 cookies

2. x 8, x 8, $n = 32$; $32 \div 8 = 4$
   x 5, x 5, $n = 45$; $45 \div 5 = 9$
   x 7, x 7, $n = 63$; $63 \div 7 = 9$

3. 1. 9
   2. 8
   3. 6
   4. total score: 40; average: 10
   5. total score: 24; average: 6
   6. Answers will vary

4. Teacher check

5. 134; 220; 152; 225; 124

6. 1. prime; 4. composite
   2. composite; 5. prime
   3. prime; 6. composite

7. 1. 3, 4 3. 16, 18
   2. 13, 14 4. 6, 8

Lesson 70

1. 2; 10; 7; 40
   50; 250; 700; 40

2. 12; 125; 9
   3; 6; 729

3. 27; 83
   57; 24

4. 77; 29; 33; 13; 39
   GRACE

5. 9,366; 11,128; 12,928; 3,240; 16,950

6. 200; 275; 80; 65
   17; 19; 32; 64

Lesson 71

1. 4 r 5; 2 r 5; 7 r 7; 7 r 1
   8 r 7; 6 r 13

2. 3; 5; 7; 4

3. $n = 36$; $n = 1$; $n = 3$; $n = 5$

4. 61; 17; 29; 16; 6; 19

5. 16; 32; 22; 29
   9; 15; 60; 20

6. 7,176; 8,823; 24,304; 8,235; 12,188

Lesson 72

1. 3; 2 r 24; 2 r 6; 3 r 7; 5; 4 r 21
   3 r 46; 6 r 13

2. Clockwise, starting from the top:
   6; 5; 9; 8; 4; 7

3. 1. 315
   2. 504
   3. 336
   4. 245

4. 271; 73; 557; 9; 287; 93

5.
1. 18 people
2. 5 people
3. 3 people
4. 37 steps

6. $n = 10$; $n = 5$; $n = 5$
$n = 6$; $n = 3$; $n = 8$

Lesson 73

1. ok; 5 instead of 6; 6 instead of 5; ok
2. 2 r 3; 7 r 10; 3 r 28; 5 r 42; 3 r 40

3. 5 r 10; 3 r 23; 6 r 20; 6 r 20; 8 r 27; 6 r 9

4. 278; 560; 242
2,230; 1,151; 5,826
PAUL

5.
1. 3–quarters; 3–1 dollar bills
Check: $10.00 – 6.25 = $3.75
2. 1–nickel; 1–10 dollar bill; 1–5 dollar bill
4–1 dollar bills
Check: $50.00 – 30.95 = $19.05
3. 3–pennies
Check: $2.00 – 1.97 = $.03
4. 1–quarter; 1– nickel; 3 pennies
Check: $3.00 – 2.67 = $.33

6. 73
22

Lesson 74

1. 7 r 41; 48 r 5; 55 r 8; 6 r 30

2. Estimate: 4; 5; 9; 1
Actual: 4 r 17; 5 r 5; 9 r 7; 1 r 89

3.
1. 3
2. 9 r 9
3. 10 r 1
4. 7
5. 8 r 1

4. Clockwise, starting from the top:
8; 3; 5; 9; 2; 4

5.
1. $.28
2. $2.01
3. $7.24

6.
1. 5 weeks
2. 6 tables; 8 people at the extra table
3. 178 miles
4. 12 pieces of candy; 16 pieces left over

Lesson 75

1. 480 r 5; Check: 480x20=9,600+ 5=9,605
231 r 9; Check: 231x34=7,854+9=7,863
486 r 77; Check: 486x87=42,282+77=42,359
348 r 25; Check: 348x65=22,620+25=22,645

2. 7 r 53; 7 r 8; 7 r 50; 5 r 33
69 r 60; 143 r 2; 21 r 17; 19 r 4
FORGIVEN

3. not reasonable; reasonable; reasonable
not reasonable; not reasonable

4.
1. 5 r 14
2. 6 r 19
3. 50 r 7
4. 6 r 1

5. $11.16; $20.26
$3.55; $150.00

6. square; oval; triangle; octagon
pentagon; hexagon; rectangle

Lesson 76

1. $.90; $1.49; $13.30; $4.97

2. 606; 500; 506 r 6; 502

3. 8 r 2; 69 r 62; 7 r 21
124 r 4; 21 r 1

4. 8 r 11; 13 r 41; 15 r 6
8 r 44; 3 r 3

5.
1. triangle
2. rectangle
3. square
4. trapezoid
5. rectangular pyramid

6.
1. $.82
2. $.38
3. $4.71
4. $33.00

Lesson 77

1. 5; 15; 4; 5; 2

2. \$.97; \$3.25; \$6.49
   \$9.67; \$3.04; \$.98

3. 50; ok; 102
   \$1.05

4. 12:47; 5:25; 9:15; 6:10

5. 8; 50; 21; 14 r 31
   65 r 18; 19 r 14; 13 r 22
   HONESTY

6. 1. \$150.61
   2. \$40.50
   3. \$.92

Lesson 78

1. 1. 12 stacks
   2. 6 trays
   3. 40 hours
   4. \$110.00

2. 50; 140; 50; 70

3. 1. \$1.05
   2. \$5.00
   3. \$26.25
   4. \$131.70

4. 11 r 41; 90 r 52; 50; 3 r 4

5. Answers will vary.

6. $n = 178$; $n = 87$; $n = 63$; $n = 378$
   $n = 30$; $n = 11$

Lesson 79

1. 1. 9 combinations
   2. 8 combinations
2. Love – COMPOSITE
   Faithfulness – COMPOSITE
   Patience – COMPOSITE
   Kindness – COMPOSITE
   Self-Control – PRIME
   Goodness – COMPOSITE
   Peace – PRIME
   Joy – PRIME
   Gentleness – COMPOSITE

3. 2:57; 11:18; 5:05; 12:45

4. $n = 20$; $n = 56$; $n = 725$; $n = 17$

5. Teacher check

6. 1. 200,556
   2. 1,300,427
   3. 762
   4. 4,040
   5. 9,600,000,020
   6. 83

Lesson 80

1. decade; centuries;
   millennium, AD.

2. 13 11 26

3. 100 x 20 = 2,000; 500 x 20 = 10,000
   800 x 10 = 8,000; 300 x 30 = 9,000

4. \$3.11; \$3.15; \$21.60 \$3.98

5. 387,420 300,000+80,000+7,000+400+20+0
   501,694 500,000+0+1,000+600+90+4
   945,107 900,000+40,000+5,000+100+0+7
   830,753 800,000+30,000+0+700+50+3

6. 55; 24; 15; 8; 17; 6

7. 6,285; 7,728; 31,089; 6,789; 11,178; 31,496

Lesson 81

1. 5:12; 11:19; 3:25
   7:45; 9:15; and 4:40.
2. 14; 4; 2
3. 300,000 + 40 + 5
   20,000,000 + 4,000,000
   60 + 5
   9,000,000 + 800,000
   2,000,000,000
4. 87; 74; 32
   71; 64; 5
5. 11,063; 11,445; 11,501; 7,868; 46,610
6. century, BC, decade, AD, millennium

Lesson 82

1. A.M., P.M., P.M., A.M.
2. 10 years — decade
   100 years — century
   BC — before Christ
   AD — anno Domini
   1,000 years — millennium
3. 6,808; 6,729; 6,395; 6,333
   9,867; 9,567; 9,365; 9,291
4. 457; 168; 81; 57; 289 260
5. 9; 4; 9; 8
6. 6 r 2; 0 r 4; 1 r 3; 6 r 2; 6 r 4

Lesson 83

1. 16th; 15th;
   19th; 18th;
   21st; 10th
2. 7:30 A.M.; 12:45 A.M.; 1:00 P.M.; 9:50 P.M.
3. 4,070; 4,406; 6,080; 9,050
   2,003; 3,002; 5,008; 6,003
4. 2,758; 4,489; 6,643; 3,150; 2,599.
5. 7 r 3; 0 r 5; 3 r 4; 1 r 3; 8 r 1; 5 r 1
6. 24; 31; 26

Lesson 84

1. C; E; F; B; D; A
2. Teacher check
3. 10:00; 2:15; 8:25; and 5:40.
4. 9; 8; 9; 6; 3
5. 2; 8; 2; 2; 3
6. Magic number is 1500
   40; 30; 80;
   90; 50; 10;
   20; 70; 60;
   New magic number is 150

Lesson 85

1. 4:15; 7:45; 11:25; 7:00; 9:45
2. 180; 72; 300; 1,800; 48; 600
3. A.M., P.M., P.M.
4. JESUS
5. 2; 3; 5; 2; 12
6. $1.25 1-$1, 1-quarter
   $2.10 2-$1, 1-dime
   $1.03 1-$1, 3-pennies
   .30¢ 1-nickel; 1-quarter

Lesson 86

1. 9/4; 19; 26; 520 (or 522 including leap years); 1200; 7; 369 days; 2 days
2. 3:30; 2:45; 7:00;
   2:40; 7:15; 9:00;
3. 5; 1 whole day & 4 hours; 240; 8
4. 13th; 16th; 20th; 3rd
5. 6 r 12; 4 r 27; 6 r 21; 3

6. $2.85 1-dime; 3-quarters; 2-one dollar bills
   $2.81 1-penny; 1-nickel; 3-quarters; 2-one dollar bills
   $5.00 1-5 dollar bill
   $4.50 2-quarters; 4-one dollar bills

Lesson 87

1. 6:00; 5:00
   10:30; 9:30; 8:30

2. 5:00; 3:50; 2:15; 8:45

3. 13; 520; 30 yrs ; 5,200

4. 900; 300; 3; 17

5. 6; 4
   1; 9
   3; 5

6. 16; 30; 32; 16

Lesson 88

1. 1st Chicken Noodle
   2nd Vegetable
   3rd Clam Chowder
   4th Tomato

2. 2:00 P.M. Alaska/Hawaii; 6:00 P.M. Eastern; 4:00 P.M. Mountain
   4:00 A.M. Central; 4:00 A.M. Central; 12:00 A.M. Alaska/Hawaii

3. February; December; June; August; November

4. 14; 13; 19; 14

Lesson 89

1. 146,356,029; 287,542

2. 100 + 80 + 6
   4,000 + 200 + 30 + 5
   70,000 + 1,000 + 200 + 30 + 5

3. 4,902; 7,749; 20,544; 35,910

4. 3/5; 12/20; 9/10; 11/11 = 1

5. $<$ $<$ $>$
   $>$ $<$ $>$

6. 5 - millions; 3 - Hundred thousands;
   2 - Ten thousands; 7 - Thousands
   6 - Billions; 9 - Hundred millions; 4 - Hundreds
   8 - Tens; 6 - Ones

7. 9:30 A.M.; 9:15 A.M.; YES

Lesson 90

1. 1. •H, Point H
   2. $\overline{AB}$, Line segment A B
   3. $\overleftrightarrow{RS}$, Line R S
   4. $\overrightarrow{BC}$, ray B C
   5. •G, Point G

2. 1. $p \parallel g$
   2. k intersects l
   3. $c \perp d$

3. 1. 3 Years old
   2. Dawn has 8 — 8 + 5 = 13; Susan has 13 — 13 – 2 = 11

4. 78; 126; 100; 182; 178

5. 1. 40,902
   2. 300,352
   3. 45,000
   4. 1,000,000
   5. 470,000,000,000

6. 1. 2:00
      1:00
      12:00
      10:00
   2. 11:00
      9:00
      6:00
      7:00

7. 1. 100 years
   2. 10 years
   3. 3,650 days
   4. 520 weeks
   5. 10
   6. 9
   7. 8

Lesson 91

1.
   1. ∠AXB acute
      ∠AXC right
      ∠BXC acute
      ∠BXD acute
      ∠AXD obtuse
   2. ∠CXA
   3. X
   4. XA and XC

2. 628; 824; 1,231; 729; 1,143; 1,280

3.
   1. m | | n
   2. G
   3. m ⊥ t or n ⊥ t
   4. sample answer: m intersects p
   5. yes

4. $\overleftrightarrow{LM}$ W $\overrightarrow{CD}$ $\overline{AB}$

5. 9,010 = O; 41,830 = T; 28,435 = E;12,800 = R
   20,307 = R; 6,201 = C; 30,723 = C
   CORRECT

6.
   1. 24
   2. 6:15 P.M.

7.
   1. 3:00 P.M.
   2. 9:00 A.M.
   3. 7:00 P.M.
   4. 3:00 P.M.

Lesson 92

1. Teacher check

2.
   1. 5
   2. 4
   3. NO. A rhombus, square, etc. are quadrilaterals.
   4. YES. A rectangle has 4 sides.
   5. Teacher check
   6. NO. It does not have straight sides.
   7. Teacher check
   8. Square
   9. Teacher check drawings. Rectangle; square; parallelogram; rhombus; trapezoid

3. 35; 24; 40; 90

4.
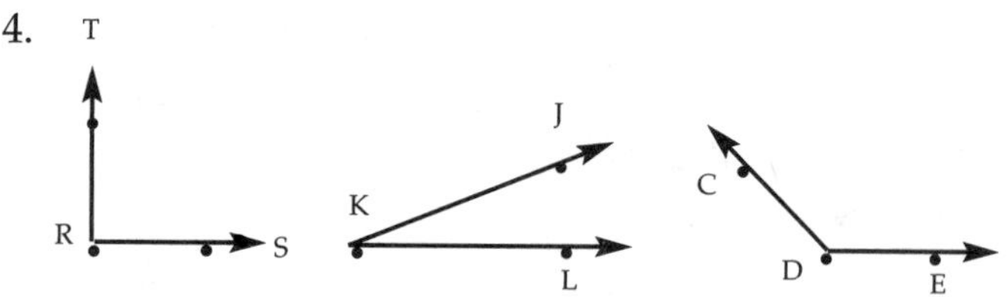

5.
   1. a 5. f
   2. c 6. d
   3. b 7. g
   4. e

6. .35¢; $6.00

7. 120; 212; 160; 200

Lesson 93

1. Answers will vary

2. quadrilateral; triangle; pentagon; hexagon; octagon

3.
   1. ∠APB, ∠APC, ∠BPC, ∠BPD, ∠BPE, ∠CPD, ∠ CPE, ∠DPE
   2. ∠APD
   3. ∠APE
   4. ∠EPA
   5. Answers may vary
   6. Answers may vary

4.

Point Label B	Line Label AB	Line Segment Labek RS
.B	A B	R S
Ray Label UV	**Intersecting Lines**	**Parallel Lines**
U V	e f	c d

5. 387; 36; 504; 226; 19

6. 6 r 6; 9 r 4; 8 r 5; 6 r 1; 4 r 2; 8 r 3

7. c. rectangle
   a. square
   e. rhombus
   d. trapezoid;
   b. parallelogram

Lesson 94

1. YES; NO; YES; NO
   Teacher check
   4; 1; 2; 2

2.

triangle	3 sides
octagon	8 sides
decagon	10 sides
quadrilateral	4 sides
hexagon	6 sides
pentagon	5 sides

3. 1. C and G
   2. B and F
   3. A ,D and E
   4. A, D and E

4. 1. Answers will vary
   2. Answers will vary
   3. Answers will vary
   4. Answers will vary

5. 3 r 1; 3; 5 r 3; 5 r 4; 9 r 5

6.

1. millennium	7. 20th century
2. century	8. 21st century
3. 7 days	9. P.M.
4. 24 hours	10. midnight
5. 60 minutes	11. decade
6. 1st century	12. A.M.

7.

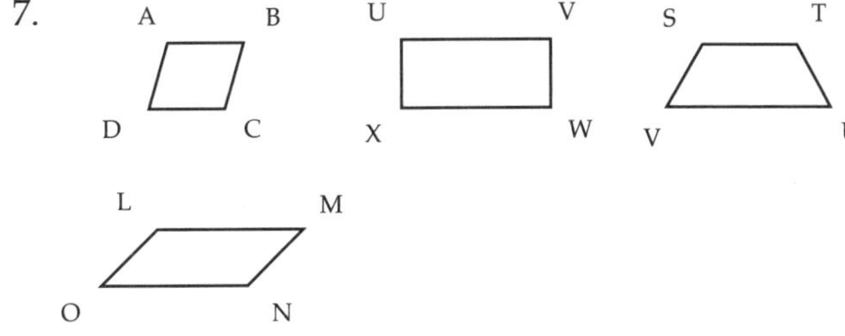

Lesson 95

1. Circle X
   $\overline{GX}$, $\overline{XH}$, $\overline{XJ}$ (letter order can be reversed)
   $\overline{GH}$ (letter order can be reversed)
   10m
   YES. All radii extend from the center of the circle to a point on the circle. All points on the circle are equidistant from the center.

2. A B C D E H I K

3. Teacher check drawings
   Trapezoid
   Parallelogram
   Rhombus

4. 1. c
   2. d
   3. e
   4. f
   5. b
   6. a

5. Octagon Pentagon Triangle Hexagon

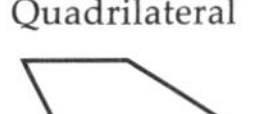

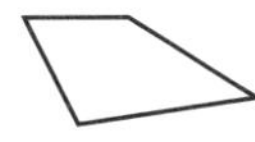

6. 10; 20; 40; 60; 102

7. 1. e
   2. g
   3. a
   4. d
   5. b
   6. c
   7. f

Lesson 96

1. 5,9,6; 6,12,8; 7,15,10
   4,6,4; 5,8,5; 7,12,7

2. Teacher check drawings

3. 1. diameter
   2. $\overline{BC}$; $\overline{BD}$ (letter order can be reversed)
   3. 5m
   4. radii

4. Teacher check lines
   rectangle; oval; square
   triangle; octagon; diamond
   pentagon; rhombus; decagon
   hexagon

5. Teacher check drawing

6. 50; 90; 20; 80; 100

7. 5
2; 5; 10
3;
3;
2; 5; 10

Lesson 97

1. 1. 210
210
840
+840
2,100
YES
2. 856 m
3. 505 m
4. 114 inches

2. 8, 18, 12; 5, 8, 5; 10, 24, 16

3.

Radius	Diameter
	6 cm
	36 cm
27 cm	
14 cm	
	144 cm
68 cm	
	206 cm
113 cm	

4. Teacher check drawing

5. 700; 1,000; 3,600; 398,700
400; 300; 8,000; 931,000

6. 7; 23; 2; 3; 13; 29; 41; 7; 3; 11; 13; 5

7. 9, 9, n = 36, 36 ÷ 9 = 4; 5, 5, n = 35, 35 ÷ 5 = 7; 8, 8, n = 64, 64 ÷ 8 = 8.
2, 2, n = 10, 10 ÷ 2 = 5; 8, 8, n = 16, 16 ÷ 8 = 2; 7, 7, n = 49, 49 ÷ 7 = 7

Lesson 98

1. 16 m^2; 12 m^2; 40 m^2

2. 30 cm; 23 cm
12 m; 20 m
3 m
4 cm, 4 cm, 4 cm,
10 m, 5 m, 5 m

3. Teacher check drawing

4. $\overline{JX}$, $\overline{XK}$, $\overline{RX}$, $\overline{LX}$ (letter order can be reversed)
Circle X
$\overline{JK}$ (letter order can be reversed)
71cm
Answers may vary by location.
Answers may vary by location.
Answers may vary by location.

5. 400; 7,900; 897,300; 302,100

6. 61, 61, n = 76, 76 + 61 = 137;
38, 38, n = 88, 88 + 38 = 126;
47, 47, n = 151, 151 + 47=198

7. 7 r 32; 6 r 16; 5 r 7; 4 r 2; 8 r 22

Lesson 99

1. 1. 72 cm^3
2. 60 cm^3
3. 72 cm^3
4. 144 cm^3

2. 6 cm^3 7 mm^3
16 m^3 37 m^3
13 cm^3 78 mm^3

3. 8 m;
16 cm; 32 m; 24 m; 32 cm
64 m^2; 48 cm^2

4. 6, 12, 8; 6, 12, 8; 7, 15, 10

5. 600; 98,300; 809,000; 1,898,000

6. 20, 20, n = 1,054, 1,054 + 20 = 1,074
328, 328, n = 878, 878 + 328 = 1,206
479, 479, n = 504, 504 + 479 = 983

7. 22; 35
106; 130

8. 1 r 62; 5 r 31; 9 r 3; 8 r 68
9 r 14; 9 r 13; 8 r 51; 7 r 23

Lesson 100

1. Teacher check
   1/2; 3/4; 4/6

2. 1. 24 cm^3 2. 8 cm^3
   3. 14 cm^3 4. 16 cm^3

3. 96; 32
   432; 64

4. fish symbol; cross

5. 1. 2,400 B 2. 68,900 U
   3. 800 R 4. 769,800 D
   5. 5,300 E 6. 1,000 N
   BURDEN

6. 10,974; 29,920; 49,032; 6,831; 35,196

Lesson 101

1. three-fourths; five-fifths; four-sevenths; six-thirteenths; zero-eights
   2/5; 1/8; 7/10; 8/16

2. 3/4; 4/6; 1/2; 3/3

3. 1. 8 cm^3
   2. 12 cm^3
   3. 25 cm^3
   4. 24 cm^3

4. 659,887,002,501

5. 1. 27,000 L; 2. 135,000 I;
   3. 2,000 G; 4. 10,000 H
   5. 15,000 T
   L I G H T

6. 13,650; 8,487; 7,326; 24,645; 27,504

Lesson 102

1. 2/4; 3/6; 1/4/;0/7

2. one-half; six-sevenths; eight-tenths; twelve-thirteenths

3. 3/4; 7/7; 3/16; 0/10

4. 6/7; 3/4; 1/4

5. 6, 6, n = 7, 6 x 7 = 42; 8, 8, n = 8, 8 x 8 = 64; 6, 6, n = 4, 6 x 4 = 24

6. 700,000 + 20,000 + 2,000 + 900 + 80 + 0
   3,000 + 900 + 4
   20,000 + 4,000 + 1
   500 + 30 + 9

7. Across
   1. 527901
   5. 28
   7. 182
   8. 17
   9. 232
   10. 63452
   11. 610857
   14. 729
   15. 7490
   16. 383
   17. 22
   18. 6417
   19. 818367

   Down
   1. 5126
   2. 28317
   3. 72204
   4. 1267
   5. 215281
   6. 872937
   12. 8928
   13. 5023
   18. 67

Lesson 103

1. 2/6; 9/12; 6/10;
   9/21; 8/24; 16/36
   4/14; 25/40; 2/20; 27/81; 16/36
2. 3/4; 1/3; 3/3;
   4/6; 3/5;

3. one-seventh; sixteen-seventeenths; nine-tenths; twelve-twelfths

4. 3/5; 7/17; 3/16; 8/10

5. 9/15; 3/4

6.

5	6	4	5	6	7			3	
1			6		0			5	
2			6		0			9	
	7	8	7		0			0	
	6				0			0	
	4			3	0	2	0	4	
3	3	2		7				2	

7. 6 r 5; 6 r 2; 8; 8 r 5; 3 r 3; 8 r 1

Lesson 104

1.
1,2,4,8	1,13
1,2,4,5,10,20	1,3,5,15
cf: 1,2,4	cf: 1
gcf: 4	gcf: 1
1,2,3,6,7,14,21,42	1,3,5,15
1,2,4,7,14,28	1,2,3,4,6,12
cf: 1,2,7,14	cf: 1,3
gcf: 14	gcf: 3
1,2,5,10	1,2,4,8,16
1,2,4,5,10,20	1,2,3,4,6,8,12,24
cf: 1,2,5,10	cf: 1,2,4,8
gcf: 10	gcf: 8

2. 2/14; 6/27; 8/10;
20/32; 18/42; 20/45

3. 12; 35; 72; 6; 3

4. 2/5
8/13
7/19
1/4
2/8
6/15

5. Teacher check

6.
1. 21 R	6. 1,010 E
2. 514 I	7. 1,021 O
3. 515 G	8. 12,000 U
4. 551 H	9. 120,000 S
5. 1,001 T	

7. 140; 211; 5768; 1779; 78;

8. 9 r 8; 4 r 2; 6 r 2; 6 r 5; 8

Lesson 105

1. 1/2; 3/5; 1/4; 1/4; 2/5
1/4; 3/5; 2/9; 3/4; 9/10

2. 12; 35; 8; 24; 24

3.
1,2,3,6	1,3,5,15
1,3,9	1,5,7,35
cf: 1,3	cf: 1,5
gcf: 3	gcf: 5
1,5	1,2,3,4,6,8,12,24
1,5,25	1,2,3,6,9,18
cf: 1,5	cf: 1,2,3,6
gcf: 5	gfc: 6
1,2,4,8	1,2,4,8,16
1,2,3,4,6,8,12,24	1,2,4,5,8,10,20,40
cf: 1,2,4,8	cf: 1,2,4,8
gfc: 8	gfc: 8

4. B. 3/4; C. 1/6; D. 3/6; E. 5/6

5.
1. 802,000,990	7. 1,000,000
2. 802,000,908	8. 29,800
3. 298,000,745	9. 2,980
4. 80,200,908	10. 840
5. 10,000,000	11. 32
6. 2,980,000	12. 23

6. Teacher check drawing

9	4 r 8
8	6
5 r 1	7 r 3
5	9 r 2
4	6 r 3
7	4 r 4
2	3

Lesson 106

1.
<	>	<	<
=	<	<	<
>	=	>	>

2.
1. 1/2	5. 1/25	9. 2/3
2. 3/4	6. 4/7	10. 7/8
3. 9/10	7. 1/3	11. 2/9
4. 4/5	8. 2/7	

F R A C T I ON
W I Z A R D

3.
1,2,7,14	1,11
1,2,4,7,14,28	1,2,3,6,9,18
cf: 1,2,7,14	cf: 1
gcf: 14	gfc: 1
1,2,3,4,6,12	1,2,4
1,2,3,6,9,18	1,2,3,4,6,12
cf: 1,2,3,6	cf: 1,2,4
gcf: 6	gcf: 4

1,3,5,9,15,45　　1,2,3,6,9,18
1,3,9,27,81　　1,3,9,27
cf: 1,3,9　　cf: 1,3,9
gcf: 9　　gcf: 9

4. 4/8; 50/100; 3/6; 6/12; 10/20
5/15; 2/6; 10/30; 3/9; 4/12
10/60; 2/12; 5/30; 3/18; 4/24
8/12; 20/30; 4/6, 16/24; 10/15

5.

↓ END

7	33	**29**	**3**	**11**	6	8	10	12	4	2	12	2
11	**3**	**23**	4	**7**	**2**	**31**	**23**	**3**	**19**	**17**	18	10
12	16	12	14	60	50	30	25	14	12	**19**	16	26
14	80	8	4	50	20	25	40	22	10	**3**	20	24
2	4	40	30	12	70	55	4	21	6	**43**	**11**	**2**
4	21	8	6	25	24	20	18	20	6	8	4	**3**

START ↑

6. 5, 3
3
2, 5, 10
2
2, 5, 10, 3

7. 50; 97; 154; 787; 189

Lesson 107

1. 1 1/2; 2 2/4; 1 7/8
8/5; 27/7; 58/8; 17/6
62/9; 52/9; 13/3; 69/8

2. <　>　>　<
>　=　>　<

3. 1/3; 2/3; 1/6; 2/7; 4/5; 6/7; 1/8; 2/11

4. 5 H; 16 E; 12 A; 6 V; 14 E; 9 N
HEAVEN

5. 45, 45, n = 44, 44 + 45 = 89;
87, 87, n = 103, 103 + 87 = 190;
78, 78, n = 565, 565 + 78 = 643

6. 3, 3, n = 15, 15 ÷ 3 = 5;
9, 9, n = 36, 36 ÷ 9 = 4;
9, 9, n = 81, 81 ÷ 9 = 9

7. decagon, rectangle, octagon
hexagon, square, trapezoid
rhombus, pentagon, triangle

Lesson 108

1. 3 4/5; 4; 3 5/6; 8 1/2
6 3/4; 3 6/9 = 3 2/3; 6; 1 3/10
5; 3 1/3; 4 2/4 = 4 1/2; 4 8/10 = 4 4/5

2. Teacher check drawing
7/4; 17/7
15/8; 19/6

3. >　>　=　<
>　=　=　<

4. 2/3 P; 1/4 O; 1/10 P; 1/9 C;
1/3 O; 4/9 R; 5/12 N
POPCORN

5. 1,900; 2,500; 9,000
600; 200; 1,000

6. 395, 395, n = 8,513, 8,513 + 395 = 8,908;
895, 895, n = 1,005, 1,005 + 895 = 1,900
708, 708, n = 895, 895 + 708 = 1,603

7. 1. 17
2. 49
3. 125
4. 357

8. rectangular pyramid; cone; hexagonal pyramid; cylinder; sphere; triangular pyramid

Lesson 109

1. 1. 90 + 110 = $200; 89.45 + 112.85 = $202.30
2. 1,300 - 800 = $500;
1,345.76 – 837.19 = $508.57
3. 80 - 40 - 10 - 5 = 25; 83 – 56 = 27
4. 8 - 4 - 4 = 0; 8 – 7 = 1
5. 4 x 4 = $16; 4 x $ 3.75 = $15.00

2. 4 1/5; 4 2/4 = 4 1/2; 8; 2
3 3/8; 9 5/9; 3 1/2; 2 4/7

3. 13/9; 15/7; 17/3; 29/8
38/9; 44/5; 15/6; 66/7

4. <　=　<　=
>　>　>　>

5. Teacher check
Answers will vary

6. 1. 315 r 2 S
   2. 775 r 5 L
   3. 255 r 12 I
   4. 140 r 3 P
   5. 136 r 22 P
   6. 109 r 56 E
   7. 100 r 8 R
   8. 119 r 6 S

   SLIPPERS

Lesson 110

1. 3/7; 5/9; 8/12 = 2/3; 4/6 = 2/3
   5/15 = 1/3; 5/5 = 1; 6/12 = 1/2; 3/3 = 1
   7/8; 9/10; 9/11; 13/18

2. 1.
   18.79 + 39.49 = $58.28
   87.95 − 58.28 = $29.67
   2. YES
   3. 2 hours 6 minutes
   4. 35.00 x 12 = $420.00
   YES, $ 420.00 could be saved in one year's time.

3. 3; 3 3/5; 7; 1 1/3
   1 5/8; 9 7/9; 5 2/3; 8 1/3

4. 5/3; 57/8; 18/4; 77/9
   72/10; 26/5; 63/5; 35/7

5. 109
   632
   106
   23
   121
   28
   87
   PANCAKE

6. Teacher check

Lesson 111

1. 5/10 = 1/2; 5/8; 2/13; 4/8 = 1/2
   2/11; 2/12 = 1/6; 6/12 = 1/2; 10/20 = 1/2
   10/15 = 2/3; 3/6 = 1/2; 2/4 = 1/2;
   3/9 = 1/3

2. 7/7 = 1; 2/9; 1; 5/6
   10/15 = 2/3; 2/5; 2/12 = 1/6; 3/8
   8/9; 8/12 = 2/3; 8/10 = 4/5; 7/8

3. 1. NO. The movie would not end till 3:10 P.M.
   2. 5:35 P.M.
   3. 11:07 P.M.
   4. 4 hours
   5. 4:00 A.M.

4. END
   2 1/8=1 7/8 4/3=1 1/3 2 1/4=9/4
   1 1/9=10/9
   4 3/4=19/4
   7/4=1 3/4
   2 7/8=23/8
   5/4=1 1/4
   3/2=1 1/2
   7/6=1 1/6
   BEGIN

   END
   2 1/4=9/4
   1 1/2=3/2
   13/5=2 3/5
   14/3=4 2/3
   6 1/3=19/3 2 1/5=11/5
   7/2=3 1/2
   3/2=1 1/2 5/2=2 1/2 1 5/8=1 7/8 8/3=2 2/3
   7/6=1 1/6
   BEGIN

5. 128; 147; 124; 122; 120

6. 3,192; 78,474; 9,548; 4,429; 54, 264

7. Teacher check

Lesson 112

1. 3/8; 5/5 = 1; 9/12 = 3/4
   5/9; 5/10 = 1/2; 10/15 = 2/3
   9/9 = 1; 6/7; 5/10=1/2
   1/12; 4/8 = 1/2; 2/11

2. Teacher check shading
   7/12; 3/8; 3/16; 5/9
   9/20; 15/21=5/7; 3/4; 6/7
   8/12 = 2/3; 5/10 = 1/2; 10/11
   BE NOT AFRAID

3. 7/10; 5/18; 9/13; 1/4
   2/9; 9/12 = 3/4; 5/15 = 1/3; 2/20 = 1/10

4. 1. 3:32 P.M.
   2. 5:34 A.M.
   3. 48 minutes
   4. 3:00 P.M.

5. 1,800; 6,601; 14,331; 36,249; 13,467

6. 7 65/82; 24 3/37; 21 22/45;
14 40/48 = 14 5/6; 14 3/27 = 14 1/9

7. Answers may vary

Lesson 113

1. 5/8; 6/6 = 1
7/10; 7/8; 5/10 = 1/2
5/6; 7/12; 10/12 = 5/6

2. 4/12 = 1/3; 6/9 = 2/3; 5/7; 5/8
1/10; 4/6 = 2/3; 2/12 = 1/6; 3/20

3. 7/12; 2/8 = 1/4; 6/6 = 1; 5/8
4/5; 2/10 = 1/5; 6/12 = 1/2; 3/15 = 1/5

4. 1, 724; 2,164; 2,160; 990; 2,132

5. 40; 51; 17; 7; 3

6.

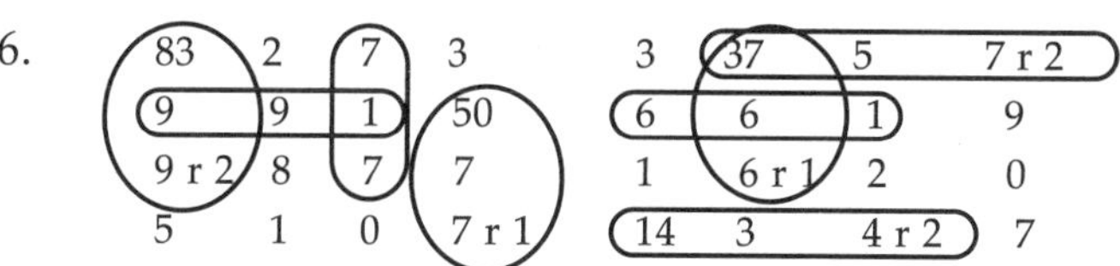

7. 1. K
2. $\overline{XY}$
3. $\overleftrightarrow{MN}$
4. $\overrightarrow{AB}$

Lesson 114

1. 1/8; 2/6 = 1/3
2/10 = 1/5; 1/10; 1/4
2/10 = 1/5; 1/6; 7/12

2. 7/8; 7/12; 4/6 = 2/3
5/10 = 1/2; 4/6 = 2/3; 9/10

3. 5/12; 8/9; 6/7
5/15 = 1/3; 2/12 = 1/6; 10/15 = 2/3
2/13; 10/10 = 1; 1/4
12/20 = 3/5; 4/8 = 1/2; 4/5
A KIDNAPPING !

4. 1,350; 16,890; 60; 190
7,000; 23,100; 100; 270
2,390; 68,000; 30; 680

5. 668; 1,755; 309; 187; 1,229

6. 6, 6, n = 8, 6 x 8 = 48;
8, 8, n = 8,8 x 8 = 64;
4, 4, n = 8, 4 x 8 = 32

7. 1. •B

2. A B (line segment)

3. P Q (line)

4. X Y (ray)

Lesson 115

1. 1. 5/6 – 4/6 = 1/6
2. 2/4 + 1/4 = 3/4
3. 1/10 + 5/10 = 6/10 = 3/5
4. 5/6 – 2/6 = 3/6 = 1/2

2. 4/8 = 1/2; 1/12; 5/6; 5/10 = 1/2; 7/12
5/10 = 1/2; 10/14 = 5/7; 4/9; 1/4; 4/8 = 1/2
9/9=1; 10/20 = 1/2; 4/6 = 2/3; 2/4 = 1/2;
6/12 = 1/2
P I G P E N S

3. 5 1/5; 2 2/6 = 2 1/3;
8 1/3; 5 2/8 = 5 1/4;
9 4/9; 7 1/7

4. 410; 800; 1,280
80; 20; 13,690
9,081,300; 810,000; 10
6,960; 45,023,880

9	S
20	E
80	C
410	R
800	E
1,280	T
6,960	P
13,690	L
810,000	A
9,081,300	C
45,023,880	E

5. 2; 3; 5; 7
11; 13; 17; 19
23; 29
31; 37
41; 43; 47

6. point; line; parallel lines
ray; intersecting lines; perpendicular lines

Lesson 116

1. 2 2/8 = 2 1/4; 10 3/6 = 10 1/2;
12 6/12 = 12 1/2; 7 6/8 = 7 3/4;
8 4/10 = 8 2/5
4 5/7; 6 8/9; 8 9/12 = 8 3/4;
4 4/8 = 4 1/2; 7 3/4

2. 4 7/8
1 3/4

3. 5/8 2/8 1/8 | 1/2 1/4, 1/4 1/6, 2/3 1/6 | 2/8 1/4, 2/4 1/3, 1/3 2/6 | 7/10 1/5 1/10

4. 7/10; 7/8; 10/10 = 1; 8/9
8/20 = 2/5; 12/18 = 2/3; 6/12 = 1/2;
5/15 = 1/3

5. 2; 5; 10
3
5
3
2

6.

1. A.M.	4. P.M.
2. A.M.	5. A.M.
3. P.M.	6. A.M.

7.

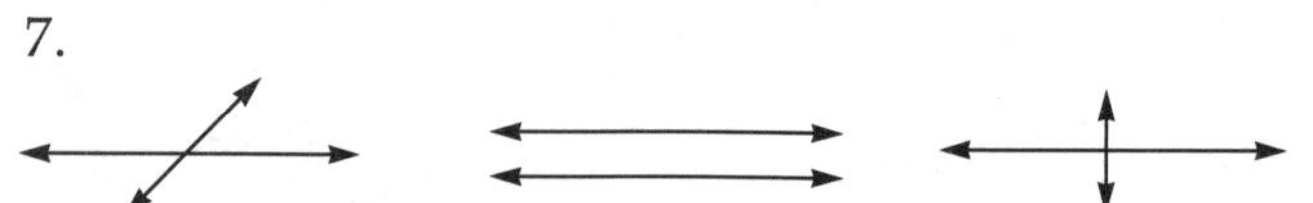

Lesson 117

1. 4/8 = 1/2; 5 3/6 = 5 1/2;
1 6/12 = 1 1/2;
1 2/8 = 1 1/4; 6 5/10 = 6 1/2
2 1/7; 12 3/9 = 12 1/3; 4 3/12 = 4 1/4;
8 1/8; 1 1/4
1 1/7; 11 1/3; 1 6/10 = 1 3/5

2. 10 5/6; 4 2/9; 6 2/4 = 6 1/2; 9 5/8; 6 5/7

3.

1. 5/50 = 1/10	2. 5/50 = 1/10
3. 1/5	4. Alaska, Hawaii
5. 1/50	

4. 3/4; 7/10; 5/6
3/9 = 1/3; 1/6; 1/4

5. A B C   X Y Z   C D E

6. 6 + n = 20, - 6, - 6, n = 14, 6 + 14 = 20;
n + 8 = 18, - 8, - 8, n = 10, 10 + 8 = 18;
4 + n = 10, - 4, - 4, n = 6, 4 + 6 = 10;
4 x n = 16, ÷ 4, ÷ 4, n = 4, 4 x 4 = 16;
8 x n = 24, ÷ 8, ÷ 8, n = 3, 8 x 3 = 24;
7 x n = 49, ÷ 7, ÷7, n = 7, 7 x 7 = 49

7. 20; 33; 64

Lesson 118

1. 3 14/8 = 4 6/8 = 4 3/4;
7 12/10 = 8 2/10 = 8 1/5;
8 9/6 = 9 3/6 = 9 1/2;
9 10/10 = 10
9 7/5 = 10 2/5;
22 4/3 = 23 1/3;
17 11/7 = 18 4/7; 24 1/2

2. 15 ¾
8 2/4 = 8 ½   7 ¼

34 ⅔
13 1/6   21 3/6 = 21 ½
5 3/6 = 5 ½   7 4/6 = 7 ⅔   13 5/6

3. 6 4/8 = 6 1/2; 5 3/9 = 5 1/3;
4 3/12 = 4 1/4; 4 1/4; 1 5/16

4.

n – 6 = 29	n – 3 = 16	n – 9 = 10
n = 35	n = 19	n = 19
35–6=40-11	19–3=18-2	19–9=29-19
29 = 29	16 = 16	10 = 10

5. 1 quarter, 1 dollar bill
2 pennies, 1 dime, 3 quarters
1 five dollar bill
4 pennies, 1 dimes, 1 nickel, 1 quarter,
3 one dollar bills, 1 five dollar bill
4 pennies, 2 dimes, 1 ten dollar bill
3 one dollar bills, 2 twenty dollar bills

6.

6th	20th
8th	12th
17th	19th
1st	21st

7. right, acute, obtuse

Lesson 119

1.
   1. 3
   2. 6
   3. 9
   4. 3
   5. 9

2. 3 pennies, 1 dime, 2 quarters
   1 dime
   2 pennies, 1 dime
   3 pennies, 1 dime
   2 pennies, 1 nickel, 2 quarters,1 one dollar bill
   3 pennies, 1 dime, 1 quarter, 2 one dollar bills,1 five dollar bill
   1 dime, 1 one dollar bill, 1 twenty dollar bill

3. C, E, B, F, D, A,

4. D
   $\overline{AD}$, $\overline{DB}$, $\overline{DX}$
   $\overline{AB}$
   50m

5. 9; 36; 54; 6; 8

6. 1/3; 1/5; 1/8; 1/5; 1/4
   1/3; 1/2; 1/2; 4/5; 1/9

7. >; <; =; >
   =; <; >; <

Lesson 120

1. 1.7 - one and seven tenths
   0.7 - seven tenths
   3.7 - three and seven tenths
   1.7 - one and seven tenths

2. 3 2/4 = 3 1/2; 15 4/11; 2 2/9; 1/12;
   22 10/17; 1 0/7 = 1

3. 2 r 2; 5 r 13; 2 r 9; 22 r 5; 2 r 4; 3 r 7
   O RG I V E N
   Word Spelled: FORGIVEN

4. C; E; F; B; D; A

5. Blue
   Red
   Teacher check labels

6. 4/8
   3/9
   3/15
   6/14
   8/18

Lesson 121

1. a. 106
   b. 166
   c. 75

2. 2.4 - Two and four tenths
   1.2 - One and two tenths
   5.1 - Five and one tenth
   2.9 - Two and nine tenths

3. 7 5/10 = 7 1/2; 1 5/16 ; 19 11/15
   11 7/20; 8 2/6 = 8 1/3; 4 3/8

4. 676; 485; 766; 395

5. 7 r 2; 5 r 6; 7 r 15; 8 r 41

6. 20th; 18th; 16th; 21st

7.

P = 46 m	P = 42 m	P = 24 m
A = 120 m^2	A = 80 m^2	A = 36 m^2

Lesson 122

1. < > > >
   < >

2. 1.43
   5.07
   2.50
   17.15

3. DATA BANK: 0.8 7.1 0.5 1.3

N	**S**	**E**	**V**	**E**	**N**	**A**	**N**	**D**	**O**	**N**	**E**	**T**	**E**	**N**	**T**	**H**
P	K	**I**	L	M	C	D	A	E	T	Y	U	A	E	M	I	O
R	A	**G**	E	A	U	I	N	D	L	B	M	X	C	Z	N	T
S	E	**H**	G	W	B	E	K	D	**F**	D	F	G	S	H	J	K
H	I	**T**	V	R	V	E	O	S	**I**	J	I	O	A	B	V	C
B	C	**T**	T	C	H	H	I	K	**V**	N	U	I	H	D	P	K
O	**N**	**E**	**A**	**N**	**D**	**T**	**H**	**R**	**E**	**E**	**T**	**E**	**N**	**T**	**H**	**S**
M	K	**N**	X	A	I	P	F	L	**T**	W	K	T	D	V	N	M
L	G	**T**	M	E	L	Z	D	M	**E**	P	P	G	D	H	J	E
C	H	**H**	O	D	B	X	X	N	**N**	Q	T	X	M	K	H	V
E	J	**S**	P	O	D	V	L	N	**T**	W	F	G	Q	R	Y	T
T	F	T	E	I	F	U	N	B	**H**	E	Z	F	J	Q	U	P
O	D	K	J	Y	T	H	B	R	**S**	D	B	N	L	S	I	O

4. 2/4 3/7 2/5 3/5

5. 4,990; 2,998; 6,990; 982
6. 37; 8 r 10; 5; 20 r 2

7. 1986
1725
1654
1854

8. A = 144 m^2 A = 54 m^2
P = 48 m P = 42 m

Lesson 123

1. .143; .147; .218; .289
.204; .309; .323

2. < < < =

3. 2.03 + 1.2 = 3.23
6.5 + 4.12 = 10.62
.07 + .1 = .17

4. 6; 9; 0; 6; 1

5. 90; 1,570; 2,480; 780; 460

6. 69; 41; 5; 8

7. 22; 33; 30; 10

8. 6 cm x 4 cm x 10 cm = 240 cm^3
4 mm x 4 mm x 20 mm = 320 m^3
3 mm x 4 mm x 15 mm = 180 mm^3

Lesson 124

1. 4; 8; 13; 9
0.3; 2.5; 4.0; 0.1

2. G 6.32
4.36 O
3.18 D
0.88 I
S 0.83
4.66 L
I 5.11
G 7.14
2..34 H
T 9.05
God is light

3. twenty–three hundredths
one and thirty-four hundredths
five and seventy-two hundredths
six and thirty-one hundredths
nine and six hundredths
eight and eleven hundredths

4. 2,340; 3,410; 20
180; 650; 980

5. 4; 8; 27
20; 21; 25

6. 14 r 12; 13 r 22; 21 r 12; 18 r 4

7. V = 12m x 10 m x 7m = 840 m^3
V = 21m x 10 m x 7 m = 1,470 m^3

Lesson 125

1. 6.31; 23.67; 22.04; 18.25; 53.30

2. 1; 8; 24; 2; 15
4.4; 9.9; 19.3; 0.1

3. 13.7; 13.61; 1.41; 0.437; 0.342

4. 1,400; 12,200; 4,900
15,300; 800; 200

5. 25 + 90 + 65 + 70 + 25 = 275
275 ÷ 5 = 55
88 + 92 + 76 + 86 + 33 = 375
375 ÷ 5 = 75

6. Pacific Mountain Central Eastern

Alaska Hawaii

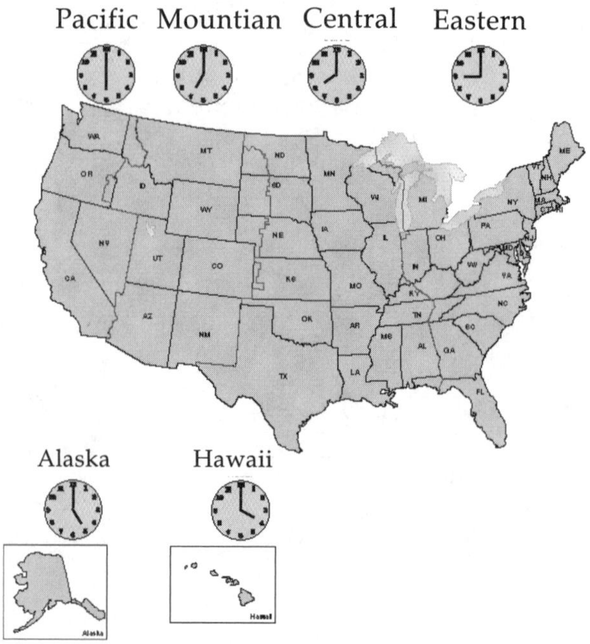

7. 2/3; 4/10 = 2/5; 1/5; 3/12 = 1/4

Lesson 126

1. 7.04; 1.01; 50.81; 34.00; 2.60; 21.12

2. 4.06; 48.33; 1.04; 44.00; 77.25

3. 4.2; 3.9
   0.29; .031
   9.30; 9.34
   10.131; 10.132

4. .025; .04; .12; .39; .42

5. Teacher check

6. 4; 11; 11

7. 11:00 A.M.; 8:00 A.M.; 7:00 A.M.

8. 2/15; 38/50 = 19/25; 3/5
   3/17

Lesson 127

1. 8 + 4 = 12; 9 - 6 = 3; 15 + 9 = 24
   7 - 1 = 6; 66 + 15 = 81; 37 - 12 = 25

2. 5; 2; 5; 4; 20

3. Answers may vary

4. Teacher check

5. 10; 17; 7

6. millennium
   decades
   centuries

7. 5.43, 0.49, and 10.42 should be circled.

Lesson 128

1. | | |
   |---|---|
   | Chocolate bars | $3.00 per bag |
   | Hard Candy | $2.00 per bag |
   | Lollipop | $1.00 per bag |
   | Bubble Gum | $3.00 per bag |
   | Licorice | $1.00 per bag |
   | Chocolate covered cherries | $3.00 per bag |

   Circled answers: Hard candy; Licorice; Lollipop

2. 13.7 + 34.8 = 45.8; (7.81 - 5.61 = 2.20) circled; (9.57 + 0.48 = 10.05) circled; 0.76 - 0.21 = 0.97; (7.86 + 0.18 = 8.04) circled

3. 16,000; 54,000; 4,000; 1,000; 124,000; 1,000

4. Order
   Zero
   Dividend
   hundred millions

5. P.M.
   A.M.
   P.M.
   A.M.

6. Answers will vary.

7. Teacher check

Lesson 129

1. P = 1,600 ft.
   L = 48 in.
   P = 144 in.
   side two = 225 ft
   side three = 240 ft.
   P = 915 ft.

2. 1 - dime; 1 - nickel; 2 - quarters, 4 - one dollar bills
   2 - quarters; 4 - one dollar bills
   1 - quarter; 4 - one dollar bills

3. Carla went to bed at 10:30 P.M..
   Sarah at lunch at 12:45 P.M..
   Mary and Becky got out of school at 3:00 P.M..

4. Parallel
   Perpendicular
   Radius
   Octagon

5. Answers will vary.
Examples are:
1/2 = 2/4
1/3 = 3/9
1/5 = 2/10
3/5 = 6/10

6. 1/2
1/2
1/2
1/2
3/4
3/7

7. 1/6; 1/4; 1/3; 1/2

8. 7/8; 5/6; 1/6; 3/8

Lesson 130

1. 2; 3; 1 1/2; 2 1/4

2. 41.20; 28.62; 15.91; 58.70; 44.41
29.65; 23.85; 28.62; 2.39
FISH

3. $9.00; $3.00; $9.00; $5.00; $8.00

4. 294; 111; 489; 103; 207; 441

5. 5 r 8; 6 r 6; 8 r 2; 5 r 9

6. $13.80
$9.75
$0.51
$2.03

7. Answers will vary.

Lesson 131

1. feet; feet; miles; yards

2. 18; 3,520; 6; 660; 8

3. 36; 72; 24; 120

4. Bag 1: $3.00+$2.00+$1.00+$4.00 = $10.00
Bag 2: $1.00+$2.00+ $3.00+$2.00 = $8.00
Bag 3: $2.00+$5.00+$2.00+$3.00+3.00 = $15.00
The most expensive bag is bag 3 at an estimated cost of $15.00.

5. 2.31; 5.28; 7.74; 14.35; 4.93

6. 178; 45; 1,799; 1,781

7. 5; 9; 3; 4

8. 13th
16th
20th
19th

9. Answers will vary.

Lesson 132

1. tons; lb; oz
oz; lb

2. feet; 9
miles; 5,280
yards; 8

3. inches; feet

4. 4 1/2; 5 1/2; 1; 6 1/4

5. $900.00; $300.00; $9,000.00; $3,000.00

6. n = 2; n = 50; n = 5; n = 25

7. 21 r 12; 11; 17 r 8; 22 r 14

8. Answers will vary.

9. 1/2; 1/3;
1/3; 1/5

Lesson 133

1. 12 2
1 1

2.

small can of soup	11 oz
a package of 2 ping pong balls	2 oz.
refrigerator	150 lb.
mini-van	1 1/2 T
a small dog	20 lb
Christmas ham	9 1/2 lb

3. > ; < ; <

4. 4 1/2 in; 2 1/2 in; 2 in; 3 3/4 in; 1 3/4 in; 1 1/2 in; 1 1/2 in; 2 1/4 in
5. n = 15; n = 14; n = 24; n = 37
6. 49; 15; 13; 30
7. 5/8; 3/14; 8/9; 3/10

Lesson 134

1. 172 ; 45 ; 78
   172° F; 45° F; 78° F
2. across: 1. sixteen, 2. twenty, 5. one
   down: 1. sixteen, 3. twelve, 4. two
3. chair 3 lb
   can 12 oz
   stapler 8 oz
   car 1 T
4. 75; 15,840; 4; 324
5. 99; 84; 38; 99; 129; 34
6. 21; 24; 35
7. 10 3/5; 4 4/12 = 4 1/3; 32 11/32

Lesson 135

1. 82°; 8° ; -10°
2. Answers will vary with the exception of the first one, which is 98.6 degrees.
3. 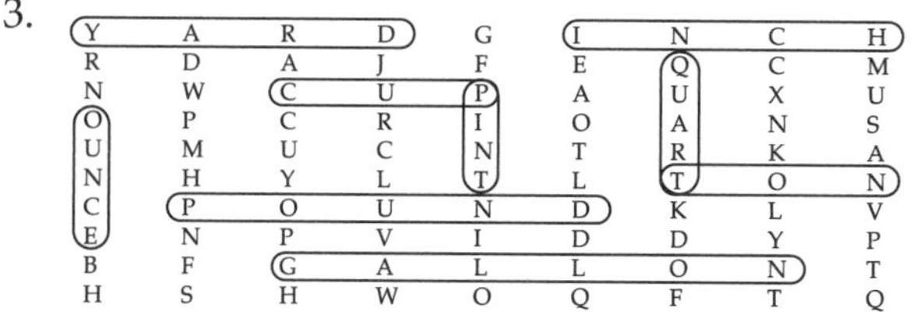
4. Right; Right; Right
   475; 804; 745
5. 0.5, 6.1, 14.8, 0.3
6. n = 22; n = 50; n = 8; n = 2
7. 7/8; 1/2; 1/3; 0/5

Lesson 136

1. 1 cm 6 mm
   1.6 cm
   16 mm

   3 cm 3 mm; 3.3 cm; 33 mm
   1 cm 4 mm; 1.4 cm; 14 mm
   2 cm 8 mm; 2.8 cm; 28 mm
   6 cm 1 mm; 6.1 cm; 61 mm
2. 1,236; 334; 689; 1,143; 1,466
3. C; F
   F; C
4. 8; 32; 1; 4; 2;
5. Teacher check
6. > >
   < =
7. Right angle
   Obtuse angle
   Acute angle

Lesson 137

1. 14.5 cm; 1,265 cm
   1.329 m; 10,400 dm
   1,890 mm; 340 mm
2. cm; mm; cm; cm or mm
3. 105° F; 0° C; 100° C

Lesson 138

1. 1 L; 587,000 ml
   0.001 L; 0.291 L
   0.033 L
2. m; m; cm; m; Km; cm

3. 40° C
   1° C
   84° C
   120° C
   0° C

4. n = 6; n = 5; n = 7

5. Teacher check
   Teacher check
   Any line which is drawn from one point on the circle to another point on the circle and goes through the center of the circle.

6. 9/9; 3/4; 1/4; 1/16

Lesson 139

1. 0.003 Kg; 0.025 Kg; 0.710 Kg
   4,000 g; 56,000 g; 529,000 g

2. L; ml; ml; ml; L

3. Km; mm; m; cm or m; cm or m; cm or m

4. 19,936; 3,472; 3,792; 10,640

5. < > >

6. 27.89; 66.41; 99.95; 44.16

Lesson 140

1. $100.00
   $200.00
   Concessions
   Moon walk
   $1100.00

2. Kilograms; gram; grams; Kilograms

3. 2 L 623,000 ml
   0.003 L 20,000 ml

4. P 105 cm
   4.2 cm R
   20 Km A
   38 dm Y
   E 31.5 Km
   R 1,760 mm
   PRAYER

5. 176; 584; 98; 277; 149; 612

6. n = 21; n = 49; n = 7; n = 3

7. 17,974; 9,396; 8,528; 19,812; 54,432

Lesson 141

1. Wednesday
   Monday and Sunday
   5° F

2.

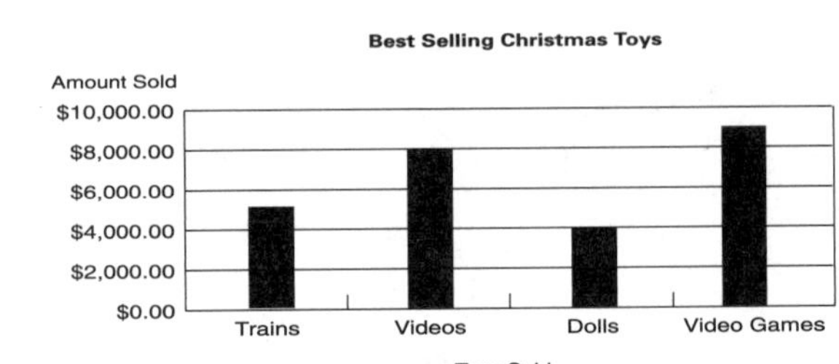

3. Bag 1- 1,100 g+800 g+150 g=2,050 g=2.05 Kg
   Bag 2- 3,000 g+1,400 g+200 g=4,600 g=4.6 Kg
   Bag 3- 2,000 g+200 g+750 g=2,950 g=2.95 Kg

4. 5,400; 39.321; 17,490; 57,020; 11,000; 9,210; 0.1252; 0.0468; 61.128; 32.31

5. 178; 267; 47; 305; 322

6. 11; 9; 13

7. 1/5; 3/4; 1/2; 1/7

Lesson 142

1. $600.00; $450.00; $250.00; Week 2; Week 3

2. Teacher check

3. Teacher check

4. 5,000 g; 1.243 g; 21 g; 0.043 Kg

5.

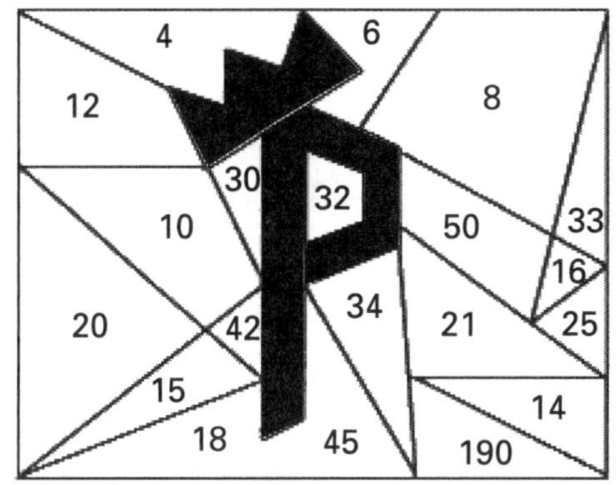

6. 18; 9; 3

7. 8/12 = 2/3   7/14 = 1/2

Lesson 143

1. Cooking
   News = 27, Sports = 25, Entertainment = 25
   23
   2

2. Teacher check line graph

3. Chocolate should have 12 cones
   Strawberry/Banana should have 15 cones
   Vanilla should have 6 cones
   Cookies and Cream should have 9 cones

4. Teacher check

5. 82; 63; 13

6. 9 r 2;   7 r 6;   7 r 4;   5 r 4

7. n = 1/4; n = 4/11; n = 7/14 = 1/2;
   n = 2/32 = 1/16

Lesson 144

1. PEACE

2. Teacher check

3. Monday should have 3 CDs
   Tuesday should have 2 1/2 CDs
   Wednesday should have 3 CDs
   Thursday should have 3 1/2 CDs
   Friday should have 6 CDs
   Saturday should have 7 1/2 CDs

4. Teacher check graph (answer may vary some)

5. 10; 8; 6

6. 6 r 23;   3 r 37; 5 r 60; 7 r 29; 6 r 62;

7. Answers will vary.

8.

1 4/8	5 3/**5**	1 1/12
+<u>2 1/8</u>	-<u>2 1/5</u>	+<u>9 5/12</u>
3 **5**/8	3 **2**/5	10 6/**12**

Lesson 145

1. 2 to 10 = 2/10
   3 to 5 = 3/5
   4 to 6 = 4/6
   7 to 10 = 7/10
   10 to 2 = 10/2

2.

3. 1 hour lunch and 1 hour recess on graph needs to be changed to 30 min. lunch and 30 min. recess.

4. Number of Sunny Days in a Year
   Jan - 7, Feb.- 8 1/2, March - 6, April - 5,
   May - 11 1/2, June- 13, July - 15, Aug. - 14 1/2
   Sept. - 12 1/2, Oct. -10, Nov. - 9, Dec. - 7.

5. n = 10; n = 12; n = 8; n = 6

6. 1 penny; 1 dime; 1 quarter; 1 one dollar bill = $1.36

   1 penny; 1 nickel; 3 quarters;1 one dollar bill = $1.81

   4 pennies; 1 dime; 2 quarters; 1 one dollar bill 1 five dollar bill = $6.64

   1 dime; 3 quarters; 2 one dollar bills; 1 ten dollar bill = $12.85

   2 quarters; 4 one dollar bills = $4.50

7. 1/12; 1/2; 3/4; 8/8

Lesson 146

1. 30; 40; 12 books
   12; 16; 20; 10 movies
   2; 3; 4; 5; 15 tickets

2.

5	2	5/2
12	1	12/1
10	6	10/6

3.

W = (1,2)	R = (7,7)
S = (3,0)	Y = (2,4)
C = (7,1)	Q = (0,7)
Z = (5,0)	U = (5,3)
T = (7,5)	P = (1,5)

4. Black-10
   White- 10
   Green- 10
   Blue- 5
   Red- 5

5. 40; 15; 13; 30

6. $5.60; $20.23; $123.75; $65.00

7. < , > , <

Lesson 147

1. n = 12; n = 35; n = 4; n = 42

2. Lemons; 18; 24
   Sugar; 3; 4.5; 6
   Water; 3

   24 lemons
   4.5 cups of sugar
   3 cups of water

3. 4/3; 3/6; 6/4; 6/7

4. (4,2) (4,3) (4,4) (4,5) (5,6) (6,7) (7,6) (8,5) (8,4) (8,3) (8,2) (7,1)

5. 26 r 24; 65 r 8; 11 r 39;

6. Acute angle; Line; Ray

7. >, >, <, =

Lesson 148

1. n = 2; n = 4; n = 2; n = 4

2. n = 30; n = 25; n = 6; n = 12

3. 3/5; 3/2; 2/3

4. 57,260; 18,000; 5,460; 71,456

5. radius – A segment from the center of a circle to any point of the circle.

   diameter – A segment containing two points of a circle and passing through the center of the circle.

   congruent angles – Two angles with the same measurement.

   similar figures – Having the same shape, but not the same size.

   symmetric figures – A figure that can be folded so that the two halves match exactly.

6. The answers may vary on the drawing section.
   2/6 = 1/3, 2/4 = 1/2

Lesson 149

1. Train Rides & Moon Walk
   $50.00
   $525.00
   1995 total was $1,025. 1996 total was $1,100.
   1996 made more money.

2. 16; 9; 1; 7

3. 6 to 2 = 6/2; 4 to 50 = 4/50; 3 to 1 = 3/1

4. n = 5; n = 11; n = 4; n = 26

5. 5,317; 6,420; 16,023; 15,050

6. 3; 9; 7

Lesson 150

1.
   1. 5/7
   2. 8/10
   3. 4/9
   4. 6/7
   5. 5/12
   6. 9/8

2. rice: 6; 8
   water: 8; 14

   cars: 3; 6; 7
   wheels: 8; 16; 20

3.

10/20	6/7	3/4
5/10	1/3	4/5
1/4	5/8	1/6
2/10	1/2	2/3

4. 96 C; 258 R; 135 A; 465 N; 52 E
   CRANE

5. 1/2; 3/4; 1/2; 1/4
   1/2; 1/2; 3/8; 1/6

6. 5/8; 8/12 = 2/3; 1/4; 3/10
   4/6 = 2/3; 3/4; 5/8; 3/6 = 1/2

Lesson 151

1. 37; 3; 17; 19; 29; 11; 5; 3
   41; 5; 7; 7
   11; 11; 2; 13; 17; 19
   2; 23; 31
   13; 5; 3; 7; 37; 47; 43

2.
   1. A.M.
   2. P.M.
   3. P.M.
   4. P.M.
   5. P.M.
   6. P.M.

3. n = 11; n = 17; n = 9

4. 4 cups ; 6 cups; 8 cups
   6 cups ; 9 cups; 12 cups

   8 cups (milk)

   2 cups ; 3 cups; 4 cups
   4 quarts; 6 quarts; 8 quarts

   4 cups (sugar)

5. Teacher check puzzle

Across	Down
368	32.75
7,299	1079.03
10,563	333.45
9856.77	55,184
106.03	17,013

6. 3/4; 5/6; 5/12
   5/8; 1/2; 3/10
   5/8; 4/6 = 2/3; 6/12 = 1/2

7. 1/5; 1/5; 2/3; 1/2; 7/10; 1/5
   1/6; 1/3; 3/20; 3/10; 1/7; 2/9

Lesson 152

1. 9; 9 r 3; 8 r 1; 1 r 4; 2
   7; 1 r 1; 3 r 1; 7 r 1; 6 r 1

2. A SPELLING BEE

3. 38° F; 84° F; -18° F; -4° F; 96° F

4. Teacher should see a sun peaking out from the mountains.

5. 45; 75; 20; 150

6. 10/20 = 1/2; 9/9 = 1; 15/25 = 3/5; 6/15 = 2/5

   9/15 = 3/5; 2/12 = 1/6; 2/16 = 1/8; 20/30 = 2/3

Lesson 153

1. HORSE PLAY

2. -20° C; 80° C; 100° C; 10° C; 34° C
3. n = 30; n = 32; n = 39

4.

20th	18th
3rd	5th
16th	12th
21st	8th
20th	13th

5. 5/8; 20/20 = 1; 4/16 = 1/4;
   8/12 = 2/3; 10/18 = 5/9; 5/15 = 1/3
   2/4 = 1/2; 7/14 = 1/2; 8/10 = 4/5

6. 1 4/12 = 1 1/3; 1 31/48; 5 9/12 = 5 3/4; 5 21/27 = 5 7/9; 4 12/20 = 4 3/5; 4 3/31

7.
1 1/2	2 1/4
1	3
1 3/4	2 3/4

Lesson 154

1. The Lord is my shepherd I shall not want

2.
3	102
1999	354
816	2089
1406	1812

3.
1. 18	6. 120
2. 3,520	7. 300
3. 3	8. 8
4. 1	9. 12
5. 15,840	10. 72

4. 78 r 6; 53 r 3; 15 r 51
33 r 16; 21 r 5; 23 r 22
Object: STAR

5. 1 quarter
2 dimes
4 pennies
1 dime

6. n = 20; n = 63; n = 49

Lesson 155

1.
1. 2	6. 96
2. 3	7. 8,000
3. 10	8. 64
4. 10,000	9. 6

2. 1 nickel, 1 dollar
1 nickel, 2 quarters
1 penny, 4 dollars
1 penny, 1 dime, 2 quarters

3. 3 5/8; 2 8/12 = 2 2/3; 24 7/8; 2 5/15 = 2 1/3
2 2/7; 38 7/8; 6 12/16 = 6 3/4; 33 12/8 = 34 4/8 = 34 1/2

4. =; <; >
=; <; <
<; =; =

5. 33; 14; 8; 47; 31
99; 11; 20; 9; 15
13; 24; 6; 7; 17
HIGH SCHOOL

6.
multiplicand	quotient
multiplier	divisor, dividend
product	
numerator	minuend
denominator	subtrahend
	difference
addend	
addend	
sum	

Lesson 156

1. >; =; <
=; >; <
=; <; =

2. 5000; 4
27,000; 12
2g; 1g
1kg; 1kg

3.
1 cm 4 mm;	14 mm;	1.4 cm
3 cm 7 mm;	37 mm;	3.7 cm
2 cm 5 mm;	25 mm;	2.5 cm

4.
2	2
4	6
4	6

5. 4/6; 5/6; 3/6; 2/6; 6/12; 7/12

6. 290.42; 1132.91; 795.13; 1805.4; 901.28
293.02; 710.39; 91.99; 361.11; 517.66

Lesson 157

1. 1 cm 9 mm; 19 mm; 1.9 cm
1 cm 1 mm; 11 mm; 1.1 cm
1 cm 8 mm; 18 mm; 1.8 cm

2.
1. point	2. line
3. intersecting	4. parallel
5. ray	6. perpendicular

3.
30	6
700	11
4,500	47

4. Teacher check

5. 137; 118; 120
131; 117; 110
30,150; 8,505; 3,124;
7,733; 14,965; 4,508

6. 2
12; 15
4; 5
36; 60

Lesson 158

1.
   1. 17/19
   2. 4/20
   3. 6/15
   4. 24/50

2.
   1. ∠ AXC
   2. ∠ AXD
   3. X
   4. XA, XB
   5. ∠ AXB, ∠ BXC,∠ CXD, ∠ BXD (any two)

3. n = 10; n = 18; n = 81; n = 28
4. A CLOCK

5. puzzle should spell: LOVE

6. 663; 1,138; 1,285
1,242; 1,196

Lesson 159

1. 241; 292; 279; 291; 290

2. n = 7; n = 6; n = 8

3. 284; 3,188

4.

100° C	boiling point	212° F
0° C	freezing point	32° F
25° C	room temp.	72° F
-20° C	inside a freezer	10° F
37° C	body temp.	98.6° F

5.
   1. millennium
   2. decade
   3. century
   4. BC
   5. 20th
   6. 21st
   7. AD

6. weight; liquid; weight
linear ; linear; liquid
linear; weight; linear
linear; liquid; weight

7. 1/2; 1/16; 1/4
1/15; 1/2; 1/7
1/2; 2/9; 1/12
1/3; 1/3; 1/10

Lesson 160

1. 1.21; 1 21/100
fifty-seven and four hundredths; 57 4/100
seven and three tenths; 7.3
3.02; 3 2/100
sixty one and 5 tenths; 61.5
four and twenty five hundredths; 4 25/100
42.5; 42 5/10
one and two hundredths; 1.02
eight and thirteen hundredths; 8 13/100

2. BASEBALL DIAMONDS

3. 50/100
4/6
33/99
12/15
10/14
4/10
12/22

4. n = 13; n = 31; n = 17

5. 7/12; 7/10; 4/8 = 1/2
4/6 = 2/3; 6/9 = 2/3; 4/10 = 2/5
2/6 = 1/3; 3/8; 4/9

6. 6; 5; 8; 3

Test 1

1. Addend Addend Sum

   Addend
   Addend
   Sum

   Order Property of Addition
   Zero Property of Addition
   Grouping Property of Addition

2.

13	8	4	11	4	7	9	8
13	8	4	11	4	7	9	8
11	10	11	15	6	11	20	19
11	10	11	15	6	11	20	19

3. Minuend
   Subtrahend
   Difference

   Minuend Subtrahend Difference

4. 6 13 90 3

5.

4	0	5	0
2	9		
5	8		

Test 2

1. Answers: 9,5,6,8,3,0

2. Answers: 30,000 + 1,000 + 700 + 50 + 6 =
   (3 x 10,000) + (1 x 1,000) + (7 x 100) + (5 x 10) + (6 x 1)

   80,000 + 5,000 + 100 + 90 + 0 =
   (8 x 10,000) + (5 x 1,000) + (1 x 100) + (9 x 10) + (0 x 1)

3.

<	=	=
>	<	=

4.

36,952	34,925	32,564	32,165
9,826	8,926	8,692	8,296
594,732	594,372	574,327	549,327

5.

3	4	2	10	1
4	3	5	7	4

6.

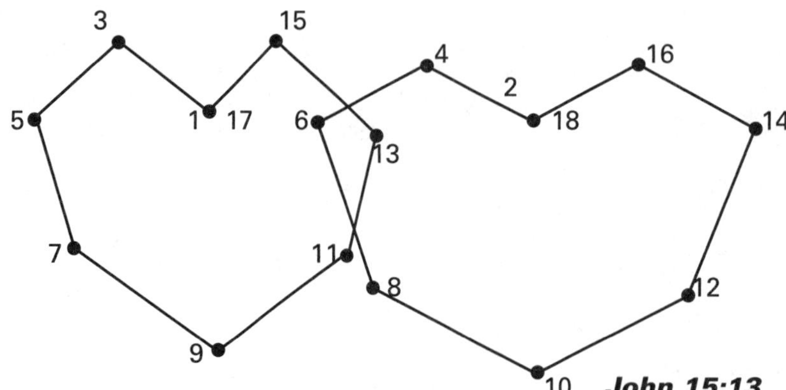

7.
1. $5.00 + $8.00 = $13.00
2. 3 + 2 = 5   24 - 5 = 19   19 brownies were left.
3. Cakes- 30 - 3 = 27 cakes sold
   Cookies - 34 dozen - 1 dozen = 33 dozen sold
   Crispy treats- 4 dozen - 0 dozen = 4 dozen sold

Test 3

1. <   <   <
   >   =   <

2. 580   8,900   43,040   70

3. Callie wants a box of popcorn, a box of candy, and a large cola.
   If she has $5.00 can she purchase all of these items?

   NO $2.50 + $1.00 + $2.50 = $6.00

   Jim purchased a box of candy and a regular soft drink. He gave the cashier $3.00.
   What was his change?

   YES $1.00 + $1.50 = $2.50 $3.00 – $2.50 = .50¢

4. 100   5,000   6,000   200   5,000

5. 23   353   966
   2,261   5,377   973
   108   129

6. 9,400   1,600   10,000   800

Test 4

1. 38   20   50   30

2.

Estimated:	$339.00	$784.00	$1,005.00	$67.00
Actual:	$338.56	$784.31	$1,004.80	$66.87

3. Addition; 62
   Addition; 152
   Subtraction and division or multiplication; 4
   Multiplication and subtraction; Monday

4. 73 97 223 6,109 3,358 59
Answer: SPIRIT

5. 260 400 600 4,000 30 10

6. 14 35 8 57

Test 5

1. $3.65 $1.12 $1.22 $2.78 $291.89

2.

$29.00	$84.00	$76.00
-14.00	- 16.00	- 46.00
15.00	$68.00	$30.00

$29.00	$85.00	$77.00
-13.00	- 16.00	- 46.00
16.00	$69.00	$31.00

3. 1 - penny, 1 - quarter, 2 - 1 dollar bills, = $2.26

1 - penny, 1 - dime, 2 - quarters, 1 - 1 dollar bill, = $1.61

1 - dime, 3 - quarters, 1 - 10 dollar bill, = $10.85

2 - quarters, 2 - 1 dollar bills, = $2.50

4. Answers:

Not Reasonable	$0.75 x 9 = $6.75 $10.00 - $6.75 = $3.25
Reasonable	4.50 x 2 = $9.00
Not Reasonable	$9.75 + $0.80 + $2.75 = $13.30

5. Multiplicand
Multiplier
Product
Multiplicand Multiplier Product

21 4 15 5 4

6. 8 x 0 = 0 —– Zero Property of Multiplication

4 x 5 = 20 so, 5 x 4 = 20 —– Order property of Multiplication

6 x 1 = 6 —– One Property of Multiplication

(3 x 2) x 4 = 3 x (2 x 4) —– Grouping Property of Multiplication

7. Answers: 16 16 60 60
35 35 30 30

8.

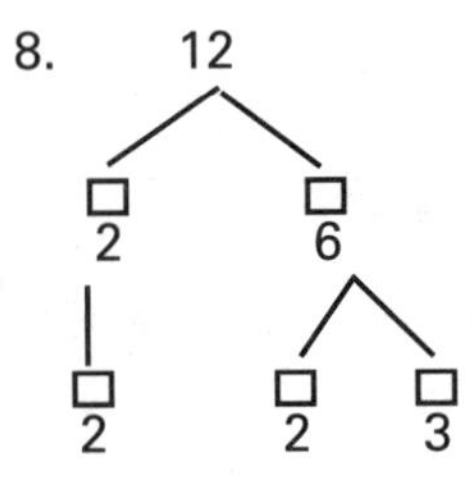

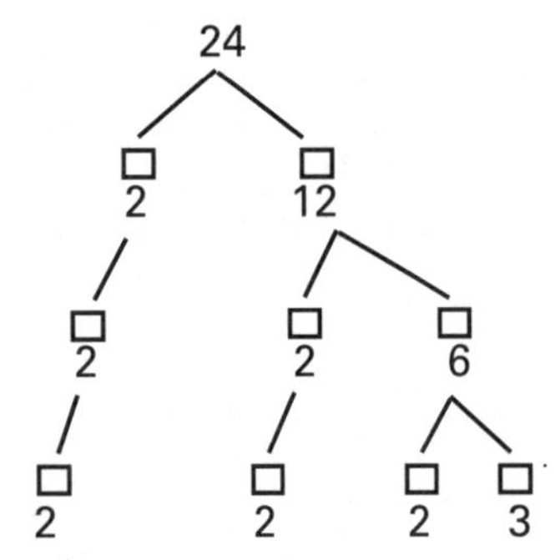

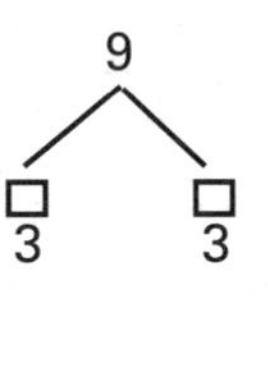

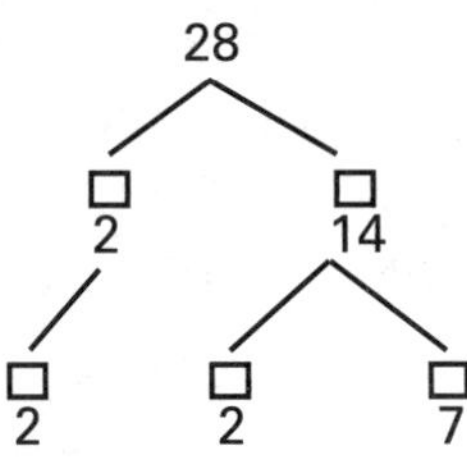

Test 6

1. Dividend Divisor Quotient

) 4
   5 20

   5 4 5 9

2. 24 ÷ 3 = 8 and, 3 x 8 = 24 — Multiplication and Division are Related

   You cannot divide by zero (0) — Division by Zero

   8 ÷ 1 = 8 — Division by One

   4 ÷ 4 = 1 — Division of a Number by Itself

3. 60 8,000 3,200 1,800,000 18,150
   22,379 18,750 71,100 26,928 5,016 200

4. 1. Jonathan purchased a baseball for $1.25, a baseball bat for $39.97, and a baseball glove for $40.00. He also purchased a set of baseball cards for $2.75. Jonathan has an extensive baseball card collection. How much did Jonathan spend on the baseball bat and baseball glove?
   $39.97 + $40.00 = $79.97

   2. Katrina ate 2 hamburgers at $0.55 each, an order of fries at $0.45, and a soft drink at $0.80. How much did lunch cost her?
   $0.55 + $0.55 + $0.45 + $0.80 = $2.35

   3. For lunch Karen purchased a slice of pizza and a drink for $1.00 each. She then bought a candy bar for dessert at a cost of $0.55. On the way home, Karen picked up a stray cat and took her home. She fed the cat a bowl of milk. How much did Karen spend on lunch?
   $1.00 + $1.00 + $0.55 = $2.55

5. 504 363 864 3,065 1,326 1,134
   Answer: PRAYER

Test 7

1. 450 240 1,500 1,400

2. 6 5 8 8

3. 1. $2.25 + $0.60 + $0.95 = $3.80

   2. $1.00 + $1.50 + $0.75 + $0.75 = $4.00

   3. Tommy - $3.95 Alex - $1.95 + $1.00 + $0.95 = $3.90
      Tommy spent $0.05 more.

   4. $3.00 + $0.60 + $0.60 = $4.20
      $4.20 ÷ 2 = $2.10

   5. The only 2 sandwiches which will total $3.75 are the Egg Salad and the Turkey.

   6. brownie - $0.75

4. 5 3 r 1 6 7
   6 r 2 20 r 3 2 r 1 50 r 1

5. $2.53 $2.05 $0.50 $0.09

6. 40 r 3 71 r 6 143
   201 908 450 r1
   Answer: CIRCLE

Test 8

1. ② 5 10 3
   2 ⑤ 10 ③
   ② ⑤ ⑩ 3
   ② 5 10 ③
   2 ⑤ 10 ③

2. 26 29 16

3. 64 54 63
   8 x 8 = 64 6 x 9 = 54 7 x 9 = 63

4. 3 20 7 40
   80 250 900 30

5. 4 r 5 7 r 2 6 r 25
   4 2 r 10 5 r 13

6. 9 r 26 45 r 41 63 r 43 46

Test 9

1. $6.52 $0.89 $3.09 $1.30 $3.14

2. 50 20 5 70 40

3. 4 tennis balls
   44 pennies
   163 suckers

4. 6 waffle (chocolate, vanilla) waffle (chocolate, strawberry) waffle (vanilla, strawberry)
   cake (chocolate, vanilla) cake (chocolate, strawberry) cake (vanilla, strawberry)

   9 red racer, red mountaineer, red space age
   black racer, black mountaineer, black space age
   gold racer, gold mountaineer, gold space age

5. BC — Before Christ
   AD — Anno Domini - in the year of our Lord
   decade — 10 years
   century — 100 years
   millennium — 1,000 years

6. Hands should read:
   1:15 4:30 10:45
   2:20 6:45 1:45

7. A.M.
   P.M.
   P.M.
   A.M.

8. 20th century 13th century
   3rd century 19th century
   1st century 7th century

9. 60 minutes — 1 hour
   60 seconds — 1 minute
   24 hours — 1 day
   48 hours — 2 days

10. New times:
    4: 05
    8: 00
    2: 34
    7: 11

Test 10

1. January 17
   January 19
   January 8
   21 days; three weeks
   January 29

2. Central Time 10:00 Eastern Time 11:00 Pacific Time 8:00 Hawaii Time 6:00

3. Carrie
   Steven Floyd
   Paula

4. (number of cards + 4) x 2 = 228 or (228 ÷ 2) – 4 = 110

5. 1. • T (point T) 2. $\overleftrightarrow{XY}$ (line XY) 3. $\overline{LM}$ (line segment LM) 4. $\overrightarrow{BC}$ (ray BC)

6. perpendicular
   parallel
   intersecting

7. 1. ∠LZN
   2. ∠LZM, ∠MZN, ∠NZO, or ∠MZO
   3. ∠LZO
   4. ∠MZL
   5. Z

8. Teacher check

9. Teacher check

10. Teacher check

11. Circle A

    $\overline{MA}$, $\overline{AN}$, $\overline{AB}$

    MN

    diameter = 6 cm; radius = 3 cm

Horizons Math 4, Test Key

Test 11

1. Triangular Prism:
Faces 5 Edges 9 Vertices 6

Rectangular Pyramid:
Faces 5 Edges 8 Vertices 5

2. 1. Sphere
2. Prism
3. Cone
4. Cylinder
5. Pyramid

3. The perimeter is 56 meters
The area is 160 meters^2

4. The volume of the figure is 216 cm^3 .

5. 2\3 4\6 4\8 1\4

6. 6\7 Numerator
Denominator

7. 1\3
0\5
7\8
6\18
4\5

8. 4\8 2\7 5\6

9. 20 20 2 27 6

10. 8: 1,2,4,8
16: 1,2,4,8,16
common factors: 1,2,4,8
greatest common factor: 8

13: 1,13
15: 1,3,5,15
common factors: 1
greatest common factor: 1

12: 1,2,3,4,6,12
16: 1,2,4,8,16
common factors: 1,2,4
greatest common factor: 4

11. 1\4 1\4 1\5 1\6 2\7

Test 12

1. 2/8 (<) 3/8 2/3 (>) 1/3 2/14 (>) 1/14 2/3 (<) 5/6

1/3 (=) 2/6 2/5 (>) 2/10 2/4 (=) 1/2 4/5 (>) 5/10

2. 10/8, 15/7, 13/4, 12/7, 22/5, 19/9, 8/3, 83/9

3. 4 1/4, 3, 6, 7, 5, 2 2/9, 5 1/2, 1 2/10 (1 1/5)

4. 300 ÷ 10 = 30 315 ÷ 9 = 35
30 x 5 = 150 27 x 5 = 135

5. 5/7 6/8 (3/4) 4/10 (2/5) 3/5

6. 8/12 (2\3) 1/4 5/7 7/8

7. 3/6 (1/2)   6/8 (3/4)   4/14 (2/7)   3/6 (1/2)

8. 4/8 (1/2)   4/6 (2/3)   6/6 (1)   5/8

9. 1/8   8/12 (2/3)   2/6 (1/3)   4/10 (2/5)

10. 1/4 hour

    7/8 cup

Test 13

1. 7 6/8 (7 3/4)   7 5/7   16 7/15   4 6/9 (4 2/3)   19 5/10 (19 1/2)

2. 3/7   4 3/8   5 6/10 (5 3/5)   2   8 1/6

3. 8 12/8 = 9 4/8 (9 1/2)   3 12/12 = 4   14 9/7 = 15 2/7   19 18/10 = 20 8/10 (20 4/5)

4.
   1. 6
   2. 3
   3. 8
   4. 1
   5. 9

5. We write: 1.2   We write: 0.3

   We read: "one and two tenths"   We read: "three tenths"

6. 0.45 — forty-five hundredths

   1.45 — one and forty-five hundredths

   0.09 — nine hundredths

   0.90 — ninety hundredths

7. 4.7 (>) 4.4   1.07 (<) 1.70   9.67 (<) 9.78   0.06 (<) 0.84

   0.760 (>) 0.740   5.070 (<) 5.700   .607 (>) .067   0.306 (<) 0.340

8. 3   8   12   123   105

9. 0.2   1.0   1.9   0.1   8.7

10. 12.99   35.64   59.71   86.88   138.02

Test 14

1.	4.71	1.09	33.78	81.02	0.08	41.97

2.	10 + 3 = 13	9 – 5 = 4	19 + 10 = 29	6 – 3 = 3

3.	Legos® $3.78 ($4.00)	truck $5.67 ($6.00)	(mini-cars $1.89) ($2.00)
	paint set $4.75 ($5.00)	game $4.55 ($5.00)	(pencil set $3.49) ($3.00)

4. 10 ft
   4 in

5. (2 1/4)
   (1 1/2)

6.	24 inches	108 inches
	6 feet	10,560 feet
	1 yard	3,520 yards
	24 oz.	32 oz.
	28oz.	40 oz.
	16 oz.	20 oz.
	48 oz.	44oz.
	2 pints	2 quarts
	3 quarts	3 gallons
	2 quarts	2 gallons
	2 cups	1 quart
	1 gallon	2 quarts

7.	98° F	32° F	-10° F	-5° F
8.	100° C	0° C	-20° C	22° C

9. 100° C — Boiling water

   0° C — Freezing

   -20° C — Inside a freezer

   22° C — Room Temperature

Test 15

1.
7.4	8.9	1.5
74	89	15

2.
19.5	8,469
6.495	75,400
9,090	301

3.
6	300,000	.200
50,000	.075	4,000

4.
.006	3,000	.023
50,000	.175	467,000

5.
1. 50
2. Baseball
3. Golf
4. Baseball, Basketball, Tennis, Football, Soccer, Golf

6. **Temp** **Daily Temperatures-Phoenix**

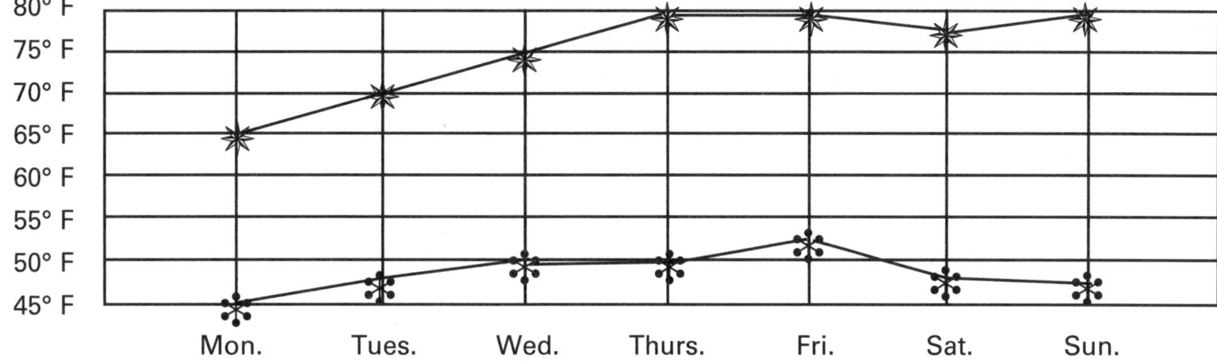

Days of the Week

High daily temperature

Low daily temperature

7.
1. 6
2. Orangeville
3. Rochester
4. Dublin, Lincoln
5. No data available

8.

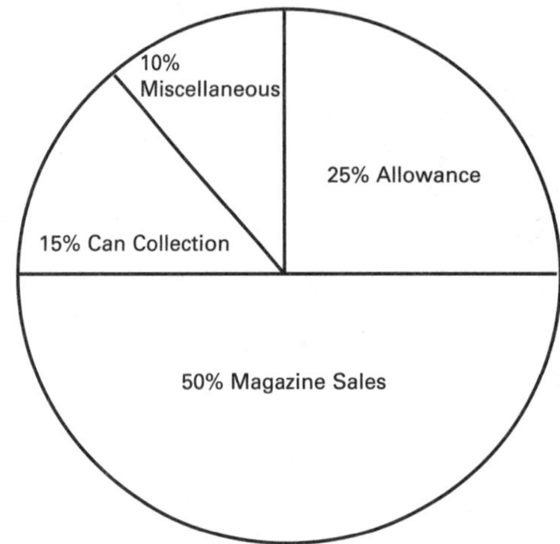

9. Teacher check

10. 3/7 4/7 5/6

Test 16

1.

cups of pudding	5	10	15	20	25	30	35
cups of milk	1	2	3	4	5	6	7

2. $n = 36$ $n = 50$ $n = 40$ $n = 48$

3. 2\4 15\30 6\8 1\2
   2\5 6\7 2\8 10\15
   2\16 3\4 3\5 4\8

4. 1\2 1\4 1\2 1\4 1\2

5. 25\25 = 1 4\18 = 2\9 10\15 = 2\3
   6\16 = 3\8 6\13 4\30 = 2\15

6. 43 85 539 192 396

7.
   1. December / December, January
   2. August / August
   3. May
   4. October

8.

x	3	6	8	2	9
2	6	12	16	4	18
7	21	42	56	14	63
9	27	54	72	18	81

9. Rectangle Square Rhombus Parallelogram Trapezoid

Horizons Mathematics 4

Worksheets

Reproducible Worksheets
for use with Horizons
Mathematics 4

① Write the answers.

9 + 8	3 + 3	4 + 6	9 + 5	5 + 7	8 + 4	3 + 9	2 + 7	2 + 6
3 + 4	4 + 4	2 + 2	8 + 5	9 + 0	4 + 2	3 + 5	4 + 9	6 + 5
5 + 5	7 + 9	8 + 7	3 + 6	2 + 8	3 + 7	4 + 5	6 + 9	9 + 9
8 + 8	3 + 2	2 + 9	7 + 7	2 + 5	3 + 8	7 + 6	4 + 7	6 + 8
1 + 8	2 + 6	3 + 4	4 + 2	1 + 7	2 + 0	3 + 2	4 + 1	1 + 3
2 + 1	3 + 0	4 + 4	1 + 0	2 + 8	4 + 5	1 + 9	2 + 5	3 + 7
1 + 1	2 + 7	2 + 2	3 + 5	4 + 0	1 + 5	2 + 9	3 + 8	1 + 6
3 + 3	3 + 9	8 + 5	4 + 9	3 + 6	6 + 9	8 + 0	7 + 6	9 + 5
4 + 6	8 + 4	6 + 0	6 + 5	8 + 7	9 + 9	7 + 7	4 + 7	6 + 6
5 + 0	5 + 7	9 + 0	5 + 5	7 + 9	8 + 8	7 + 0	6 + 8	9 + 8

① Write the answers.

10 − 6	9 − 8	6 − 3	3 − 2	12 − 9	12 − 7	8 − 2	9 − 7	12 − 8
8 − 4	13 − 8	9 − 9	7 − 3	4 − 2	6 − 6	9 − 3	10 − 5	6 − 4
8 − 5	11 − 5	10 − 8	15 − 9	16 − 9	8 − 7	4 − 4	15 − 7	18 − 9
13 − 9	9 − 4	10 − 9	8 − 8	16 − 8	5 − 2	11 − 2	11 − 4	12 − 6
3 − 2	3 − 0	8 − 4	1 − 1	10 − 8	9 − 4	10 − 9	7 − 5	10 − 3
6 − 3	12 − 9	13 − 8	9 − 3	15 − 9	13 − 9	8 − 8	13 − 6	14 − 5
5 − 0	12 − 7	9 − 9	10 − 5	16 − 9	7 − 0	16 − 8	14 − 6	17 − 9
9 − 8	8 − 2	7 − 3	6 − 4	8 − 7	2 − 0	5 − 2	5 − 4	4 − 1
2 − 1	9 − 7	4 − 2	8 − 5	4 − 4	6 − 1	11 − 2	7 − 6	11 − 8
10 − 6	12 − 8	6 − 6	11 − 5	15 − 7	18 − 9	14 − 7	11 − 4	12 − 6

1. Circle the odd numbers.

1 2 3 4 5 6 7 8 9 10

11 12 13 14 15 16 17 18 19 20

2. Circle the even numbers.

1,942 383 69 72 34 53 777

3. Circle the odd numbers.

227 2,334 123 1,098 98 699

4. Is the sum of these numbers odd or even?

1 + 1 ______	1 + 2 ______	1 + 3 ______	1 + 4 ______
1 + 5 ______	3 + 4 ______	3 + 3 ______	1 + 9 ______
8 + 15 ______	6 + 9 ______	9 + 8 ______	7 + 6 ______
6 + 5 ______	4 + 3 ______	2 + 1 ______	8 + 2 ______

5. Is the difference of these numbers odd or even?

10 – 9 ______	10 – 8 ______	10 – 7 ______	10 – 6 ______
10 – 5 ______	4 – 3 ______	9 – 1 ______	15 – 8 ______
9 – 6 ______	5 – 3 ______	16 – 2 ______	19 – 3 ______
13 – 5 ______	11 – 6 ______	18 – 2 ______	15 – 5 ______

6. For additional practice, label the sums on Worksheet 1 as odd or even?

7. For additional practice, label the differences on Worksheet 2 as odd or even?

Worksheet 4

① Write the numbers.

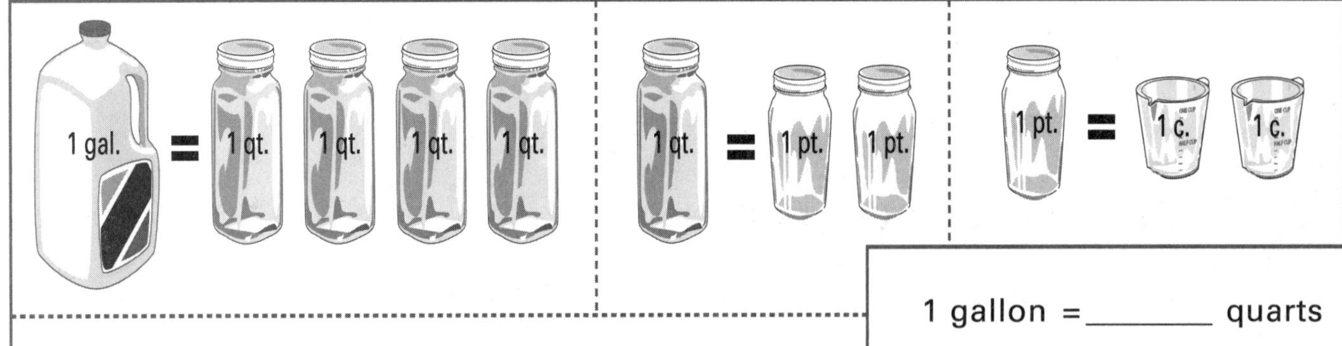

1 gallon = ________ quarts

1 quart = ________ pints

1 pint = ________ cups

1 cups = ________ ounces

② Circle the number needed.

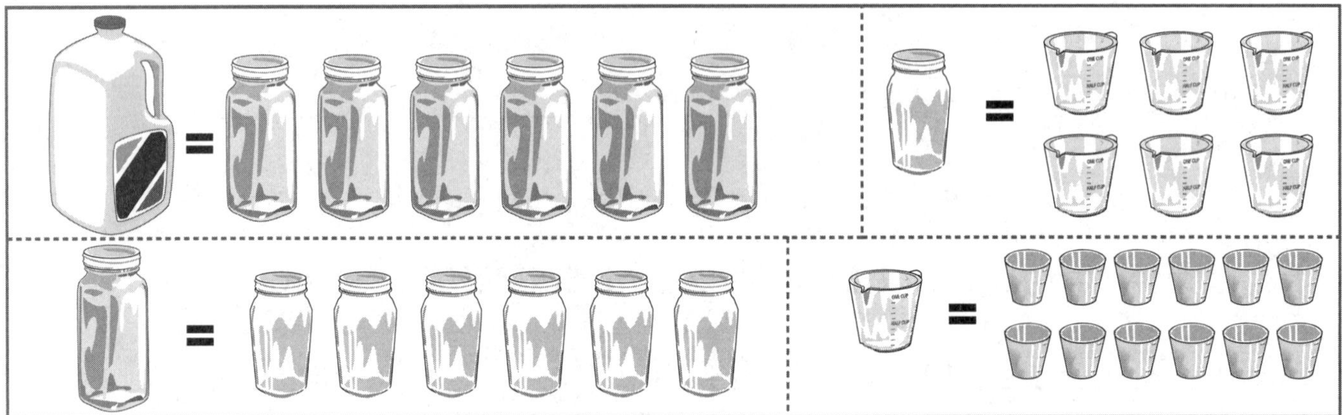

③ Write the numbers.

1 gal = _____ qts	1 qt = _____ pts	1 pt = _____ cs	1 c = _____ ozs
4 qts = _____ gal	2 pts = _____ qt	2 cs = _____ pt	8 ozs = _____ c
2 gals = _____ qts	3 qts = _____ pts	4 pts = _____ cs	5 cs = _____ ozs

① Write each digit of the number in its correct place value.

	Millions			Thousands			Units		
	hundred millions	ten millions	one millions	hundred thousands	ten thousands	one thousands	hundreds	tens	ones
43,825					4	3	8	2	5
203,780									
45,007,652									
703,647,110									
2,483,550									
723									

② Write each number on the line.

	Millions			Thousands			Units		
	hundred millions	ten millions	one millions	hundred thousands	ten thousands	one thousands	hundreds	tens	ones
403,542,807	4	0	3	5	4	2	8	0	7
____________				3	5	7	2	0	0
____________					2	3	7	8	8
____________		6	5	3	5	0	8	2	5
____________			3	0	0	0	2	9	6
____________						9	2	8	6

① Write the Arabic numbers.

LI	______	XL	______	LXI	______
IX	______	V	______	IV	______
LXX	______	XII	______	XLVII	______
XXXVI	______	XXXVII	______	XCVII	______

② Write the Roman numerals.

43	______	3	______	20	______
71	______	34	______	57	______
98	______	80	______	75	______
39	______	17	______	53	______

③ Write the Roman numerals.

72	______________	49	______________
16	______________	83	______________
58	______________	20	______________
42	______________	9	______________

④ Write the Arabic numbers.

LXIII	______	XXVIII	______
L	______	LXXI	______
XXXIV	______	I	______
LXXVI	______	XLV	______

Worksheet 7

1. Write the missing numbers.

3,692 = 3,000 + 600 + 90 + 2

3,692 = ______ + ______ + ______ + ______

3,722 = ______ + ______ + ______ + ______

1,034 = ______ + ______ + ______ + ______

9,990 = ______ + ______ + ______ + ______

8,001 = ______ + ______ + ______ + ______

4,707 = ______ + ______ + ______ + ______

2. Write the missing numbers.

63,040 = ______ + ______ + ______ + ______ + ______

50,400 = ______ + ______ + ______ + ______ + ______

21,274 = ______ + ______ + ______ + ______ + ______

83,363 = ______ + ______ + ______ + ______ + ______

3. Write the missing numbers.

423,670 = ______ + ______ + ______ + ______ + ______ + ______

205,337 = ______ + ______ + ______ + ______ + ______ + ______

480,643 = ______ + ______ + ______ + ______ + ______ + ______

265,554 = ______ + ______ + ______ + ______ + ______ + ______

① Circle the nearest ten.

16	10	(20)	30
26	10	20	30
47	30	40	50
18	10	20	30
23	10	20	30
41	30	40	50
29	10	20	30
64	50	60	70
86	70	80	90
72	60	70	80
34	20	30	40
99	80	90	100
62	50	60	70
54	40	50	60
32	20	30	40
44	40	50	60
76	60	70	80
63	60	70	80
51	40	50	60
77	60	70	80

37	30	40	50
78	70	80	90
17	10	20	30
33	30	40	50
48	30	40	50
36	30	40	50
19	0	10	20
69	60	70	80
24	10	20	30
48	30	40	50
53	40	50	60
42	30	40	50
73	60	70	80
84	70	80	90
49	30	40	50
57	50	60	70
21	10	20	30
93	80	90	100
11	10	20	30
59	50	60	70

① Circle the nearest ten.

37	30	(40)	50
52	50	60	70
31	20	30	40
46	40	50	60
59	50	60	70
72	60	70	80
28	20	30	40
76	60	70	80
93	80	90	100

② Circle the nearest hundred.

568	400	500	(600)
422	300	400	500
386	300	400	500
975	800	900	1,000
244	200	300	400
716	600	700	800
258	200	300	400
496	300	400	500
132	100	200	300

③ Circle the nearer thousand.

3,750	3,000	(4,000)
2,240	2,000	3,000
1,575	1,000	2,000
4,680	4,000	5,000
8,180	8,000	9,000
7,320	7,000	8,000
9,980	9,000	10,000
2,765	2,000	3,000
1,246	1,000	2,000
3,824	3,000	4,000
9,421	9,000	10,000

5,777	5,000	6,000
6,428	6,000	7,000
4,800	4,000	5,000
2,200	2,000	3,000
3,900	3,000	4,000
7,664	7,000	8,000
5,303	5,000	6,000
8,911	8,000	9,000
6,543	6,000	7,000
7,944	7,000	8,000
9,210	9,000	10,000

① Write the correct answer.

75 + 13	42 + 35	47 + 12	44 + 25
19 + 32	49 + 24	66 + 16	46 + 29
26 + 15	39 + 47	48 + 45	32 + 38
76 + 51	84 + 22	47 + 71	93 + 93
15 + 32	63 + 24	32 + 38	26 + 45
39 + 58	28 + 64	73 + 85	92 + 44

① Write the correct answer.

$$\begin{array}{r} 543 \\ +\ 323 \\ \hline \end{array} \quad \begin{array}{r} 462 \\ +\ 423 \\ \hline \end{array} \quad \begin{array}{r} 860 \\ +\ 138 \\ \hline \end{array} \quad \begin{array}{r} 252 \\ +\ 433 \\ \hline \end{array}$$

$$\begin{array}{r} 468 \\ +\ 271 \\ \hline \end{array} \quad \begin{array}{r} 344 \\ +\ 274 \\ \hline \end{array} \quad \begin{array}{r} 399 \\ +\ 410 \\ \hline \end{array} \quad \begin{array}{r} 283 \\ +\ 284 \\ \hline \end{array}$$

$$\begin{array}{r} 585 \\ +\ 246 \\ \hline \end{array} \quad \begin{array}{r} 446 \\ +\ 396 \\ \hline \end{array} \quad \begin{array}{r} 359 \\ +\ 369 \\ \hline \end{array} \quad \begin{array}{r} 436 \\ +\ 476 \\ \hline \end{array}$$

$$\begin{array}{r} 536 \\ +\ 123 \\ \hline \end{array} \quad \begin{array}{r} 342 \\ +\ 517 \\ \hline \end{array} \quad \begin{array}{r} 465 \\ +\ 273 \\ \hline \end{array} \quad \begin{array}{r} 634 \\ +\ 181 \\ \hline \end{array}$$

$$\begin{array}{r} 273 \\ +\ 179 \\ \hline \end{array} \quad \begin{array}{r} 185 \\ +\ 279 \\ \hline \end{array} \quad \begin{array}{r} 387 \\ +\ 251 \\ \hline \end{array} \quad \begin{array}{r} 583 \\ +\ 283 \\ \hline \end{array}$$

① Write the correct answer.

$\begin{array}{r} 2 \\ 5 \\ +\ 2 \\ \hline \end{array}$	$\begin{array}{r} 5 \\ 0 \\ +\ 3 \\ \hline \end{array}$	$\begin{array}{r} 3 \\ 2 \\ +\ 1 \\ \hline \end{array}$	$\begin{array}{r} 4 \\ 3 \\ +\ 1 \\ \hline \end{array}$
$\begin{array}{r} 14 \\ 61 \\ +\ 24 \\ \hline \end{array}$	$\begin{array}{r} 34 \\ 22 \\ +\ 42 \\ \hline \end{array}$	$\begin{array}{r} 33 \\ 43 \\ +\ 13 \\ \hline \end{array}$	$\begin{array}{r} 62 \\ 23 \\ +\ 13 \\ \hline \end{array}$
$\begin{array}{r} 4 \\ 6 \\ +\ 2 \\ \hline \end{array}$	$\begin{array}{r} 5 \\ 2 \\ +\ 4 \\ \hline \end{array}$	$\begin{array}{r} 4 \\ 3 \\ +\ 8 \\ \hline \end{array}$	$\begin{array}{r} 7 \\ 6 \\ +\ 3 \\ \hline \end{array}$
$\begin{array}{r} 35 \\ 23 \\ +\ 38 \\ \hline \end{array}$	$\begin{array}{r} 63 \\ 19 \\ +\ 12 \\ \hline \end{array}$	$\begin{array}{r} 14 \\ 27 \\ +\ 14 \\ \hline \end{array}$	$\begin{array}{r} 55 \\ 25 \\ +\ 15 \\ \hline \end{array}$
$\begin{array}{r} 29 \\ 55 \\ +\ 8 \\ \hline \end{array}$	$\begin{array}{r} 38 \\ 48 \\ +\ 6 \\ \hline \end{array}$	$\begin{array}{r} 34 \\ 19 \\ +\ 19 \\ \hline \end{array}$	$\begin{array}{r} 39 \\ 15 \\ +\ 27 \\ \hline \end{array}$
$\begin{array}{r} 27 \\ 6 \\ +\ 38 \\ \hline \end{array}$	$\begin{array}{r} 29 \\ 29 \\ +\ 16 \\ \hline \end{array}$	$\begin{array}{r} 58 \\ 18 \\ +\ 6 \\ \hline \end{array}$	$\begin{array}{r} 7 \\ 28 \\ +\ 46 \\ \hline \end{array}$

① Write the correct answer for each problem.

4,332 + 2,662	3,371 + 1,473	2,786 + 2,516
6,925 + 3,325	7,317 + 1,732	5,825 + 3,567
4,962 + 1,249	2,527 + 2,638	1,465 + 1,383
7,340 + 2,684	5,425 + 4,246	3,284 + 6,293
6,780 + 4,316	8,560 + 9,262	4,573 + 2,742
5,258 + 2,785	1,763 + 2,275	5,280 + 2,469
9,420 + 8,632	4,256 + 7,325	2,961 + 3,874
6,892 + 2,163	3,428 + 2,647	6,843 + 2,537

① Solve the equations.

$n + 7 = 9$	$n + 4 = 7$	$n + 2 = 10$	$n + 5 = 8$
$n + 9 = 12$	$n + 8 = 12$	$n + 5 = 11$	$n + 9 = 14$
$n + 6 = 12$	$n + 6 = 14$	$n + 5 = 12$	$n + 2 = 11$
$n + 3 = 11$	$n + 9 = 15$	$n + 8 = 17$	$n + 8 = 15$
$n + 4 = 13$	$n + 7 = 15$	$n + 9 = 17$	$n + 2 = 4$
$n + 5 = 10$	$n + 7 = 13$	$n + 4 = 11$	$n + 4 = 12$

① Write the correct answer.

87 − 31	89 − 10	83 − 23	87 − 24	77 − 35
87 − 51	79 − 61	84 − 22	66 − 23	32 − 11
89 − 15	47 − 32	57 − 32	89 − 25	68 − 26
95 − 15	67 − 23	88 − 13	58 − 41	75 − 25
85 − 52	99 − 17	58 − 12	49 − 30	85 − 13
59 − 25	73 − 35	95 − 76	85 − 27	78 − 46
79 − 23	82 − 27	81 − 39	86 − 47	93 − 48
70 − 38	73 − 27	61 − 14	74 − 25	66 − 38
78 − 39	82 − 58	61 − 29	75 − 46	83 − 37

① Write the correct answer.

995 − 580	575 − 250	859 − 517	487 − 224	883 − 423
866 − 323	886 − 114	885 − 114	687 − 431	849 − 619
668 − 247	757 − 623	787 − 251	983 − 123	777 − 435
958 − 512	685 − 433	799 − 582	758 − 341	689 − 310
836 − 142	618 − 274	445 − 172	458 − 192	914 − 431
739 − 271	546 − 184	445 − 172	616 − 393	728 − 341
567 − 284	738 − 273	938 − 141	777 − 194	419 − 195
346 − 194	457 − 185	769 − 483	728 − 382	949 − 191
715 − 181	927 − 463	727 − 382	619 − 369	747 − 256

① Find the difference and check.

502 − 374	706 − 697	701 − 465	906 − 438	301 − 219	805 − 516	608 − 539	406 − 277
804 − 349	502 − 169	302 − 125	801 − 627	705 − 138	507 − 459	902 − 564	406 − 379
801 − 784	402 − 183	603 − 259	905 − 648	502 − 296	705 − 527	807 − 418	904 − 367
901 − 388	403 − 376	802 − 197	906 − 49	703 − 235	603 − 448	903 − 846	508 − 159
402 − 137	504 − 19	603 − 175	704 − 488	504 − 167	803 − 314	901 − 256	306 − 98
403 − 277	802 − 298	605 − 359	901 − 124	201 − 153	904 − 726	701 − 362	506 − 489

① Circle the nearest ten.

16	0	10	20
11	0	10	20
92	80	90	100
58	50	60	70
18	0	10	20

87	70	80	90
37	20	30	40
53	40	50	60
98	80	90	100
47	40	50	60

② Circle the nearest hundred.

485	400	500	600
560	400	500	600
247	100	200	300
251	100	200	300
562	400	500	600
648	500	600	700
765	600	700	800
375	300	400	500

598	500	600	700
841	700	800	900
462	400	500	600
958	800	900	1,000
158	100	200	300
662	600	700	800
937	800	900	1,000
423	300	400	500

③ Circle the nearest thousand.

2,358	2,000	3,000
6,420	6,000	7,000
1,582	1,000	2,000
7,688	7,000	8,000
4,298	4,000	5,000
3,565	3,000	4,000
9,250	9,000	10,000
6,628	6,000	7,000

1,120	1,000	2,000
4,280	4,000	5,000
7,630	7,000	8,000
9,489	9,000	10,000
3,650	3,000	4,000
2,410	2,000	3,000
9,685	9,000	10,000
8,286	8,000	9,000

① Write the correct answers.

7,809 − 3,523	9,906 − 2,096	9,953 − 4,272	3,897 − 1,719
3,726 − 1,253	5,658 − 2,492	6,677 − 3,483	9,483 − 4,191
4,968 − 2,382	5,495 − 3,723	8,355 − 3,724	7,488 − 4,863
9,593 − 6,642	4,398 − 2,629	6,350 − 2,173	8,675 − 4,898
4,968 − 2,382	5,398 − 2,629	7,685 − 4,896	3,474 − 2,786

1. Solve and check the following equations.

$n - 2 = 6$ $n - 5 = 7$ $n - 10 = 2$ $n - 14 = 1$

$n - 1 = 0$ $n - 8 = 3$ $n - 1 = 9$ $n - 20 = 1$

$n - 6 = 11$ $n - 4 = 7$ $n - 8 = 15$ $n - 5 = 8$

$n - 12 = 12$ $n - 6 = 6$ $n - 1 = 6$ $n - 4 = 9$

Worksheet 21

① Solve each verbal problem.

Find the number that is 16 more than 58.

Find the number that is 32 less than 96.

Find the number that is 56 more than 102.

Find the number that is 18 less than 82.

Find the number that is 142 more than 68.

Find the number that is 53 more than 243.

Find the number that is 19 less than 384.

Find the number that is 6 feet longer than 79 feet

Find the number that is 62 miles longer than 456 miles.

Find the number that is 30 meters shorter than 86 meters.

Find the number that is 73 inches shorter than 108 inches.

Find the number that is 6 times 78 centimeters.

① Multiply to find the product.

9 x 5	10 x 6	9 x 3	9 x 2	3 x 9	8 x 1	2 x 8	1 x 9	2 x 2
1 x 3	6 x 5	4 x 0	5 x 8	6 x 1	9 x 0	4 x 3	5 x 1	6 x 0
9 x 8	9 x 6	2 x 4	8 x 3	8 x 9	10 x 9	4 x 2	4 x 8	8 x 2
10 x 2	6 x 2	8 x 7	10 x 5	5 x 3	6 x 7	7 x 3	2 x 3	3 x 8
5 x 0	1 x 2	5 x 4	8 x 6	4 x 7	3 x 6	6 x 8	3 x 3	6 x 4
2 x 7	5 x 7	10 x 3	9 x 0	4 x 5	6 x 6	1 x 8	7 x 4	8 x 5
4 x 1	5 x 5	9 x 9	6 x 5	2 x 1	8 x 8	6 x 9	1 x 9	3 x 7
3 x 8	8 x 5	7 x 4	6 x 0	10 x 6	7 x 9	4 x 6	5 x 0	4 x 9
7 x 1	2 x 6	7 x 8	1 x 1	8 x 6	7 x 3	8 x 0	5 x 6	5 x 9

Multiplication Chart

X	0	1	2	3	4	5	6	7	8	9	10
0	0	0	0	0	0	0	0	0	0	0	0
1	0	1	2	3	4	5	6	7	8	9	10
2	0	2	4	6	8	10	12	14	16	18	20
3	0	3	6	9	12	15	18	21	24	27	30
4	0	4	8	12	16	20	24	28	32	36	40
5	0	5	10	15	20	25	30	35	40	45	50
6	0	6	12	18	24	30	36	42	48	54	60
7	0	7	14	21	28	35	42	49	56	63	70
8	0	8	16	24	32	40	48	56	64	72	80
9	0	9	18	27	36	45	54	63	72	81	90
10	0	10	20	30	40	50	60	70	80	90	100

1. Find the prime factors of these numbers. Write each prime number as a product of itself and one.

2 3 4 5 6 7 8 9

10 11 12 13 14 15 16

17 18 19 20 21 22

23 24 25

1 **This game will let you find all the prime numbers less than 100.** (1 is crossed out because prime numbers are greater than 1.)

~~1~~	2	3	4	5	6	7	8	9	10
11	12	13	14	15	16	17	18	19	20
21	22	23	24	25	26	27	28	29	30
31	32	33	34	35	36	37	38	39	40
41	42	43	44	45	46	47	48	49	50
51	52	53	54	55	56	57	58	59	60
61	62	63	64	65	66	67	68	69	70
71	72	73	74	75	76	77	78	79	80
81	82	83	84	85	86	87	88	89	90
91	92	93	94	95	96	97	98	99	100

Follow these rules.

1. Draw a line through every number greater than 2 that is divisible by 2 (use divisibility rule).
2. Draw a line through every number that is left that is greater than 5 and that is divisible by 5 (use divisibility rule).
3. Draw a line through every number that is left that is greater than 3 and that is divisible by 3 (use divisibility rule).
4. Draw a line through every number that is left that is greater than 7 and that is divisible by 7 (divide by 7).

You should have twenty-five prime numbers that are not crossed out.

2 **Write** ***prime*** **or** ***composite*** **by the following numbers.**

13 ______________ 67 ______________ 76 ______________ 91 ______________

39 ______________ 47 ______________ 49 ______________ 53 ______________

31 ______________ 51 ______________ 23 ______________ 81 ______________

Prime number chart.

2	3	5	7	11
13	17	19	23	29
31	37	41	43	47
53	59	61	67	71
73	79	83	89	97

① Divide to find the quotient.

$5\overline{)20}$ $6\overline{)54}$ $8\overline{)24}$ $3\overline{)21}$

$4\overline{)16}$ $7\overline{)49}$ $9\overline{)45}$ $6\overline{)36}$

② Write the missing numbers.

7 x 9 = ______
9 x 7 = ______
63 ÷ 9 = ______
63 ÷ 7 = ______

4 x 8 = ______
8 x 4 = ______
32 ÷ 8 = ______
32 ÷ 4 = ______

8 x 5 = ______
5 x 8 = ______
40 ÷ 5 = ______
40 ÷ 8 = ______

5 x 6 = ______
6 x 5 = ______
30 ÷ 6 = ______
30 ÷ 5 = ______

7 x 6 = ______
6 x 7 = ______
42 ÷ 6 = ______
42 ÷ 7 = ______

3 x 5 = ______
5 x 3 = ______
15 ÷ 5 = ______
15 ÷ 3 = ______

① Work each problem correctly.

342 x 2	689 x 6	128 x 4	742 x 5
898 x 7	662 x 3	523 x 7	750 x 5
436 x 2	718 x 4	932 x 9	488 x 7
679 x 8	935 x 5	820 x 7	486 x 4
630 x 5	189 x 6	782 x 4	936 x 2
218 x 4	463 x 2	372 x 3	515 x 6

① Write the correct answers.

62 x 10 =	______	32 x 100 =	______
58 x 10 =	______	85 x 100 =	______
74 x 10 =	______	16 x 100 =	______
23 x 10 =	______	12 x 100 =	______
16 x 10 =	______	55 x 100 =	______
92 x 10 =	______	63 x 100 =	______
88 x 10 =	______	47 x 100 =	______
74 x 10 =	______	10 x 100 =	______
51 x 10 =	______	90 x 100 =	______
10 x 10 =	______	458 x 100 =	______

15 x 1,000 =	______	47 x 100 =	______
33 x 1,000 =	______	15 x 10 =	______
51 x 1,000 =	______	31 x 100 =	______
60 x 1,000 =	______	43 x 1,000 =	______
24 x 1,000 =	______	62 x 10 =	______
92 x 1,000 =	______	55 x 10 =	______
114 x 1,000 =	______	88 x 1,000 =	______
725 x 1,000 =	______	16 x 100 =	______
400 x 1,000 =	______	7 x 100 =	______
812 x 1,000 =	______	81 x 1,000 =	______

① Write the correct answers.

318 x 32	118 x 31	128 x 24	523 x 34
424 x 61	124 x 32	216 x 37	322 x 45
117 x 34	716 x 24	234 x 28	165 x 29
413 x 43	328 x 14	168 x 23	282 x 62
542 x 54	124 x 26	318 x 43	452 x 26
125 x 22	548 x 56		

1 Solve and check the following equations.

$2 \times n = 6$

$4 \times n = 12$

$5 \times n = 20$

$n \times 6 = 12$

$n \times 3 = 36$

$3 \times n = 3$

$14 \times n = 42$

$n \times 5 = 100$

$5 \times n = 10$

$3 \times n = 6$

$3 \times n = 12$

$n \times 7 = 21$

$3 \times n = 24$

$n \times 2 = 6$

$4 \times n = 20$

$11 \times n = 22$

$5 \times n = 45$

$2 \times n = 24$

$n \times 3 = 9$

$6 \times n = 18$

Prices at the Grocery Store	
crackers (box) . . . . .92¢	bread (loaf) $1.59
oranges (bag) . . . . .93¢	candy (bag) $1.24
eggs (dozen) . . . . .73¢	tuna (can) . . . . .89¢
bananas (pound) . . . . .59¢	cheese (pound) $3.99
cookies (package) $2.39	peanut butter (jar) $2.49
jelly (jar) $1.89	flour (5 pounds) $1.69

1. How much for 8 boxes of crackers?

2. How much would 7 bags of oranges cost?

3. J.C. would like to make peanut butter and jelly sandwiches. How much will it cost for the supplies?

4. How much would a customer pay for a package of cookies, a bag of oranges, and a loaf of bread?

5. How much would 4 dozen eggs cost?

6. How much more does a bag of oranges cost than a box of crackers?

7. If Ashley gets 50¢ each day for doing the dishes how many days will she need to work to buy a bag of candy?

8. What change will be given to the customer if they purchase a bag of flour with a $5.00 dollar bill?

① Find the product.

7	8	2	4	5	0	6	3	1	9
x 8	x 3	x 2	x 6	x 8	x 7	x 8	x 5	x 1	x 3
1	0	4	9	2	7	1	0	9	2
x 5	x 2	x 9	x 8	x 9	x 3	x 9	x 8	x 7	x 3
5	1	4	0	3	6	5	6	3	9
x 7	x 6	x 5	x 1	x 4	x 7	x 4	x 4	x 9	x 4
0	2	7	1	6	9	0	3	4	8
x 6	x 8	x 4	x 4	x 6	x 5	x 3	x 3	x 8	x 8
1	8	2	8	2	9	4	1	0	3
x 8	x 4	x 4	x 5	x 7	x 9	x 4	x 2	x 0	x 7
0	5	5	0	7	8	2	1	4	3
x 9	x 6	x 9	x 4	x 5	x 9	x 5	x 7	x 7	x 8
6	2	1	8	3	7	9	0	5	7
x 9	x 6	x 3	x 6	x 6	x 7	x 6	x 5	x 5	x 6

① Find the quotient.

$3\overline{)10}$	$6\overline{)35}$	$2\overline{)11}$	$4\overline{)11}$	$5\overline{)21}$	$8\overline{)35}$
$5\overline{)29}$	$4\overline{)13}$	$6\overline{)21}$	$3\overline{)17}$	$2\overline{)15}$	$7\overline{)39}$
$6\overline{)25}$	$2\overline{)19}$	$4\overline{)18}$	$5\overline{)12}$	$3\overline{)14}$	$9\overline{)64}$
$5\overline{)18}$	$3\overline{)19}$	$6\overline{)14}$	$2\overline{)13}$	$4\overline{)23}$	$7\overline{)55}$
$9\overline{)57}$	$7\overline{)34}$	$8\overline{)23}$	$5\overline{)43}$	$3\overline{)25}$	$6\overline{)44}$

① Find the quotient.

$3\overline{)213}$ $3\overline{)186}$ $3\overline{)129}$ $3\overline{)156}$ $4\overline{)484}$

$4\overline{)128}$ $4\overline{)448}$ $4\overline{)248}$ $5\overline{)155}$ $5\overline{)205}$

$5\overline{)240}$ $5\overline{)180}$ $5\overline{)150}$ $5\overline{)225}$ $5\overline{)120}$

$5\overline{)145}$ $6\overline{)384}$ $6\overline{)456}$ $6\overline{)546}$ $6\overline{)510}$

$7\overline{)287}$ $7\overline{)371}$ $7\overline{)175}$ $7\overline{)518}$ $8\overline{)648}$

$8\overline{)744}$ $8\overline{)600}$ $8\overline{)184}$ $9\overline{)369}$ $9\overline{)387}$

$9\overline{)306}$ $9\overline{)675}$ $3\overline{)645}$ $5\overline{)455}$ $2\overline{)720}$

$6\overline{)144}$ $2\overline{)450}$ $4\overline{)468}$ $8\overline{)176}$ $9\overline{)279}$

$8\overline{)200}$ $7\overline{)371}$ $9\overline{)675}$ $5\overline{)145}$ $5\overline{)265}$

$7\overline{)581}$ $9\overline{)297}$ $4\overline{)368}$ $5\overline{)650}$ $9\overline{)747}$

① Divide money.

$4\overline{)\$6.48}$	$2\overline{)\$3.58}$	$3\overline{)\$1.53}$	$5\overline{)\$5.75}$
$2\overline{)\$4.64}$	$3\overline{)\$5.67}$	$4\overline{)\$8.84}$	$2\overline{)\$9.50}$
$6\overline{)\$7.32}$	$5\overline{)\$4.20}$	$7\overline{)\$9.31}$	$6\overline{)\$8.64}$
$9\overline{)\$11.07}$	$8\overline{)\$12.24}$	$6\overline{)\$13.92}$	$7\overline{)\$15.75}$
$4\overline{)\$9.00}$	$2\overline{)\$12.78}$	$3\overline{)\$10.32}$	$2\overline{)\$3.50}$

Worksheet 36

① Divide.

$6\overline{)1209}$	$7\overline{)2102}$	$8\overline{)8567}$
$7\overline{)6374}$	$9\overline{)9818}$	$4\overline{)2561}$
$6\overline{)2163}$	$3\overline{)2345}$	$8\overline{)2163}$
$4\overline{)3245}$	$6\overline{)4329}$	$5\overline{)8757}$

① Check the appropriate column for divisibility.

	2	5	10	3
459				
76				
500				
84				
321				
450				
210				
685				
143				
243				
68				
305				
264				
455				
288				
462				
430				
255				
168				
4,569				

② Write the divisibility rule on each line.

324 is divisible by 2 because ______________________________

____

324 is divisible by 3 because ______________________________

____

250 is divisible by 5 because ______________________________

____

250 is divisible by 10 because ______________________________

____

1 Solve the equations and check.

$n \div 3 = 6$

$n \div 2 = 3$

$n \div 6 = 7$

$n \div 2 = 5$

$n \div 6 = 3$

$n \div 9 = 3$

$n \div 3 = 2$

$n \div 7 = 2$

$n \div 5 = 4$

$n \div 8 = 4$

$n \div 6 = 6$

$n \div 5 = 2$

$n \div 9 = 2$

$n \div 7 = 3$

$n \div 3 = 4$

$n \div 9 = 4$

$n \div 6 = 2$

$n \div 4 = 2$

$n \div 4 = 3$

$n \div 3 = 7$

$n \div 8 = 2$

$n \div 7 = 4$

$n \div 9 = 5$

$n \div 8 = 3$

① Divide.

$2\overline{)42}$	$2\overline{)36}$	$2\overline{)28}$	$2\overline{)44}$
$3\overline{)69}$	$3\overline{)75}$	$4\overline{)72}$	$4\overline{)84}$
$5\overline{)80}$	$5\overline{)25}$	$6\overline{)96}$	$6\overline{)72}$
$5\overline{)95}$	$4\overline{)64}$	$3\overline{)81}$	$2\overline{)18}$
$8\overline{)32}$	$4\overline{)16}$	$3\overline{)24}$	$9\overline{)18}$
$9\overline{)477}$	$6\overline{)342}$	$5\overline{)730}$	$7\overline{)567}$
$7\overline{)749}$	$6\overline{)120}$	$5\overline{)635}$	$8\overline{)568}$

① Find each quotient and remainder.

$45\overline{)325}$ $82\overline{)736}$ $91\overline{)398}$

$66\overline{)497}$ $78\overline{)518}$ $46\overline{)386}$

$73\overline{)320}$ $52\overline{)326}$ $32\overline{)256}$

$82\overline{)685}$ $68\overline{)526}$ $54\overline{)367}$

$23\overline{)214}$ $16\overline{)156}$ $82\overline{)902}$

$74\overline{)198}$ $35\overline{)283}$ $56\overline{)489}$

$88\overline{)843}$ $13\overline{)116}$ $45\overline{)205}$

1 Write the coins and bills you would give in change. Total the change and check your answer.

A helium balloon costs $6.99. What is the change from $10.00?

Coins: ________________ Check:

Bills: ________________

Total: ________________

Two candy apples at the carnival cost $2.29 each.
What is the change from $20.00?

Coins: ________________ Check:

Bills: ________________

Total: ________________

A pencil costs 18¢, an eraser 29¢, and a plastic case 39¢.
What is the change from $1.00?

Coins: ________________ Check:

Bills: ________________

Total: ________________

At the drive-in restaurant a hamburger is $1.19, french fries are 99¢, and a chocolate shake is $1.09. If two of each items are ordered what would be the change from $20.00?

Coins: ________________ Check:

Bills: ________________

Total: ________________

2 Complete the chart.

Cost	Money	Change
$8.75	$10.00	
$23.89	$50.00	
$46.79	$100.00	
$11.28	$20.00	
$27.43	$40.00	
$.08	$.25	
$.35	$.50	

① Find each quotient and remainder.

$23\overline{)4266}$ $16\overline{)356}$ $82\overline{)902}$ $74\overline{)981}$

$32\overline{)5382}$ $56\overline{)894}$ $28\overline{)345}$ $88\overline{)9843}$

$13\overline{)416}$ $38\overline{)5622}$ $45\overline{)605}$ $31\overline{)738}$

$33\overline{)947}$ $28\overline{)642}$ $17\overline{)389}$ $12\overline{)328}$

$32\overline{)5736}$ $38\overline{)8324}$

① Find the correct answers.

$3\overline{)\$3.15}$	$7\overline{)\$58.10}$	$2\overline{)\$19.80}$	$8\overline{)\$7.36}$
$7\overline{)\$20.30}$	$6\overline{)\$8.52}$	$9\overline{)\$83.97}$	$5\overline{)\$65.80}$
$4\overline{)\$45.68}$	$3\overline{)\$23.79}$	$9\overline{)\$192.87}$	$4\overline{)\$58.52}$
$4\overline{)\$126.80}$	$8\overline{)\$65.92}$	$6\overline{)\$58.74}$	

(1) Solve the problems.

Each student in Mrs. Jenkins class was treated to ice cream. There was vanilla, chocolate, and strawberry ice cream with butterscotch or fudge topping. If each student was allowed to choose one ice cream flavor and one topping, how many combinations would there be?

Jessica needs to pick out an outfit for the party. She has a pink, blue, or green top and a pair of black, white, or tan pants from which to choose. How many top and pant combinations are there?

The car dealership has 15 vehicles parked in the front of the lot. If every fifth vehicle is a truck, how many cars were?

The sandwich shop was offering specials on their soup and sandwich combinations. The choice of soups were tomato, chicken noodle, and vegetable. The choice of sandwiches were ham, turkey, and chicken. How many choices of soup and sandwich combinations were there?

① Write the numbers.

To change seconds to minutes, divide the number of seconds by 60.
To change minutes to seconds, multiply the number of minutes by 60.
To change minutes to hours, divide the number of minutes by 60.
To change hours to minutes, multiply the hours by 60.
To change hours to days, divide the number of hours by 24.
To change days to hours, multiply the number of days by 24.

1 Write the correct number to complete the following rules.

The number of hours x ______ equals the number of minutes.

The number of days x ______ equals the number of hours.

The number of minutes ÷ ______ equals the number of hours.

The number of seconds ÷ ______ equals the number of minutes.

2 Write the correct number.

2 hours = ______ minutes

300 seconds = ______ minutes

3 days = ______ hours

720 hours = ______ days

60 seconds = ______ minute

60 minutes = ______ hour

How many minutes are in twelve hours? ______________

How many days are in 120 hours? ______________

How many minutes equal 720 seconds? ______________

How many seconds are in two hours? ______________

3,000 seconds = _______ minutes

8 hours = _______ minutes

96 hours = _______ days

2 days = _______ hours

① In the following sentences, write A.M. or P.M. correctly.

Two o'clock in the afternoon is 2:00 ________.

It is still dark at 3:00 ________.

We ate lunch at 12:15 ________.

The baby started to cry a little before midnight at 11:50 ________.

② Answer the following questions.

Megan and her dad walked to the park. They left the house at 8:30 A.M. The walk took them 45 minutes. What time did they arrive at the park? ________.

Ben had a soccer game that started at 4:00 P.M. They played two 40-minute periods and had a 15 minute halftime break. What time did the game end if there were no timeouts called? ________.

Annette and Stephen were going to the zoo. They planned to arrive at the zoo at 9:05 A.M. and leave for home at 11:50 A.M. What is the maximum number of minutes they could stay at the zoo? ________.

It takes Lisa one hour and fifteen minutes to get ready for school. What time must she begin to get ready if her bus stops by her door at 7:45 A.M.? ________.

Mark needs to have some repair work done on his car. The mechanic tells him to bring it into the shop at 2:30 P.M. It will take three hours and fifteen minutes to make the repairs. What is the earliest Mark can expect his car to be ready to drive again? ________.

If a plane leaves New York at 10:05 A.M. on a trip that will arrive in Denver at 12:55 P.M. New York time, how many minutes will the plane be in the air? ________.

① Solve the problems.

Grandmother Walker sent a box containing a present for each of her grandchildren. They were wrapped in different colors of paper and stacked in order. The yellow one was between the blue and red. The orange one was on the bottom next to the red one. There was also a green one. In what order were they?

Chad, Tyler, Mike, and James live on opposites sides of town from each other. Chad lives on the west side of town and Mike lives on the east side. If James lives on the south side of town, in what part of town does Tyler live?

Mary, Nancy, Steve, and Alan were standing in line at the lunch counter. Nancy was first in line, and Alan was last in line behind Steve. In what order were they standing?

The P.E coach was making up teams for a new game. He had the kids line up and count off by fours. All the same numbers would be on the same team. Tim was third in line. David and Jerry wanted to be on the same team as Tim. If there were sixteen students in the class, what places in line could they stand in order to be on the same team?

(1) Solve.

Bill and Mike added 21 inches of rope to their sister Emily's jump rope. If the rope now measures 87 inches, how long was it in the beginning?

If it took 48 cups of water to fill 8 water bottles, how many cups did each water bottle hold?

Five hundred tickets were sold for the class play. If $375.00 was the total amount the class collected for tickets, how much did each ticket cost?

The fifteen member youth group was going on a hay ride. If each person brought the same number of friends, how many people did each bring if 60 people went on the hay ride?

For three straight years Theresa went backpacking with her youth group. The first two years the group spent 7 days each year in the wilderness. This year, however, they spent 12 days. Altogether, how many more days did they spend the first two years than this year?

A fish aquarium has a capacity of 2 gallons. If it was already filled with two quarts plus one pint of water, how much water would need to be added to completely fill the tank?

Geometry Terms	Geometry in Pictures	Geometry in Symbols	Geometry in Words
Point	K	K	Point K
Line	D E	$\overleftrightarrow{DE}$	Line DE
Line Segment	S T	$\overline{ST}$	Line Segment
Ray	X Y	$\overrightarrow{XY}$	Ray XY Always name the end point first.
Intersecting Lines	l m	l intersects m	Line l intersects line m.
Parallel Lines	x y	$x \parallel y$	Line x is parallel to line y.
Perpendicular Lines	b a	$a \perp b$	Line a is perpendicular to line b.
Angle	A B C	∠A, ∠ ABC, ∠CAB	Angle ABC is two rays that share a common end point.
Right Angle			A right angle measures 90°.
Acute			An acute angle measures less than 90°.
Obtuse			An obtuse angle measures greater than 90°.

1) Put an "X" on the shape that is congruent to the first shape in each row. Circle the shapes that are similar to the first shape in each row.

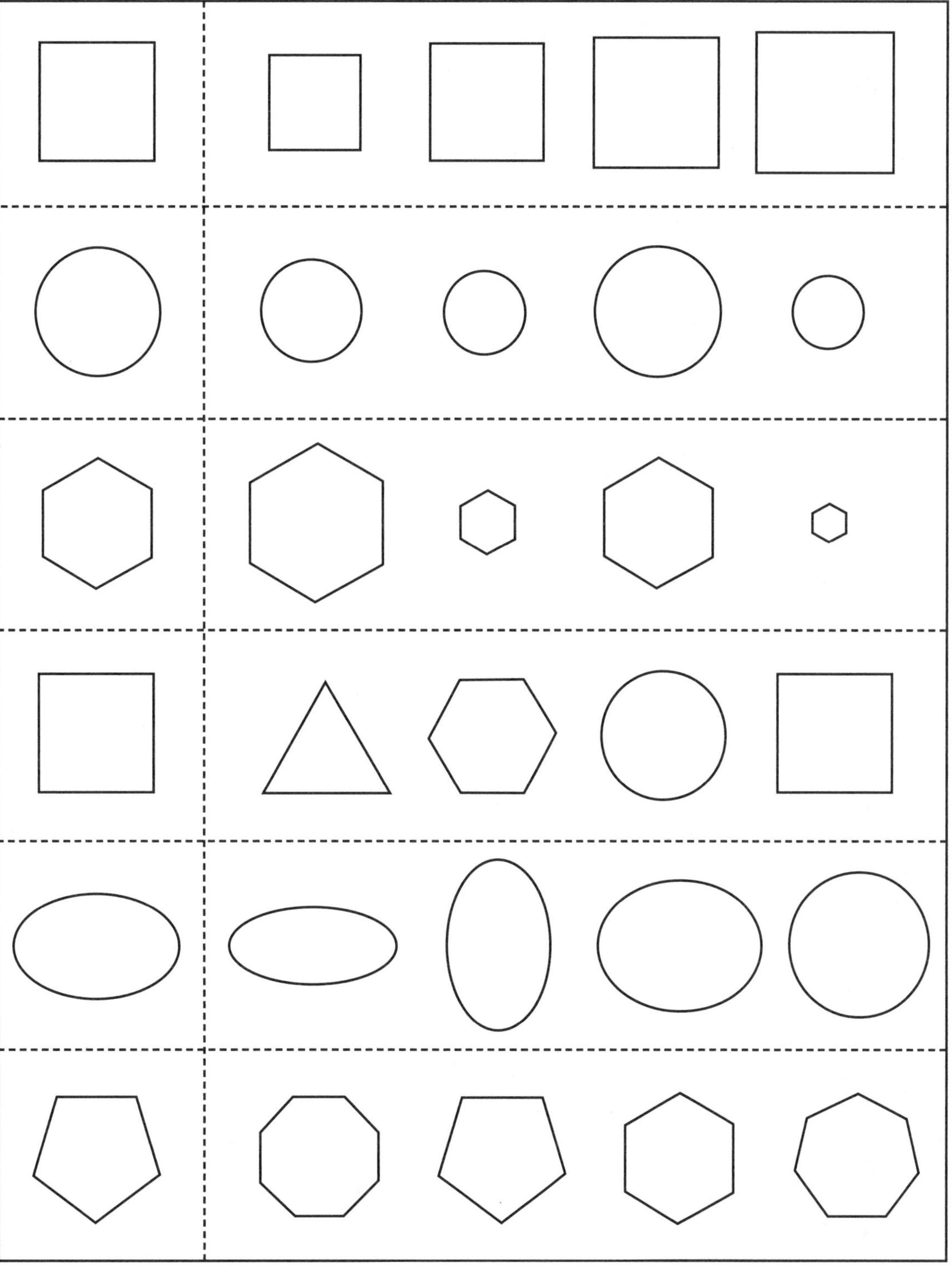

① Fold and cut out to form symmetrical shapes.

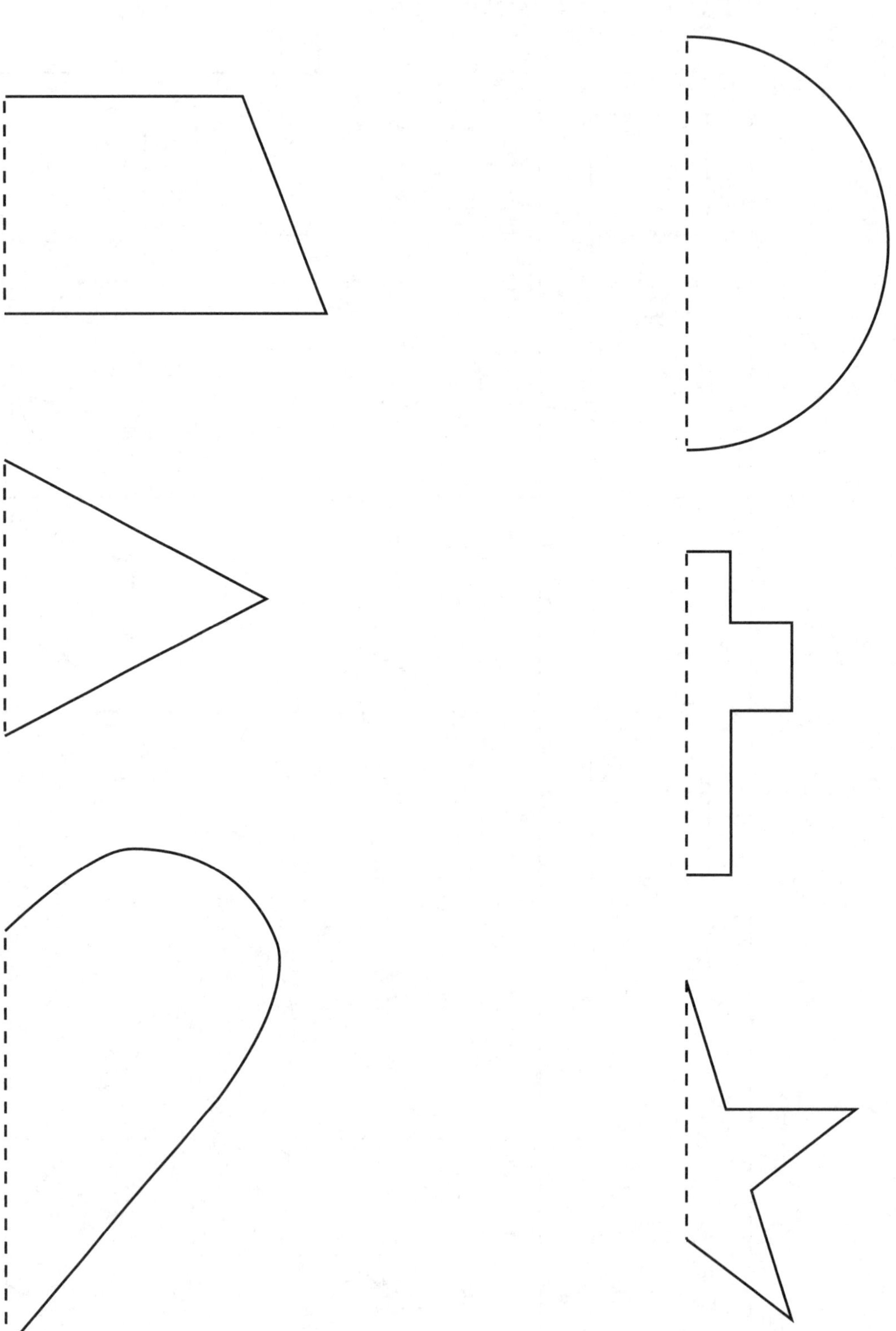

① Each pattern on the left can be folded to make one of the three-dimensional figures on the right. Circle the letter of that figure.

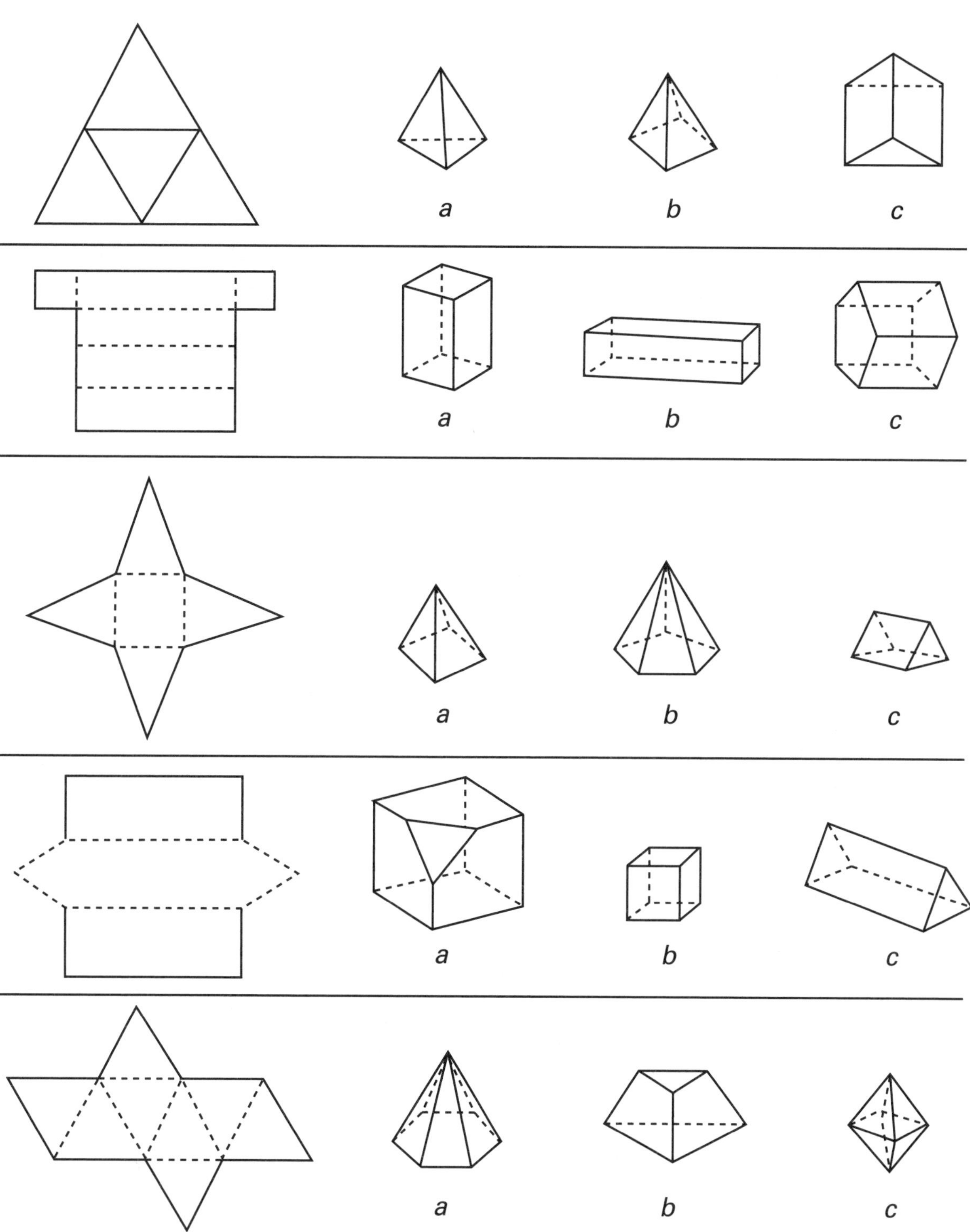

① Find the perimeter.

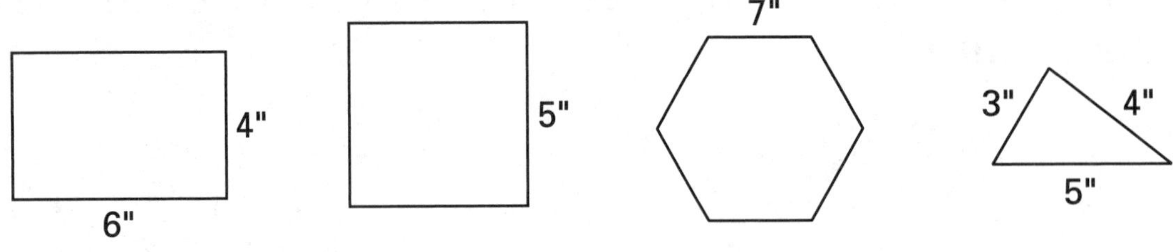

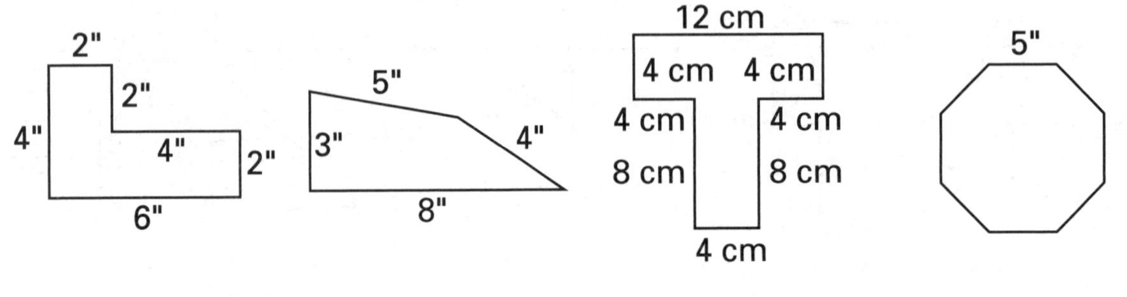

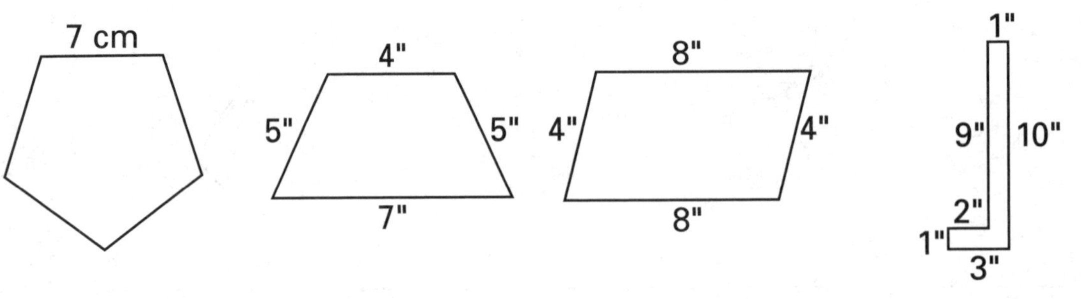

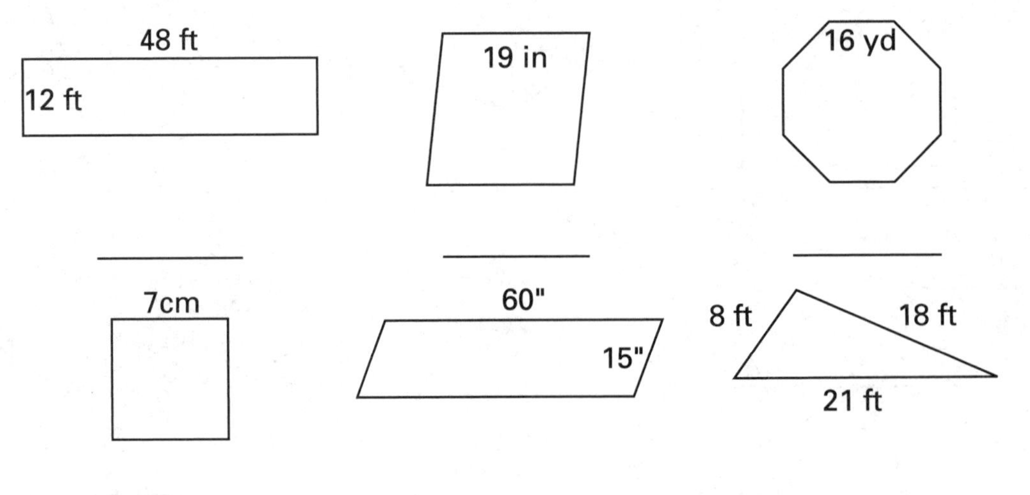

Centimeter Graph Paper

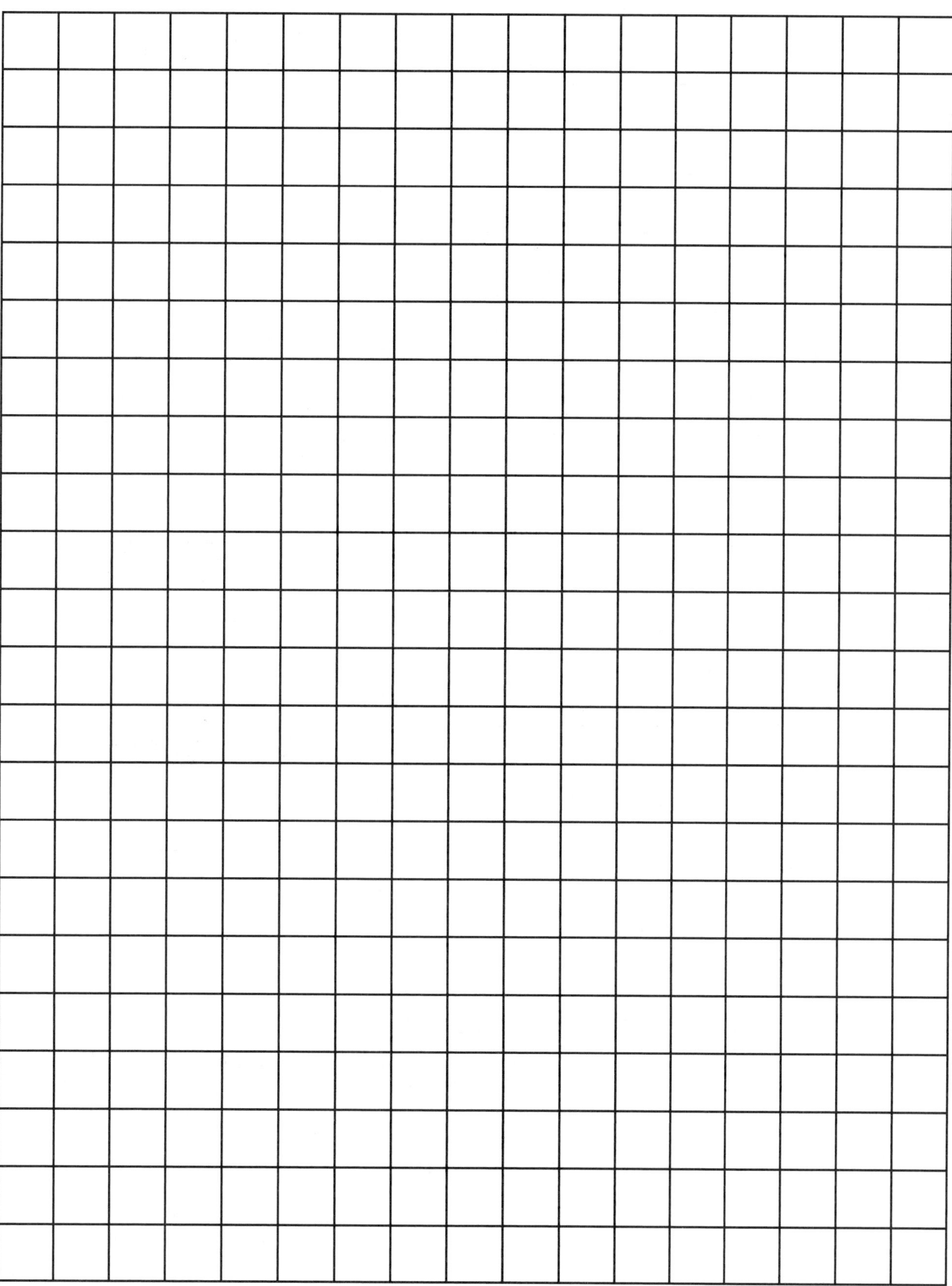

(1) Find the volume.

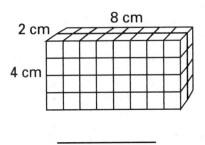

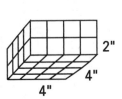

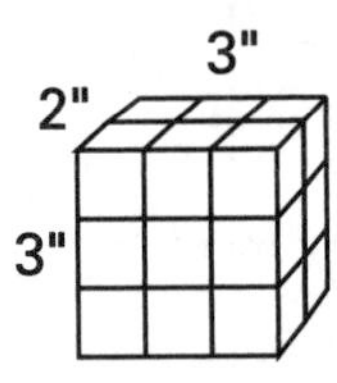

4 cm
2 cm
2 cm

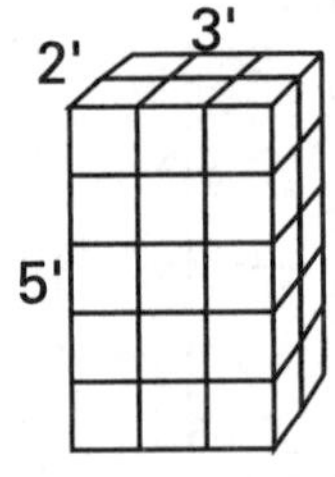

2"
4"
4"

8 cm
2 cm
4 cm

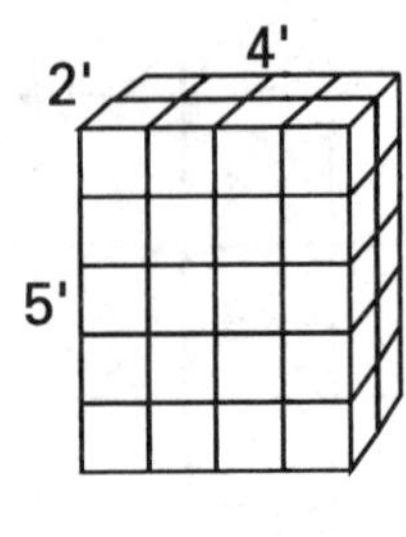

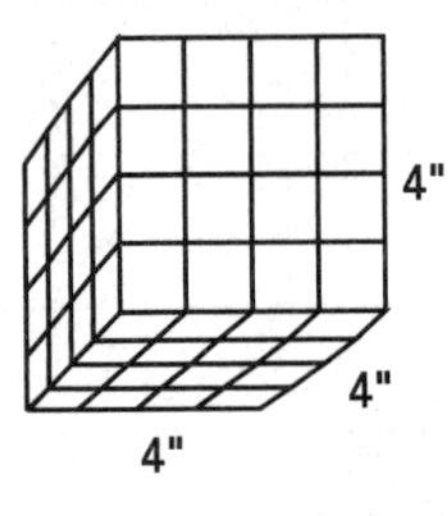

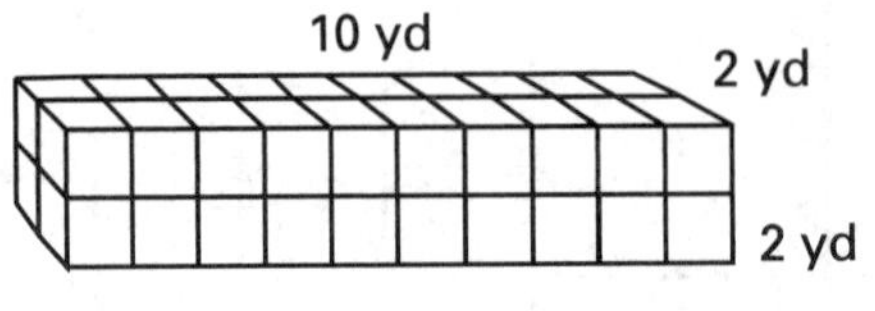

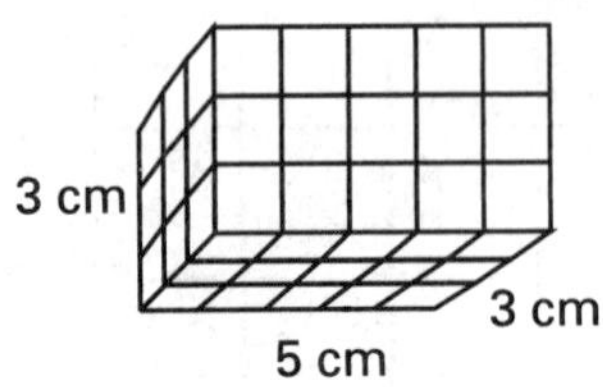

2 cm
2 cm
2 cm

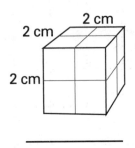

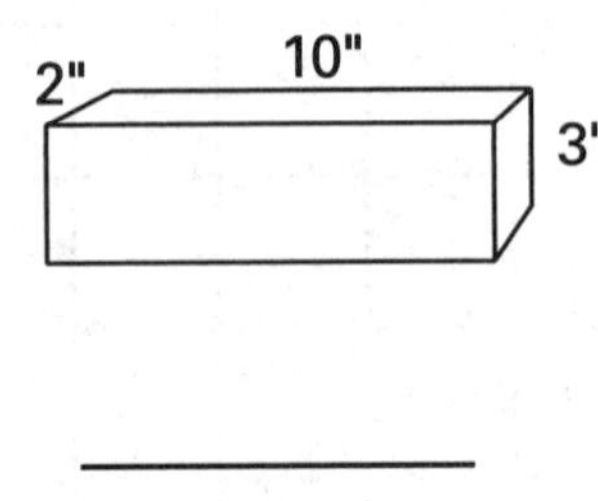

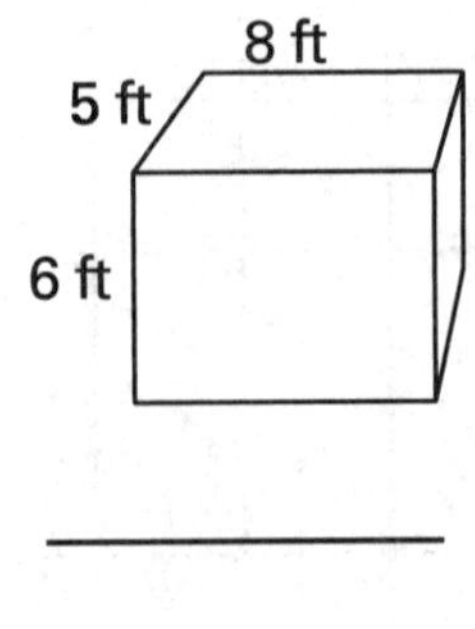

Fraction Strips

One Whole	1

One-half	$\frac{1}{2}$

One-third	$\frac{1}{3}$	$\frac{1}{3}$

One-fourth	$\frac{1}{4}$	$\frac{1}{4}$	$\frac{1}{4}$

One-fifth	$\frac{1}{5}$	$\frac{1}{5}$	$\frac{1}{5}$	$\frac{1}{5}$

One-sixth	$\frac{1}{6}$	$\frac{1}{6}$	$\frac{1}{6}$	$\frac{1}{6}$	$\frac{1}{6}$

One-eighth	$\frac{1}{8}$	$\frac{1}{8}$	$\frac{1}{8}$	$\frac{1}{8}$	$\frac{1}{8}$	$\frac{1}{8}$	$\frac{1}{8}$

One-tenth	$\frac{1}{10}$	$\frac{1}{10}$	$\frac{1}{10}$	$\frac{1}{10}$	$\frac{1}{10}$	$\frac{1}{10}$	$\frac{1}{10}$	$\frac{1}{10}$	$\frac{1}{10}$

One-twelfth	$\frac{1}{12}$	$\frac{1}{12}$	$\frac{1}{12}$	$\frac{1}{12}$	$\frac{1}{12}$	$\frac{1}{12}$	$\frac{1}{12}$	$\frac{1}{12}$	$\frac{1}{12}$	$\frac{1}{12}$	$\frac{1}{12}$

1. Draw lines to match the fraction with the fraction word.

$\frac{3}{4}$	seven-eighths	$\frac{7}{8}$	$\frac{1}{2}$	four-sixths	$\frac{3}{5}$
$\frac{2}{3}$	three-fourths	$\frac{4}{5}$	$\frac{1}{3}$	one-half	$\frac{4}{6}$
$\frac{5}{6}$	five-sixths	$\frac{6}{7}$	$\frac{2}{4}$	one-third	$\frac{5}{8}$
$\frac{1}{4}$	six-sevenths	$\frac{3}{7}$	$\frac{3}{6}$	three-fifths	$\frac{4}{7}$
$\frac{2}{5}$	two-thirds	$\frac{6}{8}$	$\frac{2}{9}$	five-eighths	$\frac{3}{8}$
$\frac{2}{6}$	four-fifths	$\frac{5}{9}$	$\frac{7}{12}$	two-fourths	$\frac{3}{11}$

2. Write the fraction words.

$\frac{4}{4}$	________________	$\frac{1}{6}$	________________
$\frac{1}{5}$	________________	$\frac{2}{7}$	________________
$\frac{5}{7}$	________________	$\frac{2}{8}$	________________
$\frac{3}{11}$	________________	$\frac{4}{13}$	________________
$\frac{8}{14}$	________________	$\frac{8}{15}$	________________
$\frac{5}{9}$	________________	$\frac{7}{10}$	________________

① What fraction of each set is in the box?

1.   

____

2.   

____

3. 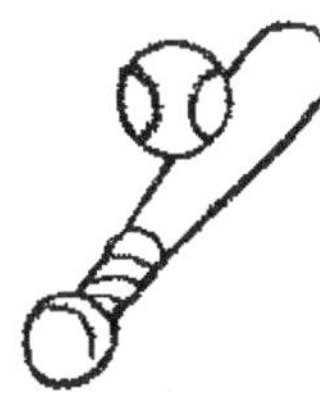 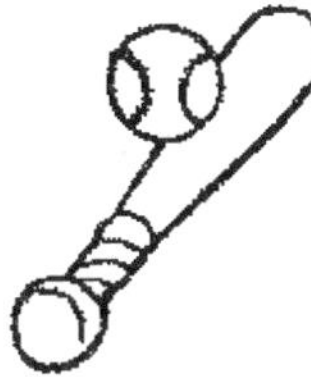  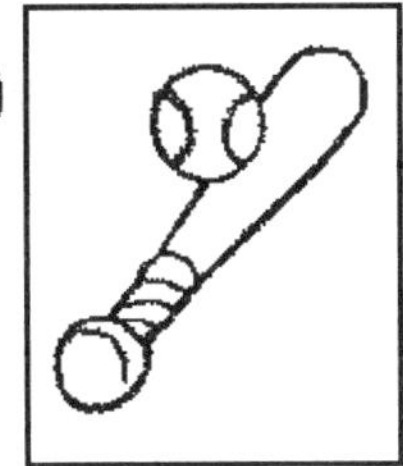

____

4.      

____

① Write = or ≠.

$\frac{2}{3}$ ☐ $\frac{8}{12}$	$\frac{3}{4}$ ☐ $\frac{9}{12}$	$\frac{4}{5}$ ☐ $\frac{15}{20}$	$\frac{3}{6}$ ☐ $\frac{6}{18}$
$\frac{5}{7}$ ☐ $\frac{10}{21}$	$\frac{1}{4}$ ☐ $\frac{5}{24}$	$\frac{3}{5}$ ☐ $\frac{6}{10}$	$\frac{2}{6}$ ☐ $\frac{3}{9}$
$\frac{1}{3}$ ☐ $\frac{4}{15}$	$\frac{1}{4}$ ☐ $\frac{6}{10}$	$\frac{5}{6}$ ☐ $\frac{10}{11}$	$\frac{2}{7}$ ☐ $\frac{8}{18}$
$\frac{3}{8}$ ☐ $\frac{7}{20}$	$\frac{4}{7}$ ☐ $\frac{12}{21}$	$\frac{4}{6}$ ☐ $\frac{6}{8}$	$\frac{1}{5}$ ☐ $\frac{5}{25}$

1. Circle the multiples of these numbers.

4 1, 2, 3, 4, 5, 6, 7, 8, 9, 10, 11, 12, 13, 14, 15, 16, 17, 18, 19, 20, 21, 22, 23, 24

7 1, 2, 3, 4, 5, 6, 7, 8, 9, 10, 11, 12, 13, 14, 15, 16, 17, 18, 19, 20, 21, 22, 23, 24

9 1, 2, 3, 4, 5, 6, 7, 8, 9, 10, 11, 12, 13, 14, 15, 16, 17, 18, 19, 20, 21, 22, 23, 24

3 1, 2, 3, 4, 5, 6, 7, 8, 9, 10, 11, 12, 13, 14, 15, 16, 17, 18, 19, 20, 21, 22, 23, 24

5 1, 2, 3, 4, 5, 6, 7, 8, 9, 10, 11, 12, 13, 14, 15, 16, 17, 18, 19, 20, 21, 22, 23, 24

6 1, 2, 3, 4, 5, 6, 7, 8, 9, 10, 11, 12, 13, 14, 15, 16, 17, 18, 19, 20, 21, 22, 23, 24

2 1, 2, 3, 4, 5, 6, 7, 8, 9, 10, 11, 12, 13, 14, 15, 16, 17, 18, 19, 20, 21, 22, 23, 24

8 1, 2, 3, 4, 5, 6, 7, 8, 9, 10, 11, 12, 13, 14, 15, 16, 17, 18, 19, 20, 21, 22, 23, 24

2. Name the divisors (2, 3, 5, 6, 9, and 10) of these numbers.

62 ________________

93 ________________

95 ________________

50 ________________

10 ________________

1. In each of the following groups, circle the fraction that is in lowest terms.

$\frac{3}{18}$	$\frac{2}{3}$	$\frac{2}{8}$
$\frac{4}{8}$	$\frac{6}{12}$	$\frac{5}{9}$
$\frac{2}{9}$	$\frac{5}{20}$	$\frac{3}{12}$
$\frac{6}{13}$	$\frac{7}{14}$	$\frac{8}{12}$
$\frac{2}{4}$	$\frac{2}{18}$	$\frac{2}{7}$

2. Reduce these fractions by dividing by one of these numbers. Choose the largest one.

2	3	4	5	6

$\frac{3}{9}$	$\frac{4}{16}$
$\frac{6}{12}$	$\frac{3}{12}$
$\frac{5}{10}$	$\frac{6}{10}$

3. Reduce these fractions to lowest terms.

$\frac{5}{25}$	$\frac{4}{6}$	$\frac{2}{12}$
$\frac{4}{12}$	$\frac{2}{18}$	$\frac{6}{24}$
$\frac{15}{30}$	$\frac{20}{24}$	$\frac{12}{24}$
$\frac{16}{24}$	$\frac{16}{20}$	

(1) Using the diagrams at the right, compare the two fractions given. Place the correct symbol inside the circle between each pair of fractions.

$\frac{1}{2}$ ◯ $\frac{1}{3}$　　$\frac{1}{3}$ ◯ $\frac{1}{2}$

$\frac{1}{3}$ ◯ $\frac{1}{4}$　　$\frac{1}{2}$ ◯ $\frac{1}{4}$

$\frac{1}{4}$ ◯ $\frac{1}{2}$　　$\frac{1}{3}$ ◯ $\frac{1}{3}$

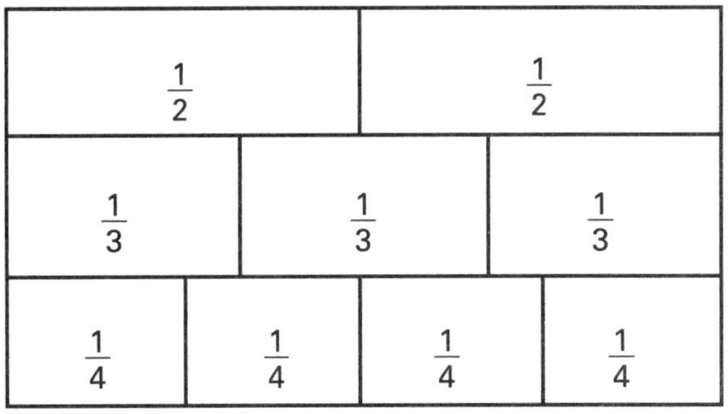

$\frac{1}{2}$	$\frac{1}{2}$		
$\frac{1}{3}$	$\frac{1}{3}$	$\frac{1}{3}$	
$\frac{1}{4}$	$\frac{1}{4}$	$\frac{1}{4}$	$\frac{1}{4}$

$\frac{1}{4}$ ◯ $\frac{1}{6}$　　$\frac{1}{6}$ ◯ $\frac{1}{8}$

$\frac{1}{6}$ ◯ $\frac{1}{4}$　　$\frac{1}{8}$ ◯ $\frac{1}{4}$

$\frac{1}{8}$ ◯ $\frac{1}{6}$　　$\frac{1}{4}$ ◯ $\frac{1}{8}$

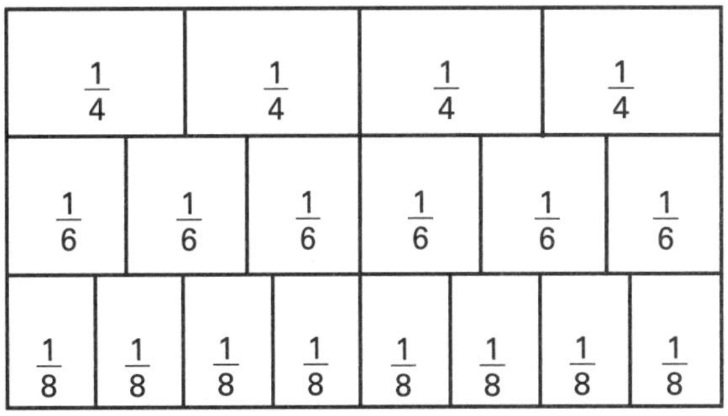

$\frac{1}{4}$	$\frac{1}{4}$	$\frac{1}{4}$	$\frac{1}{4}$				
$\frac{1}{6}$	$\frac{1}{6}$	$\frac{1}{6}$	$\frac{1}{6}$	$\frac{1}{6}$	$\frac{1}{6}$		
$\frac{1}{8}$	$\frac{1}{8}$	$\frac{1}{8}$	$\frac{1}{8}$	$\frac{1}{8}$	$\frac{1}{8}$	$\frac{1}{8}$	$\frac{1}{8}$

$\frac{1}{6}$ ◯ $\frac{1}{5}$　　$\frac{1}{5}$ ◯ $\frac{1}{5}$

$\frac{1}{5}$ ◯ $\frac{1}{3}$　　$\frac{1}{3}$ ◯ $\frac{1}{6}$

$\frac{1}{6}$ ◯ $\frac{1}{3}$　　$\frac{1}{3}$ ◯ $\frac{1}{5}$

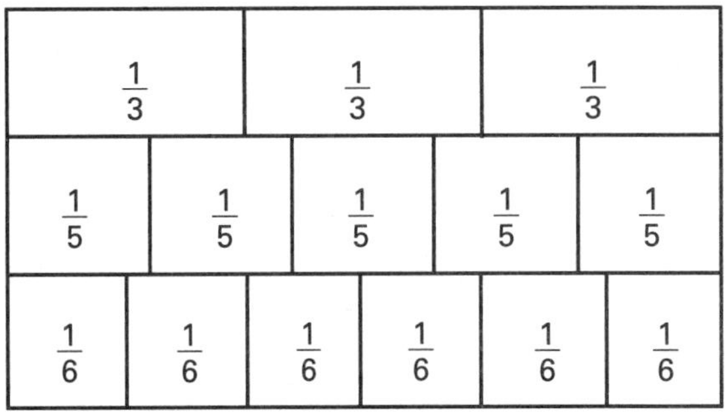

$\frac{1}{3}$	$\frac{1}{3}$	$\frac{1}{3}$			
$\frac{1}{5}$	$\frac{1}{5}$	$\frac{1}{5}$	$\frac{1}{5}$	$\frac{1}{5}$	
$\frac{1}{6}$	$\frac{1}{6}$	$\frac{1}{6}$	$\frac{1}{6}$	$\frac{1}{6}$	$\frac{1}{6}$

① Change each mixed number to an improper fraction.

a. $1\frac{1}{3}$

b. $2\frac{1}{2}$

c. $7\frac{1}{5}$

d. $4\frac{2}{3}$

e. $6\frac{1}{3}$

f. $1\frac{4}{5}$

g. $2\frac{1}{3}$

h. $7\frac{1}{2}$

i. $3\frac{2}{3}$

j. $3\frac{1}{8}$

k. $4\frac{4}{5}$

l. $1\frac{1}{6}$

m. $5\frac{2}{3}$

n. $2\frac{1}{5}$

o. $6\frac{1}{8}$

p. $5\frac{1}{3}$

q. $7\frac{2}{3}$

r. $6\frac{1}{2}$

s. $4\frac{3}{5}$

t. $3\frac{2}{5}$

② Change these improper fractions to whole numbers or mixed numbers. Show all work.

$\frac{14}{7}$ ____________________

$\frac{21}{5}$ ____________________

$\frac{50}{13}$ ____________________

$\frac{17}{2}$ ____________________

$\frac{11}{4}$ ____________________

$\frac{24}{6}$ ____________________

$\frac{17}{9}$ ____________________

$\frac{20}{4}$ ____________________

$\frac{9}{3}$ ____________________

$\frac{12}{3}$ ____________________

1. Add or subtract. Simplify.

a. $\frac{3}{8} + \frac{1}{8}$

b. $\frac{4}{10} + \frac{2}{10}$

c. $\frac{3}{9} + \frac{3}{9}$

d. $\frac{7}{21} + \frac{7}{21}$

e. $\frac{1}{6} + \frac{3}{6}$

f. $\frac{6}{12} + \frac{3}{12}$

g. $\frac{5}{14} + \frac{3}{14}$

h. $\frac{6}{16} + \frac{8}{16}$

i. $\frac{2}{15} + \frac{8}{15}$

j. $\frac{5}{20} + \frac{10}{20}$

2. Add these fractions. REMEMBER! Add just the numerators.

a. $\frac{1}{4} + \frac{2}{4}$

b. $\frac{9}{12} + \frac{2}{12}$

c. $\frac{3}{9} + \frac{1}{9}$

d. $\frac{5}{16} + \frac{2}{16}$

e. $\frac{4}{6} + \frac{1}{6}$

f. $\frac{11}{15} + \frac{2}{15}$

g. $\frac{5}{11} + \frac{3}{11}$

h. $\frac{6}{13} + \frac{4}{13}$

1. Subtract these fractions. REMEMBER! Subtract just the numerator.

a. $\frac{5}{6} - \frac{2}{6}$

b. $\frac{9}{12} - \frac{5}{12}$

c. $\frac{8}{16} - \frac{3}{16}$

d. $\frac{5}{11} - \frac{2}{11}$

e. $\frac{12}{15} - \frac{9}{15}$

f. $\frac{4}{5} - \frac{2}{5}$

g. $\frac{3}{9} - \frac{2}{9}$

h. $\frac{9}{18} - \frac{4}{18}$

2. Subtract like fractions; simplify answers.

a. $\frac{9}{12} - \frac{5}{12}$

b. $\frac{6}{7} - \frac{3}{7}$

c. $\frac{5}{4} - \frac{2}{4}$

d. $\frac{3}{8} - \frac{1}{8}$

e. $\frac{6}{12} - \frac{3}{12}$

f. $\frac{4}{10} - \frac{2}{10}$

Worksheet 67

① Solve. Reduce answers to lowest terms.

a. $\frac{2}{3} = \frac{\quad}{\quad}$

$+ \frac{1}{6} = \frac{\quad}{\quad}$

______ = ______

b. $\frac{5}{8} = \frac{\quad}{\quad}$

$+ \frac{3}{4} = \frac{\quad}{\quad}$

______ = ______

c. $\frac{4}{9} = \frac{\quad}{\quad}$

$+ \frac{2}{3} = \frac{\quad}{\quad}$

______ = ______

d. $\frac{3}{15} = \frac{\quad}{\quad}$

$+ \frac{2}{5} = \frac{\quad}{\quad}$

______ = ______

e. $\frac{3}{5} = \frac{\quad}{\quad}$

$+ \frac{1}{10} = \frac{\quad}{\quad}$

______ = ______

f. $\frac{4}{12} = \frac{\quad}{\quad}$

$+ \frac{3}{4} = \frac{\quad}{\quad}$

______ = ______

g. $\frac{1}{16} = \frac{\quad}{\quad}$

$+ \frac{1}{2} = \frac{\quad}{\quad}$

______ = ______

h. $\frac{2}{5} = \frac{\quad}{\quad}$

$+ \frac{3}{10} = \frac{\quad}{\quad}$

______ = ______

① Solve. Reduce answers to lowest terms.

a. $\frac{5}{7} = \frac{}{}$

$- \frac{2}{14} = \frac{}{}$

b. $\frac{7}{12} = \frac{}{}$

$- \frac{1}{3} = \frac{}{}$

c. $\frac{7}{8} = \frac{}{}$

$- \frac{3}{4} = \frac{}{}$

d. $\frac{11}{16} = \frac{}{}$

$- \frac{5}{8} = \frac{}{}$

e. $\frac{3}{4} = \frac{}{}$

$- \frac{5}{12} = \frac{}{}$

f. $\frac{9}{12} = \frac{}{}$

$- \frac{2}{6} = \frac{}{}$

g. $\frac{11}{24} = \frac{}{}$

$- \frac{1}{4} = \frac{}{}$

h. $\frac{2}{3} = \frac{}{}$

$- \frac{4}{9} = \frac{}{}$

① Add mixed numbers with like fractions. Simplify answers.

a. $4\frac{1}{3} + 7\frac{1}{3}$

b. $2\frac{1}{5} + 5\frac{3}{5}$

c. $6\frac{1}{2} + 4$

d. $3\frac{4}{15} + 7\frac{6}{15}$

e. $4\frac{4}{9} + 8\frac{2}{9}$

f. $13\frac{3}{6} + 3\frac{2}{6}$

g. $20\frac{5}{8} + 8\frac{2}{8}$

h. $13\frac{9}{20} + 9\frac{4}{20}$

i. $10\frac{1}{8} + 4\frac{6}{8}$

j. $3\frac{1}{3} + 1\frac{1}{3}$

k. $5\frac{3}{5} + 4\frac{1}{5}$

l. $2\frac{1}{6} + 1\frac{4}{6}$

1. Subtract mixed numbers with like fractions. Simplify answers. Borrow from the whole number if necessary.

a. $6\frac{4}{6} - 2\frac{2}{6}$

b. $12\frac{5}{8} - 8\frac{1}{8}$

c. $10\frac{8}{10} - 3\frac{3}{10}$

2. Subtract these mixed numbers. Simplify your answer. Show all work.

a. $7\frac{6}{15} - 3\frac{4}{15}$

b. $8\frac{4}{9} - 4\frac{2}{9}$

c. $13\frac{5}{6} - 3\frac{2}{6}$

d. $20\frac{10}{16} - 8\frac{8}{16}$

e. $13\frac{15}{20} - 9\frac{9}{20}$

f. $10\frac{7}{8} - 4\frac{5}{8}$

g. $3\frac{3}{6} - 1\frac{1}{6}$

h. $5\frac{6}{10} - 4\frac{4}{10}$

i. $2\frac{10}{12} - 1\frac{8}{12}$

Worksheet 71

1 Write each common fraction as a decimal.

$\frac{2}{10}$	=	______	$\frac{8}{10}$	=	______
$\frac{4}{100}$	=	______	$\frac{166}{1,000}$	=	______
$\frac{23}{100}$	=	______	$\frac{7}{100}$	=	______
$\frac{6}{10}$	=	______	$\frac{10}{100}$	=	______
$\frac{46}{1,000}$	=	______	$\frac{425}{1,000}$	=	______
$\frac{125}{1,000}$	=	______	$\frac{58}{1,000}$	=	______
$\frac{40}{100}$	=	______	$\frac{12}{100}$	=	______

2 Write each decimal as a common fraction.

.25	=	______	.625	=	______
.2	=	______	.15	=	______
.5	=	______	.32	=	______
.20	=	______	.200	=	______
.125	=	______	.075	=	______
.75	=	______	.99	=	______
.16	=	______	.50	=	______

1. Arrange each group of numbers from smallest to largest.

5.4, 15, 0.54, 1.5 ______________________

0.3, 3, 30, 0.03, 0.003 ______________________

0.45, 4.5, 450, 0.045, 45 ______________________

0.82, 0.7, 0.25 ______________________

0.13, 0.08, 0.46 ______________________

0.16, 0.9, 0.03 ______________________

0.64, 0.38, 0.57, 0.4 ______________________

0.6, 0.23, 0.11, 0.06 ______________________

32.7, 5.11, 0.25, 0.58 ______________________

0.21, 83.74, 61.97, 32.7 ______________________

14.07, 0.38, 2.43, 16.634 ______________________

25.632, 72.694, 32.609, 25.912 ______________________

① Write the correct answers.

2.68 + 34.2	4.56 + 7.6	3.75 + 46.26	46.23 + 9.63
136.20 + 72.96	43.7 + 21.5	64.75 + 25.33	4.73 + 16.30
26.72 + 3.56	40.32 + 7.64	7.35 + 132.68	68.47 + 75.20
26.00 + 38.6	75.32 − 46.20	89.7 − 37.3	84.6 − 28.4
4.67 − 1.04	843.2 − 675.0	46.35 − 19.43	20.72 − 12.06
36.45 − 18.26	16.42 − 8.36		

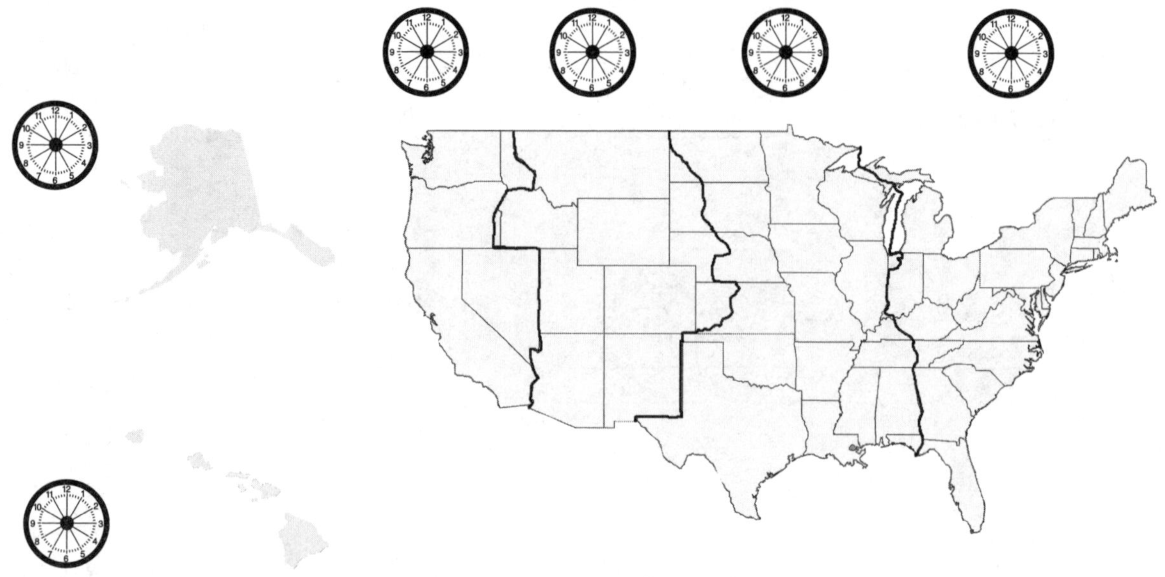

1. Complete the following chart.

HAWAII	ALASKA	PACIFIC	MOUNTAIN	CENTRAL	EASTERN
10:25 A.M.	______	______	______	______	______
______	______	4:35 P.M.	______	______	______
______	______	______	______	______	11:30 P.M.
______	1:00 A.M.	______	______	______	______
______	______	______	2:31 A.M.	______	______
______	______	______	______	1:10 P.M.	______
______	______	9:46 A.M.	______	______	______
6:45 P.M.	______	______	______	______	______
______	______	______	______	12:50 A.M.	______

① Estimate the totals.

\$34.20 + \$ 20.38	\$ 4.56 + \$ 7.60	\$ 3.75 + \$ 9.30
\$ 46.23 + \$ 72.40	\$ 136.20 + \$ 240.32	\$ 43.70 + \$ 21.50
\$ 3.62 + \$ 5.87	\$ 4.75 + \$ 5.33	\$ 4.73 + \$ 6.30
\$ 6.72 + \$ 3.56	\$ 7.64 + \$ 8.56	\$ 103.96 + \$ 212.34
\$ 7.35 + \$ 28.50	\$ 68.47 + \$ 75.20	\$ 26.00 + \$ 38.60

____

① Answer these questions.

How many feet are in one yard? _______________

How many inches are in a yard? _______________

Which is longer, a yard or a meter? _______________

How many feet are in a mile? _______________

How many inches are in 2 yards, 3 feet? _______________

② Work these following problems.

4 feet = ________ inches.

4 feet, 8 inches = ________ inches.

2 yards, 1 foot, 6 inches = ________.

8,169 feet = ________ miles ________ feet.

45 inches = ________ feet, ________ inches.

$\frac{1}{2}$ of a foot = ________ inches.

2 miles, 24 feet = ________ feet.

③ Answer these questions.

What is the English unit of measure for weight? _______________

What is the English unit of measure for length? _______________

What is the English unit of measure for liquid volume? _______________

(1) Write the English units of measure for the following.

length ____ ____ ____ ____

weight ____ ____ ____

liquid volume ____ ____ ____ ____

(2) Write the metric units of measure for the following.

length ____ ____ ____

weight ____ ____

liquid volume ____ ____

(3) Convert these measurements.

16 ounces = ____ pound(s)

____ pounds = 1 ton

2 tons, 1,235 pounds = ____ pounds

65 ounces = ____ pounds ____ ounce(s)

31,492 pounds = ____ tons ____ pounds

8 ounces = ____ pound(s)

1.75 tons = ____ pounds

1. Write the English units of measure for the following.

length ________ ________ ________ ________

liquid volume ________ ________ ________ ________ ________

weight ________ ________ ________

2. Write the metric units of measure for the following.

length ________ ________ ________

liquid volume ________ ________

weight ________ ________

3. Write English or metric.

tons	________	pounds	________	cups	________
grams	________	inches	________	milliliters	________
gallons	________	liters	________	yards	________
feet	________	kilograms	________	pints	________
quarts	________	meters	________	centimeters	________
ounces	________	miles	________		

4. Convert these measurements.

1,000 millimeters = ________ meters

876 centimeters = ________ meters

1 kilometer = ________ meters

2 meters = ________ millimeters

100 centimeters = ________ meters

2 meters = ________ centimeters

2,500 millimeters = ________ meters

2 meters = ________ kilometers

4.8 kilometers = ________ meters

1 Write the unit of measure (English or metric).

pounds	__________	quarts	__________	feet	__________
inches	__________	liters	__________	gallons	__________
grams	__________	tons	__________	kilograms	__________
cups	__________	yards	__________	milliliters	__________
meters	__________	pints	__________	centimeters	__________
ounces	__________	miles	__________	kiloliters	__________

2 Convert these measurements.

1,000 ml =	__________ L	625 L =	__________ ml
1 ml =	__________ L	2.8 L =	__________ ml
43 ml =	__________ L	.5 L =	__________ ml
1,000 grams =	__________ Kg	48 grams =	__________ milligrams
1 milligram =	__________ grams	16 centimeters =	__________ meters
6.75 Kg =	__________ grams	243 decigrams =	__________ Kg

① Complete the sentences using the graph.

Ashley read some books one summer about four different subjects.

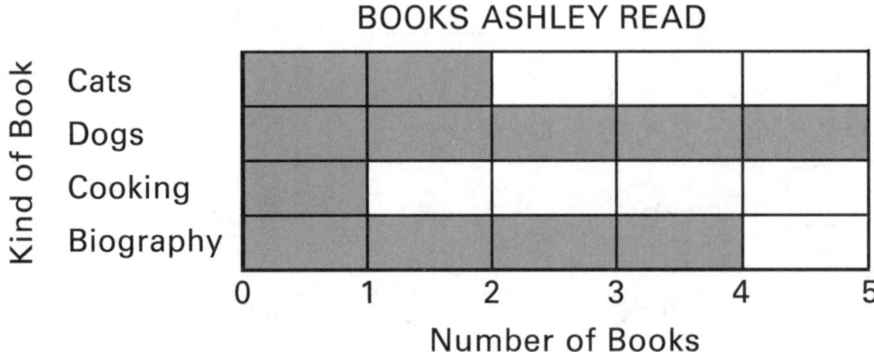

During the summer, Ashley read the most number of books about the subject of

__________________.

Ashley read exactly one-half as many books about cats as she read about

__________________.

The total number of books that Ashley read in the summer was __________________.

② Complete the sentences using the graph.

Lindsey made a graph that showed her summer activities.

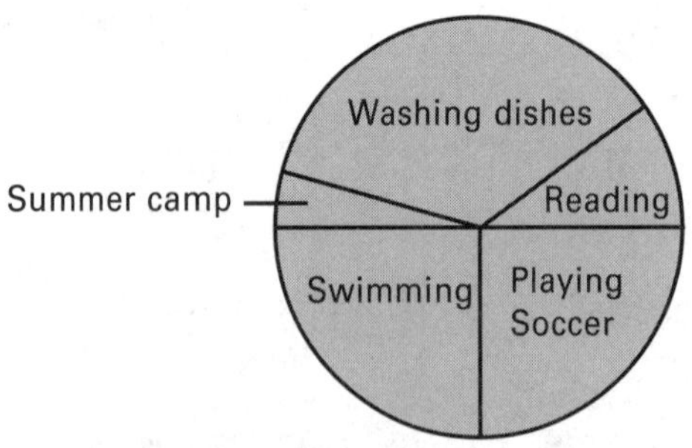

Lindsey spent most of her summertime __________________.

Lindsey spent the same amount of time __________________ and __________________.

Lindsey spent the least amount of time at __________________.

③ Answer the questions using the graph.

AGES OF CHILDREN ATTENDING SUMMER CAMP

10 years old
11 years old
12 years old
13 years old
14 years old
15 years old
16 years old

Each stands for 10 children

How many children were 13 years old? ______________

Which age group had the most number of children? ______________

What was the total number of children attending summer camp? ______________

What is this kind of graph called? ______________

Which age groups had twenty children? ______________ and ______________

How many children were in the youngest three age groups? ______________

④ Study the graph. Answer *true* or *false*.

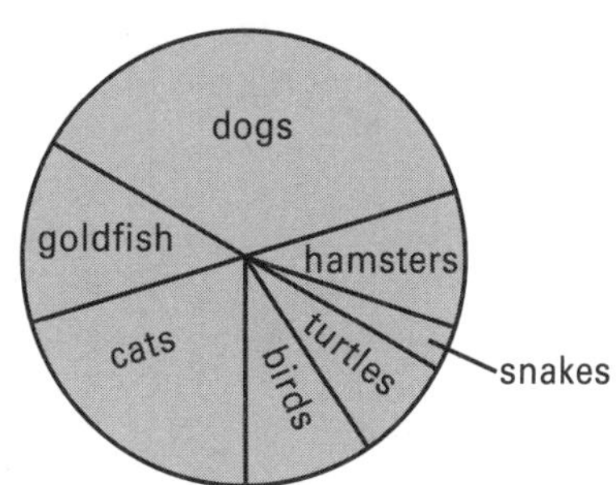

__________ More people have hamsters than dogs for pets.

__________ The number of bird pets is not as great as the number of cat pets.

__________ The goldfish outnumber the turtles.

__________ The number of snakes is small.

(5) Study the graph. Answer the questions.

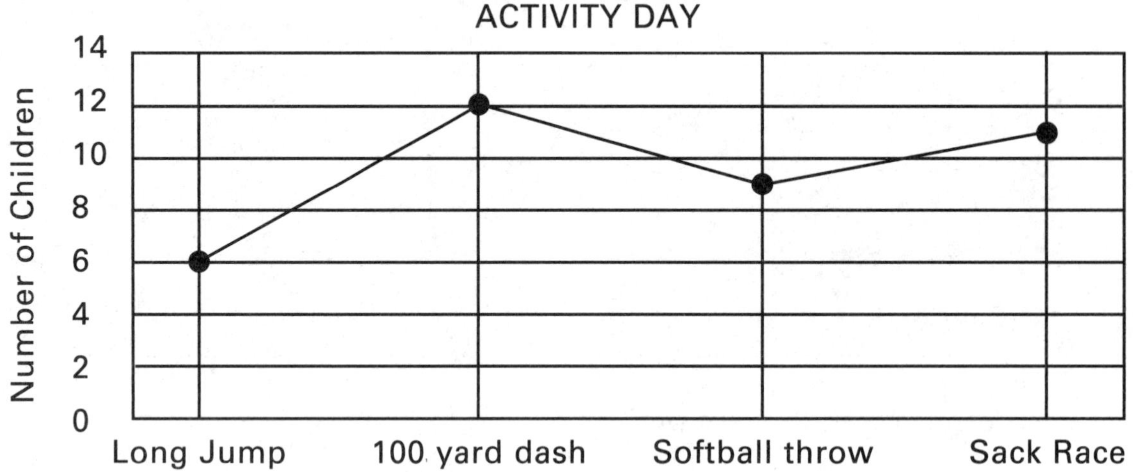

How many children took part in the sack race? ________________.

In which activity did the most children take part? ________________.

How many more children took part in the 100 yard dash than in the long jump?

________________.

What was the total number of children who took part in field day?

________________.

Horizons Mathematics 4

Worksheet Answer Key

Worksheet 1

17, 6, 10, 14, 12, 12, 12, 9, 8

7, 8, 4, 13, 9, 6, 8, 13, 11

10, 16, 15, 9, 10, 10, 9, 15, 18

16, 5, 11, 14, 7, 11, 13, 11, 14

9, 8, 7, 6, 8, 2, 5, 5, 4

3, 3, 8, 1, 10, 9, 10, 7, 10

2, 9, 4, 8, 4, 6, 11, 11, 7

6, 12, 13, 13, 9, 15, 8, 13, 14

10, 12, 6, 11, 15, 18, 14, 11, 12

5, 12, 9, 10, 16, 16, 7, 14, 17

Worksheet 2

4, 1, 3, 1, 3, 5, 6, 2, 4

4, 5, 0, 4, 2, 0, 6, 5, 2

3, 6, 2, 6, 7, 1, 0, 8, 9

4, 5, 1, 0, 8, 3, 9, 7, 6

1, 3, 4, 0, 2, 5, 1, 2, 7

3, 3, 5, 6, 6, 4, 0, 7, 9

5, 5, 0, 5, 7, 7, 8, 8, 8

1, 6, 4, 2, 1, 2, 3, 1, 3

1, 2, 2, 3, 0, 5, 9, 1, 3

4, 4, 0, 6, 8, 9, 7, 7, 6

Worksheet 3

1. 1, 3, 5, 7, 9, 11, 13, 15, 17, 19
2. 1,942, 72, 34,
3. 227, 123, 699
4. even, odd, even, odd, even, odd, even, even,
   odd, odd, odd, odd, odd, odd, odd, even
5. odd, even, odd, even, odd, odd, even, odd,
   odd, even, even, even, even, odd, even, even
6. Teacher check
7. Teacher check

Worksheet 4

1. 4 quarts, 2 pints, 2 cups, 8 ounces,
2. 4 quarts, 2 cups, 2 pints, 8 ounces
3. 4 qt, 2 pt, 2 c, 8 oz,
   1 gal, 1 qt, 1 pt, 1 c,
   8 qt, 6 pt, 8 cups , 40 oz.

Worksheet 5

Problem 1: Teacher check

Problem 2: 357,200; 23, 788; 65,350, 825; 3,000,296; 9,286

Worksheet 6

Problem 1: 51, 40, 61

9, 5, 4

70, 12, 47

36, 37, 97

Problem 2: XLIII, III, XX

LXXI, XXXIV, LVII

XCVIII, LXXX, LXXV

XXXIX, XVII, LIII

Problem 3: LXXII, XLIX

XVI, LXXXIII

LVIII, XX

XLII, IX

Problem 4: 63, 28

50, 71

34, 1

76, 45

Worksheet 7

3,000 + 600 + 90 + 2

3,000 + 700 + 20 + 2

1,000 + 0 + 30 + 4

Worksheet 7 cont.

1. 9,000 + 900 + 90 + 0

   8,000 + 0 + 0 + 1

   4,000 + 700 + 0 + 7

2. 60,000 + 3,000 + 0 + 40 + 0

   50,000 + 0 + 400 + 0 + 0

   20,000 + 1,000 + 200 + 70 + 4

   80,000 + 3,000 + 300 + 60 + 3

3. 400,000 + 20,000 + 3,000 + 600 + 70 + 0

   200,000 + 0 + 5,000 + 300 + 30 + 7

   400,000 + 80,000 + 0 + 600 + 40 + 3

   200,000 + 60,000 + 5,000 + 500 + 50 + 4

Worksheet 8

30, 50, 20, 20, 40, 30, 60, 90, 70, 30, 100, 60, 50,

30, 40, 80, 60, 50, 80, 40, 80, 20, 30, 50, 40, 20,

70, 20, 50, 50, 40, 70, 80, 50, 60, 20, 90, 10, 60

Worksheet 9

50, 30, 50, 60, 70, 30, 80, 90

400, 400, 1,000, 200, 700, 300, 500, 100

2,000, 2,000, 5,000, 8,000, 7,000, 10,000, 3,000, 1,000, 4,000, 9,000

6,000, 6,000, 5,000, 2,000, 4,000, 8,000, 5,000, 9,000 7,000, 8,000, 9,000

Worksheet 10

88, 77, 59, 69

51, 73, 82, 75

41, 86, 93, 70

127, 106, 118, 186

47, 87, 70, 71

97, 92, 158, 136

Worksheet 11

866, 885, 998, 685

739, 618, 809, 567

831, 842, 728, 912

659, 859, 738, 815

452, 464, 638, 866

Worksheet 12

9, 8, 6, 8

99, 98, 89, 98

12, 11, 15, 16

96, 94, 55, 95

92, 92, 72, 81

71, 74, 82, 81

Worksheet 13

6,994; 4,844; 5,302

10,250; 9,049; 9,392

6,211; 5,165; 2,848

10,024; 9,671; 9,577

11,096;17,822; 7,315

8,043; 4,038; 7,749

18,052; 11,581; 6,835

9,055; 6,075; 9,380

Worksheet 14

$n = 2$, $n = 3$, $n = 8$, $n = 3$

$n = 3$, $n = 4$, $n = 6$, $n = 5$

$n = 6$, $n = 8$, $n = 7$, $n = 9$

$n = 8$, $n = 6$, $n = 9$, $n = 7$

$n = 9$, $n = 8$, $n = 8$, $n = 2$

$n = 5$, $n = 6$, $n = 7$, $n = 8$

Worksheet 15

56, 79, 60, 63, 42

36, 18, 62, 43, 21

74, 15, 25, 64, 42

80, 44, 75, 17, 50

33, 82, 46, 19, 72

34, 38, 19, 58, 32

56, 55, 42, 39, 45

32, 46, 47, 49, 28

39, 24, 32, 29, 46

Worksheet 16

415, 325, 342, 263, 460

543, 772, 771, 256, 230

421, 134, 536, 860, 342

446, 252, 217, 417, 379

694, 344, 273, 266, 483

468, 362, 273, 223, 387

283, 465, 797, 583, 224

152, 272, 286, 346, 758

534, 464, 345, 250, 491

Worksheet 17

128, 9, 236, 468, 82, 289, 69, 129

455, 333, 177, 174, 567, 48, 338, 27

17, 219, 344, 257, 206, 178, 389, 537

513, 27, 605, 857, 468, 155, 57, 349

265, 485, 428, 216, 337, 489, 645, 208

126, 504, 246, 777, 48, 178, 339, 17

Worksheet 18

1. 20, 10, 90, 60, 20
   90, 40, 50, 100, 50
2. 500, 600, 200, 300, 600, 600, 800, 400
   600, 800, 500, 1,000, 200, 700, 900, 400
3. 2,000, 6,000, 2,000, 8,000, 4,000, 4,000, 9,000, 7,000
   1,000, 4,000, 8,000, 9,000, 4,000, 2,000, 10,000, 8,000

Worksheet 19

4286, 7810, 5681, 2178

2473, 3166, 3194, 5292

2586, 1772, 4631, 2625

2951, 1769, 4177, 3777

2586, 2769, 2789, 688

Worksheet 20

$n = 8$, $n = 12$, $n = 12$, $n = 15$

$n = 1$, $n = 11$, $n = 10$, $n = 21$

$n = 17$, $n = 11$, $n = 23$, $n = 13$

$n = 24$, $n = 12$, $n = 7$, $n = 13$

Worksheet 21

74, 64, 158, 64, 210, 296, 365, 85 ft, 518 mi, 56 m, 35 in, 468 cm

Worksheet 22

45, 60, 27, 18, 27, 8, 16, 9, 4

3, 30, 0, 40, 6, 0, 12, 5, 0

72, 54, 8, 24, 72, 90, 8, 32, 16

20, 12, 56, 50, 15, 42, 21, 6, 24,

0, 2, 20, 48, 28, 18, 48, 9, 24

14, 35, 30, 0, 20, 36, 8, 28, 40,

4, 25, 81, 30, 2, 64, 54, 9, 21,

24, 40, 28, 0, 60, 63, 24, 0, 36

7, 12, 56, 1, 48, 21, 0, 30, 45

Worksheet 23

Chart is for reference only.

Horizons Math 4, Worksheet Key

Worksheet 24

2 = 2 • 1; 3 = 3 • 1; 4 = 2 • 2; 5 = 5 • 1; 6 = 3 • 2;

7 = 7 • 1; 8 = 2 • 2 • 2; 9 = 3 • 3; 10 = 5 • 2; 11 = 11 • 1;

12 = 3 • 2 • 2; 13 = 13 • 1; 14 = 7 • 2; 15 = 5 • 3;

16 = 2 • 2 • 2 • 2; 17 = 17 • 1; 18 = 2 • 3 • 3; 19 = 19 • 1

20 = 2 • 2 • 5; 21 = 3 • 7; 22 = 2 • 11; 23 = 23 • 1;

24 = 2 • 2 • 2 • 3; 25 = 5 • 5

Worksheet 25

1. Teacher check
2. prime, prime, composite, composite
   composite, prime, composite, prime
   prime, composite, prime, composite

Worksheet 26

4, 9, 3, 7, 4, 7, 5, 6

63, 63, 7, 9; 30, 30, 5, 6;

32, 32, 4, 8; 42, 42, 7, 6;

40, 40, 8, 5; 15, 15, 3, 5

Worksheet 27

684; 4,134; 512; 3,710

6,286; 1,986; 3,661; 3,750

872; 2,872; 8,388; 3,416

5,432; 4,675; 5,740; 1,944

3,150; 1,134; 3,128; 1,872

872; 926; 1,116; 3,090

Worksheet 28

620, 580, 740, 230, 160, 920, 880, 740, 510, 100,

3,200, 8,500, 1,600, 1,200, 5,500, 6,300, 4,700, 1,000, 9,000, 45,800

15,000; 33,000; 51,000; 60,000; 24,000; 92,000; 114,000;
725,000; 400,000; 812,000;

4,700; 150; 3,100; 43,000; 620; 550; 88,000; 1,600; 700; 81,000

Worksheet 29

10,176; 3,658; 3,072; 17,782

25,864; 3,968; 7,992; 14,490

3,978; 17,184; 6,552; 4,785

17,759; 4,592; 3,864; 17,484

29,268; 3,224; 13,674; 11,752

2,750; 30,688

Worksheet 30

$n = 3$, $n = 4$, $n = 12$, $n = 3$, $n = 2$, $n = 4$, $n = 8$, $n = 5$, $n = 9$, $n = 3$

$n = 3$, $n = 2$, $n = 1$, $n = 20$, $n = 2$, $n = 3$, $n = 3$, $n = 2$, $n = 12$, $n = 3$

Worksheet 31

$7.36, $6.51, $5.97,$4.91, 2.92, 1¢, 2.48 or 3 days, $3.31

Worksheet 32

56, 24, 4, 24, 40, 0, 48, 15, 1, 27

5, 0, 36, 72, 18, 21, 9, 0, 63, 6

35, 6, 20, 0, 12, 42, 20, 24, 27, 36

0, 16, 28, 4, 36, 45, 0, 9, 32, 64

8, 32, 8, 40, 14, 81, 16, 2, 0, 21

0, 30, 45, 0, 35, 72, 10, 7, 28, 24

54, 12, 3, 48, 18, 49, 54, 0, 25, 42

Worksheet 33

3 r 1, 5 r 5, 5 r 1, 2 r 3, 4 r 1, 4 r 3

5 r 4, 3 r 1, 3 r 3, 5 r 2, 7 r 1, 5 r 4

4 r 1, 9 r 1, 4 r 2, 2 r 2, 4 r 2, 7 r 1

3 r 3, 6 r 1, 2 r 2, 6 r 1, 5 r 3, 7 r 6

6 r 3, 4 r 6, 2 r 7, 8 r 3, 8 r 1, 7 r 2

Worksheet 34

71, 62, 43, 52, 121

32, 112, 62, 31, 41

48, 36, 30, 45, 24

29, 64, 76, 91, 85

41, 53, 25, 74, 81

93, 75, 23, 41, 43

34, 75, 215, 91, 360

24, 225, 117, 22, 31

25, 53, 75, 29, 53

83, 33, 92, 130, 83

Worksheet 35

$1.62, $1.79, $0.51, $1.15

$2.32, $1.89, $2.21, $4.75

$1.22, $0.84, $1.33, $1.44

$1.23, $1.53, $2.32, $2.25

$2.25, $6.39, $3.44, $1.75

Worksheet 36

201 r 3, 300 r 2, 1070 r 7

910 r 4, 1090 r 8, 640, r 1

360 r 3, 781 r 2, 270 r 3

811 r 1, 721 r 3, 1751 r 2

Worksheet 37

1. Teacher check

2. by 2: Any number whose ones' place digit is an even number (0, 2, 4, 6, 8).
   by 3: Any number whose digits add up to 3,6, 9, or 12.
   by 5: Any number whose ones' place digit is 0 or 5.
   by 10: Any number whose ones' place digit is 0.

Worksheet 38

$n = 18$, $n = 42$, $n = 18$, $n = 6$, $n = 20$, $n = 36$, $n = 18$, $n = 12$, $n = 12$, $n = 12$, $n = 16$, $n = 45$

$n = 6$, $n = 10$, $n = 27$, $n = 14$, $n = 32$, $n = 10$, $n = 21$, $n = 36$, $n = 8$, $n = 21$, $n = 28$, $n = 24$

Worksheet 39

21, 18, 14, 22

23, 25, 18, 21

16, 5, 16, 12

19, 16, 27, 9

4, 4, 8, 2

53, 57, 146, 81

107, 20, 127, 71

Worksheet 40

7 r 10, 8 r 80, 4 r 34

7 r 35, 6 r 50, 8 r 18

4 r 28, 6 r 14, 8 r 0

8 r 29, 7 r 50, 6 r 43

9 r 7, 9 r 12, 11 r 0

2 r 50, 8 r 3, 8 r 41

9 r 51, 8 r 12, 4 r 25

Worksheet 41

1. 1¢, 3- $1, = $3.01
   Check: $10.00 – $6.99 = $3.01;

   2¢, 5¢, 10¢, 25¢, 1– $5.00 , 1 – $10.00 = $15.42
   Check: $20.00 – $4.58 = $15.42;

   4¢, 10¢ = 14¢
   Check: $1.00 – 86¢ = 14¢;

   1¢, 2 – 10¢, 25¢, 3 – $1.00, 1 – $10.00 = $13.46,
   Check: $20.00 – $6.54 = $13.46;

Worksheet 41 cont.

2. 25¢, 1 – $1.00 = $1.25; 1¢, 10¢, 1 – $1.00, 1 – $5.00, 1 – $20.00 = $26.11; 1¢, 2 – 10¢, 3 – $1.00, 1 – $50.00 = $53.21; 02¢, 2 – 10¢, 2 – 25¢, 3 – $1.00, 1 – $5.00 = $8.72; 02¢, 05¢, 2 – 25¢, 2 – $1.00, 1 – $10.00 = $12.57; 02¢, 5¢, 10¢ = 17¢; 5¢, 10¢ = 15¢

Worksheet 42

185 r 11, 22 r 4, 11 r 0, 13 r 19

168 r 6, 15 r 54, 12 r 9, 111 r 75

32 r 0, 147 r 36, 13 r 20, 23 r 25

28 r 23, 22 r 26, 22 r 15, 27 r 4, 179 r 8, 219 r 2

Worksheet 43

$1.05, $8.30, $9.90, $0.92

$2.90, $1.42, $9.33, $13.16

$11.42, $7.93, $21.43, $14.63

$31.70, $8.24, $9.79

Worksheet 44

6, 9, 12, 9

Worksheet 45

7:53, 12:42, 4:44, 2:01, 5:55

1:45, 11:37, 8:16, 5:24, 1:56

2:33, 10:37, 7:19, 9:58, 8:11

11:02, 10:21, 3:40, 4:08, 6:29

Worksheet 46

1. 60, 24, 60, 60

2. 120, 5, 72, 30, 1, 1, 720, 5, 12, 7200, 50, 480, 4, 48

Worksheet 47

1. PM, AM, PM, PM

2. 9:15, 5:35, 165, 6:30, 5:45, 170

Worksheet 48

green, blue, yellow, red, orange; north; Nancy, Mary, Steve, Alan; 7th, 11th, 15th

Worksheet 49

66 in; 6 cups; 75¢; 3; 2 days; 5 qts and 1 pt or 1 gal,

1 qt, 1 pt

Worksheet 50

see chart for reference

Worksheet 51

Teacher check

Worksheet 52

Teacher check

Worksheet 53

a, b, a, c, c

Worksheet 54

20″, 20″, 42″, 12′

20″, 20″, 48 cm, 40″

35″, 21″, 24″, 26″

120 ft, 76 in, 128 yd

28 cm, 150″, 47 ft

Worksheet 55

Centimeter graph paper

Worksheet 56

V = L x W x H
V = 3 x 2 x 3
V = 18 in^3

V = L x W x H
V = 2 x 2 x 4
V = 16 cm^3

V = L x W x H
V = 5 x 2 x 3
V = 30 ft^3

V = L x W x H
V = 4 x 4 x 2
V = 32 in^3

V = L x W x H
V= 4 x 2 x 8
V = 64cm^3

Worksheet 56 cont.

V = L x W x H
V = 5 x 4 x 2
V = 40 in^3

V = L x W x H
V = 4 x 4 x 4
V = 64 in^3

V = L x W x H
V = 2 x 2 x 10
V = 40 yd^3

V = L x W x H
V = 3 x 3 x 5
V = 45 cm^3

V = L x W x H
V = 2 x 2 x 2
V = 8 cm^3

V = L x W x H
V = 2 x 10 x 3
V = 60 in^3

V = L x W x H
V = 8 x 5 x 6
V = 240 ft^3

Worksheet 57

Fraction strip chart

Worksheet 58

1. $\frac{3}{4}$—three-fourths, $\frac{7}{8}$—seven-eighths,

   $\frac{1}{2}$—one-half, $\frac{3}{5}$—three-fifths, $\frac{2}{3}$—two-thirds,

   $\frac{4}{5}$—four-fifths, $\frac{1}{3}$—one-half, $\frac{4}{6}$—four-sixths

   $\frac{5}{6}$—five-sixths, $\frac{6}{7}$—six-sevenths,

   $\frac{2}{4}$—two-fourths, $\frac{5}{8}$—five-eighths

2. $\frac{1}{4}$—one-fourth, $\frac{3}{7}$—three-sevenths,

   $\frac{3}{6}$—three-sixths, $\frac{4}{7}$—four-sevenths

   $\frac{2}{5}$—two-fifths, $\frac{6}{8}$—six-eighths, $\frac{2}{9}$—two-ninths

   $\frac{3}{8}$—three-eighths, $\frac{2}{6}$—two-sixths,

   $\frac{5}{9}$—five-ninths, $\frac{7}{12}$—seven-twelfths,

   $\frac{3}{11}$—three-elevenths

3. four-fourths, one-sixth,
   one-fifth, two-sevenths
   five-sevenths, two-eighths
   three-elevenths, four-thirteenths
   eight-fourteenths, eight-fifteenths
   five-ninths, seven-tenths

Worksheet 59

$\frac{2}{4}, \frac{3}{5}, \frac{1}{4}, \frac{0}{7}$

Worksheet 60

$=, =, \neq, \neq$
$\neq, \neq, =, \neq$
$\neq, \neq, \neq, \neq$
$\neq, =, \neq, =$

Worksheet 61

1. multiples of 4: 4, 8, 12, 16, 20, 24

   multiples of 7: 7, 14, 21

   multiples of 9: 9, 18

   multiples of 3: 3, 6, 9, 12, 15, 18, 21, 24

   multiples of 5: 5, 10, 15, 20

   multiples of 6: 6, 12, 18, 24

   multiples of 2: 2, 4, 6, 8, 10, 12, 14, 16, 18, 20, 22, 24

2. divisors of 62: 2
   divisors of 93: 3
   divisors of 95: 5
   divisors of 50: 2, 5, 10
   divisors of 10: 2, 5, 10

Horizons Math 4, Worksheet Key

Worksheet 62

1. $\frac{2}{3}, \frac{5}{9}, \frac{2}{9}, \frac{6}{13}, \frac{2}{7}$

2. $\frac{1}{3}, \frac{1}{4}, \frac{1}{2}, \frac{3}{4}, \frac{1}{2}, \frac{3}{5}$

3. $\frac{1}{5}, \frac{2}{3}, \frac{1}{6}, \frac{1}{3}, \frac{1}{9}, \frac{1}{4}, \frac{1}{2}, \frac{5}{6}, \frac{1}{2}, \frac{4}{5}$

Worksheet 63

1. $>, <, >, >, <, =, >, >, <, <, <, >, <, =, <, >, <, >$

Worksheet 64

1. a. $\frac{4}{3}$ b. $\frac{5}{2}$ c. $\frac{36}{5}$ d. $\frac{14}{3}$ e. $\frac{19}{3}$ f. $\frac{9}{5}$ g. $\frac{7}{3}$

   h. $\frac{15}{2}$ i. $\frac{11}{3}$ j. $\frac{25}{8}$ k. $\frac{24}{5}$ l. $\frac{7}{6}$ m. $\frac{17}{3}$ n. $\frac{11}{5}$

   o. $\frac{49}{8}$ p. $\frac{16}{3}$ q. $\frac{23}{3}$ r. $\frac{13}{2}$ s. $\frac{23}{5}$ t. $\frac{17}{5}$

2. 2; $4\frac{1}{5}$; $3\frac{11}{13}$; $8\frac{1}{2}$; $2\frac{3}{4}$; 4; $1\frac{8}{9}$; 5; 3; 4

Worksheet 65

1. a. $\frac{4}{8} = \frac{1}{2}$ b. $\frac{6}{10} = \frac{3}{5}$ c. $\frac{6}{9} = \frac{2}{3}$ d. $\frac{14}{21} = \frac{2}{3}$;

   e. $\frac{4}{6} = \frac{2}{3}$ f. $\frac{9}{12} = \frac{3}{4}$ g. $\frac{8}{14} = \frac{4}{7}$ h. $\frac{14}{16} = \frac{7}{8}$;

   i. $\frac{10}{15} = \frac{2}{3}$ j. $\frac{15}{20} = \frac{3}{4}$

2. a. $\frac{3}{4}$ b. $\frac{11}{12}$ c. $\frac{4}{9}$ d. $\frac{7}{16}$ e. $\frac{5}{6}$ f. $\frac{13}{15}$ g. $\frac{8}{11}$ h. $\frac{10}{13}$

Worksheet 66

1. a. $\frac{3}{6} = \frac{1}{2}$ b. $\frac{4}{12} = \frac{1}{3}$ c. $\frac{5}{16}$ d. $\frac{3}{11}$ e. $\frac{3}{15} = \frac{1}{5}$

   f. $\frac{2}{5}$ g. $\frac{1}{9}$ h. $\frac{5}{18}$

2. a. $\frac{4}{12} = \frac{1}{3}$ b. $\frac{3}{7}$ c. $\frac{3}{4}$ d. $\frac{2}{8} = \frac{1}{4}$ e. $\frac{3}{12} = \frac{1}{4}$

   f. $\frac{2}{10} = \frac{1}{5}$

Worksheet 67

1. a. $\frac{5}{6}$ b. $\frac{11}{8} = 1\frac{3}{8}$ c. $\frac{10}{9} = 1\frac{1}{9}$ d. $\frac{9}{15} = \frac{3}{5}$ e. $\frac{7}{10}$

   f. $\frac{13}{12} = 1\frac{1}{12}$ g. $\frac{9}{16}$ h. $\frac{7}{10}$

Worksheet 68

1. a. $\frac{8}{14} = \frac{4}{7}$ b. $\frac{3}{12} = \frac{1}{4}$ c. $\frac{1}{8}$ d. $\frac{1}{16}$ e. $\frac{4}{12} = \frac{1}{3}$

   f. $\frac{5}{12}$ g. $\frac{5}{24}$ h. $\frac{2}{9}$

Worksheet 69

1. a. $11\frac{2}{3}$ b. $7\frac{4}{5}$ c. $10\frac{1}{2}$ d. $10\frac{10}{15} = 10\frac{2}{3}$

   e. $12\frac{6}{9} = 12\frac{2}{3}$ f. $16\frac{5}{6}$ g. $28\frac{7}{8}$ h. $22\frac{13}{20}$

   i. $14\frac{7}{8}$ j. $4\frac{2}{3}$ k. $9\frac{4}{5}$ l. $3\frac{5}{6}$

Worksheet 70

1. a. $4\frac{2}{6} = 4\frac{1}{3}$ b. $4\frac{4}{8} = 4\frac{1}{2}$ c. $7\frac{5}{10} = 7\frac{1}{2}$

2. a. $4\frac{2}{15}$ b. $4\frac{2}{9}$ c. $10\frac{3}{6} = 10\frac{1}{2}$ d. $12\frac{2}{16} = 12\frac{1}{8}$

   e. $4\frac{6}{20} = 4\frac{3}{10}$ f. $6\frac{2}{8} = 6\frac{1}{4}$ g. $2\frac{2}{6} = 2\frac{1}{3}$

   h. $1\frac{2}{10} = 1\frac{1}{5}$ i. $1\frac{2}{12} = 1\frac{1}{6}$

Worksheet 71

1. 0.2, 0.8, 0.04, 0.166, 0.23, 0.07, 0.6, 0.10, 0.046, 0.425, 0.125, 0.058, 0.40, 0.12

2. $\frac{25}{100}$, $\frac{625}{1,000}$, $\frac{2}{10}$, $\frac{15}{100}$, $\frac{5}{10}$, $\frac{32}{100}$, $\frac{20}{100}$, $\frac{2}{1,000}$,

$\frac{125}{1,000}$, $\frac{75}{1,000}$, $\frac{75}{100}$, $\frac{99}{100}$, $\frac{16}{100}$, $\frac{50}{100}$

Worksheet 72

0.54, 1.5, 5.4, 15
0.003, 0.03, 0.3, 3, 30
0.045, 0.45, 4.5, 45, 450
0.25, 0.7, 0.82
0.08, 0.13, 0.46
0.03, 0.16, 0.9
0.38, 0.4, 0.57, 0.64
0.06, 0.11, 0.23, 0.6
0.25, 0.58, 5.11, 32.7
0.21, 32.7, 61.97, 83.74
0.38, 2.43, 14.07, 16.634
25.632, 25.912, 32.609, 72.694

Worksheet 73

36.88, 12.16, 50.01, 55.86
209.16, 65.2, 90.08, 21.03
30.28, 88.28, 140.03, 143,67
64.6, 29.12, 52.4, 56.2
3.63, 168.2, 26.92, 8.66, 18.19, 8.06

Worksheet 74

11:25 am, 12:25 pm, 1:25 pm, 2:25 pm, 3:25 pm;
2:35 pm, 3:35 pm, 5:35 pm, 6:35 pm, 7:35 pm;
6:30 pm, 7:30 pm, 8:30 pm, 9:30 pm, 10:30 pm;
12:00 am, 2:00 am, 3:00 am, 4:00 am, 5:00 am;
11:31 pm, 12:31 am, 1:31 am, 3:31 am, 4:31 am;
9:10 am, 10:10 am, 11:10 am, 12:10 pm, 2:10 pm;
7:46 am, 8:46 am, 10:46 am, 11:46 am, 12:46 pm;
7:45 pm, 8:45 pm, 9:45 pm, 10:45 pm, 11:45 pm;
8:50 pm, 9:50 pm, 10:50 pm, 11:50 pm, 1:50 am

Worksheet 75

$54.58; $30.00 + $20.00 = $50.00
$12.16; $5.00 + $8.00 = $13.00
$13.05; $4.00 + $9.00 = $13.00
$118.00; $50.00 + $70.00 = $120.00
$376.52; $140.00 + $240.00 = $380.00
$65.20; $40.00 + $20.00 = $60.00
$9.49; $4.00 + $6.00 = $10.00
$10.08; $5.00 + $5.00 = $10.00
$11.03; $5.00 + $6.00 = $11.00
$10.28; $7.00 + $4.00 = $11.00
$16.20; $8.00 + $9.00 = $17.00
$35.85; $7.00 + $30.00 = $37.00
$143.67; $70.00 + $80.00 = $150.00

Worksheet 76

1. 3, 36, yard, 5,280, 108
2. 48in., 56in., 90, 1 mi., 2889 ft; 3ft 9 in., 6in., 10584 ft.
3. pounds, inches, ounces

Worksheet 77

1. inch, foot, yard, mile
   pounds, ounces, tons
   cup, pint, quart, gallon
2. meter, kilometer, centimeter
   gram kilogram
   liter, milliliter
3. 1; 2,000; 5,235; 4 lbs., 1 oz.; 15 tons, 1,492 lbs.;
   $\frac{1}{2}$ lbs.; 3,500 lbs.

Worksheet 78

1. inch, foot, yard, mile
   ounce, cup, pint, quart, gallon
   ounce, pound, ton
2. centimeter, meter, kilometer
   mililiter, liter
   grams, kilograms
3. English, English, English,
   metric, English, metric
   English, metric, English
   English, metric, English
   English, metric, metric
   English, English
4. 1; 8.76; 1,000; 2,000; 1; 200; 2.5, .002; 4,800

Worksheet 79

1. English, English, English
   English, metric, English
   metric, English, metric
   English, English, metric
   metric, English, metric
   English, English, metric

2. 1; 62,500; 0.001; 2,800; 0.043; 500; 1; 48,000; 0.001; 0.16; 6,750; 0.0243

Worksheet 80

1. dogs, biography, 12
2. washing dishes, swimming and playing soccer, summer camp
3. 40, 14 years old, 230, picture graph, 10 and 12, 70
4. F, T, T, T
5. 11, 100 yard dash, 6, 38

Unit Tests

(1) Label using the Word Bank. 11 pts.

4 + 6 = 10

_______ _______ _______

8 − 5 = 3

_______ _______ _______

4 − 0 = 4   20 − 20 = 0

____

(2 + 4) + 5 = 11, (so) 2 + (4 + 5) = 11

____

5 − 3 = 2, (so) 2 + 3 = 5

____

5 + 0 = 5   7 + 0 = 7

____

3 + 9 = 12, (so) 9 + 3 = 12

____

WORD BANK:

Order Property of Addition   Zero Property of Addition   Opposites Property
Zero Property   Grouping Property of Addition   addend   difference
minuend   subtrahend   sum

(2) Find the difference. 12 pts.
Find the odd and even numbered answers to decode the message.

11 – 9 = ____ J	8 – 7 = ____ S	16 – 8 = ____ E	10 – 7 = ____ A	4 – 2 = ____ S
11 – 6 = ____ V	6 – 2 = ____ U	15 – 8 = ____ E	19 – 9 = ____ S	10 – 5 = ____ S

____ ____ ____ ____ ____
Even numbered answers in order worked.

____ ____ ____ ____ ____
Odd numbered answers in order worked.

(3) Fill in the four steps which are used in the Four-Step Problem Solving Process
Use the Four-Step Problem Solving Process to solve the following questions. 7 pts.

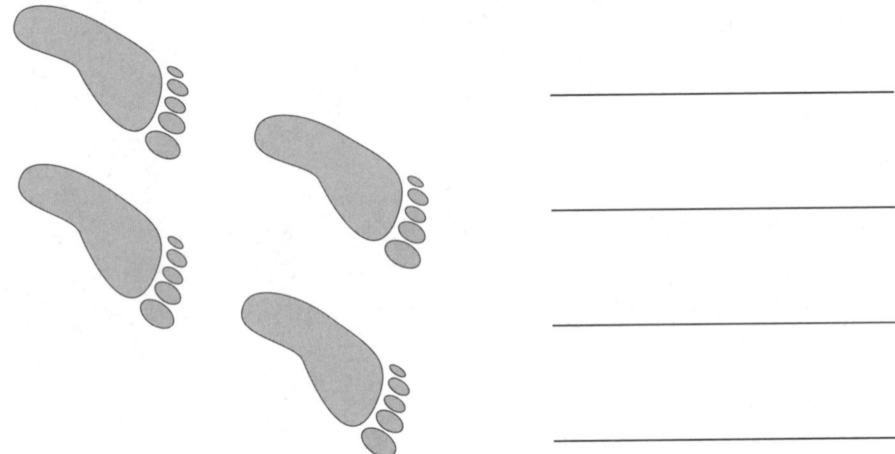

Carolyn had $400.00 in her checking account. She received a paycheck for $800.00. How much money does she have now?

Kitty went to the store and purchased a new computer program at a cost of $69.99. If she gave the cashier a $100.00 bill, how much change should she receive?

Thomas paid a workman to cut his grass and clean out his gutters. If the workman took 5 hours to complete this job, and Thomas paid him $5.00 per hour, how much money did the workman earn?

④ Write the numbers in expanded form. 18 pts.

8,926 = __________ + __________ + ______________ + _________

Which number is in the thousands' place? __________

32,065 = ____________ + ____________ + ____________ +

____________ + ____________

Which number is in the ones' place? __________

874,231 = ____________ + ____________ + ___________ +

____________ + ______________ + __________

Which number is in the hundred thousands' place? __________

⑤ Convert the Roman numerals to standard numbers. 15 pts.

XV	VII	XXVII	XXXI	LXI	XL
____	____	____	____	____	____

Round the numbers to the nearest ten and write <, >, or = in the circle.

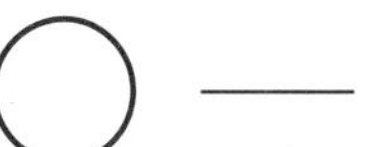

⑥ Add. 4 pts.

$$\begin{array}{r} 15 \\ +\ 12 \\ \hline \end{array} \qquad \begin{array}{r} 329 \\ +\ 154 \\ \hline \end{array} \qquad \begin{array}{r} 5{,}138 \\ +\ 1{,}259 \\ \hline \end{array} \qquad \begin{array}{r} 204 \\ 52 \\ +\ 602 \\ \hline \end{array}$$

7. Estimate by rounding each 2-digit number to the tens, each 3-digit number to the hundreds, each 4-digit number to the thousands, and each dollar amount to the nearest dollar. 10 pts.

958 L	7,256 B	$451.25 V	34 G	$17.25 N
− 41	− 2,561	− 158.97	− 27	− 9.54

268 I	472 E	$804.65 I	9,001 E
− 40	− 97	− 210.03	− 5,521

Order your answers from the largest to the smallest to reveal the mystery word.

____ ____ ____ ____ ____ ____ ____ ____ ____

Acts 24:14

8. Write a question which can be answered using the data given. Then solve the problem. 2 pts.

Joe has 28 Bible verses memorized. He needs to memorize 50 in order to receive a certificate of achievement.

Kirby has pledged to give $125.00 to the church building project. He has $175.00 in his savings account.

79 points total

1. Estimate by rounding to the nearest dollar. 4 pts.

$49.55	$35.64	$272.49	$84.83
− 13.79	− 31.58	− 185.25	− 9.85

2. Count the change due. Use the fewest bills possible. 3 pts.

Price	Paid	Change Due
Example: $36.00	$40.00	$4.00 = 4-1 dollar bills
$4.00	$5.00	
$87.00	$100.00	
$75.00	$100.00	

3. Match. 14 pts.

8 x 0 = 0	Zero Property of Multiplication
4 x 5 = 20 (so) 5 x 4 = 20	Grouping Property of Multiplication
6 x 1 = 6	Order property of Multiplication
(3 x 2) x 4 = 3 x (2 x 4)	One Property of Multiplication

4 ÷ 4 = 1	Division of a Number by Itself
24 ÷ 3 = 8 and, 3 x 8 = 24	Division by Zero
You cannot divide by zero (0)	Multiplication and Division are Related
8 ÷ 1 = 8	Division by One

(35) ÷ 5 = 7	product
35 ÷ (5) = 7	quotient
35 ÷ 5 = (7)	divisor
(6) x 4 = 24	multiplier
6 x (4) = 24	multiplicand
6 x 4 = (24)	dividend

4. Complete the factor trees. Multiply the prime numbers on the bottom of the tree to check your answers. 7 pts.

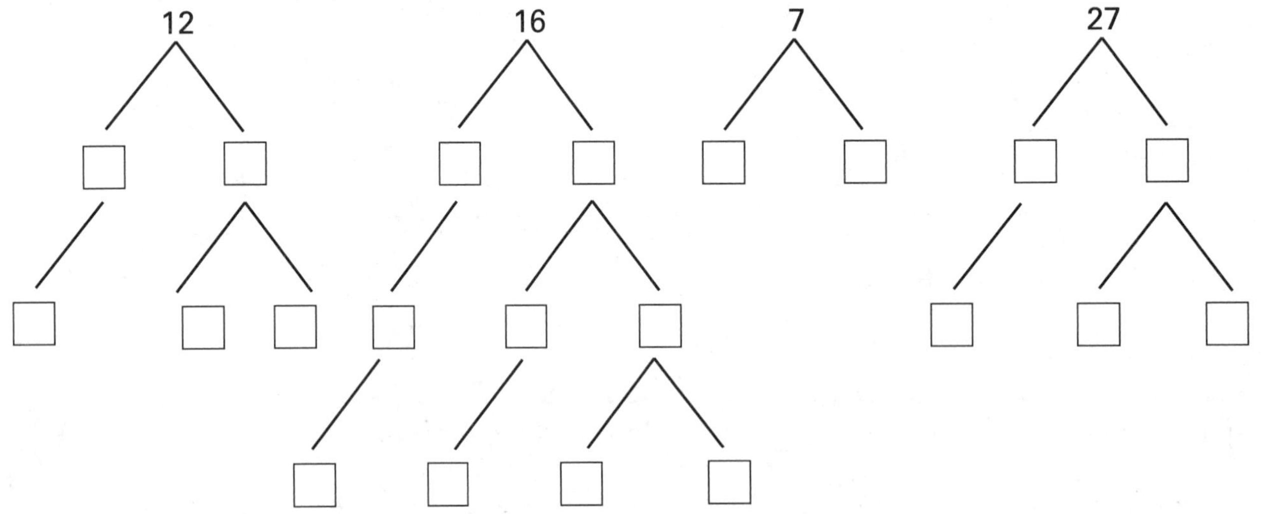

Example: 3 x 2 x 2 = 12 ______________ ______________ ______________

5. Rewrite each problem vertically and multiply. 7 pts.

17 x 7 = _____ 300 x 50 = _____ 299 x 21 = _____ 692 x 5 = _____

24 x 11 = _____ 223 x 3 = _____ 6,000 x 4,000 = _____

(6) Use data from the menu below to answer the questions. 2 pts.

Lori's Cafe

Sandwiches		Side Dishes		Desserts		Beverages		
Egg Salad	$1.75	Chips	$.60	Cheesecake	$2.75	Coke		
Tuna Salad	$1.95	Fries	$.95	w/ topping	$3.00		Sm.	$.50
Roast Beef	$2.25	Coleslaw	$.80				Lg.	$.95
Turkey	$2.00	Soup (cup)	$1.00	Brownie	$.75	Coffee		
Ham	$1.95			Sundae	$1.00		Sm.	$.60
Club	$2.50	Salad	$1.50				Lg.	$.95
						Milk		$.75

Lunch special: $3.95 Sandwich, side dish & small drink
(Monday-Friday-12:00-2:00 only)

1. Tabitha and a friend split a roast beef sandwich, two orders of fries, and two large cokes. They left a $0.95 tip for the waitress. How much did each girl spend on lunch?

2. Mrs. Kelly & Mrs. Honey split a piece of cheesecake with a topping, and two small coffees. How much money did they each spend?

(7) Average the following numbers. 3 pts.

38, 25, 21　　　　48, 53, 36, 31, 27　　　　56, 66, 74, 64, 70

8 Divide. 8 pts.

$40\overline{)166}$ $20\overline{)140}$ $50\overline{)327}$

$22\overline{)88}$ $45\overline{)100}$ $32\overline{)160}$

$44\overline{)2,021}$ $63\overline{)4,012}$

55 points total

(1) Find the quotient. 5 pts.

4) $24.08   2) $2.38   3) $23.67   11) $26.07   15) $77.70

(2) Estimate by rounding one- and two-digit numbers to the 10's and three-digit numbers to the 100's. 5 pts.

8) 678   14) 896   87) 913   28) 609   18) 792

(3) Draw a picture to solve the problem. 1 pt.

Four girls were in line for the movies. Dottie was behind Elaine. Karen was last. Tami was ahead of Elaine. Who was first in line?

④ Match. Place the appropriate letter next to the definition. 15 pts.

____ 1.	1665	a.	12:00 midnight to 12:00 noon.
____ 2.	BC	b.	Anno Domini–in the year of our Lord
____ 3.	AD	c.	1 hour
____ 4.	decade	d.	1 minute
____ 5.	century	e.	eight-sided figure
____ 6.	millennium	f.	3-sided figure
____ 7.	60 minutes	g.	1,000 years
____ 8.	24 hours	h.	10 years
____ 9.	60 seconds	i.	Before Christ
____10.	AM	j.	17th century
____11.	pentagon	k.	five-sided figure
____12.	hexagon	l.	1 day
____13.	octagon	m.	100 years
____14.	triangle	n.	four-sided figure
____15.	quadrilateral	o.	six-sided figure

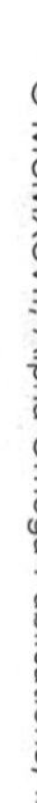

4 pts.

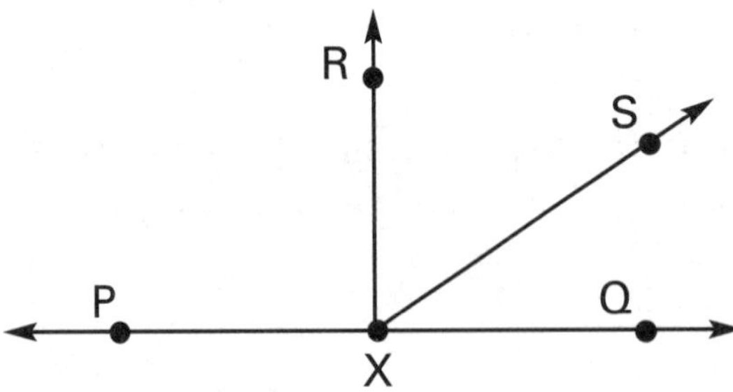

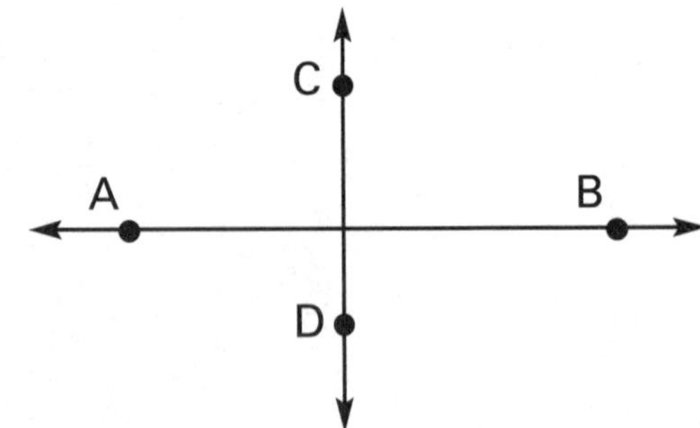

1. Name two angles that are acute. ______________________
2. Name two angles that are right angles. ______________________
3. Name two lines that are parallel. ______________________
4. Name two lines that are perpendicular. ______________________

6) 5 pts.

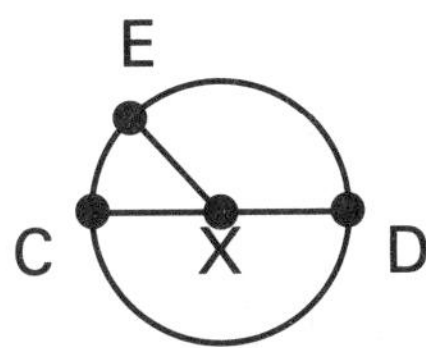

1. Name the circle. __________
2. The diameter is 4 cm. What is the length of $\overline{XD}$? __________
3. What is the length of $\overline{CX}$? __________
4. Name the diameter. __________
5. Circle M is twice as big as the circle pictured above.
   What is the diameter of Circle M? __________

7) Draw a similar and congruent figure. Draw the lines of symmetry. 4 pts.

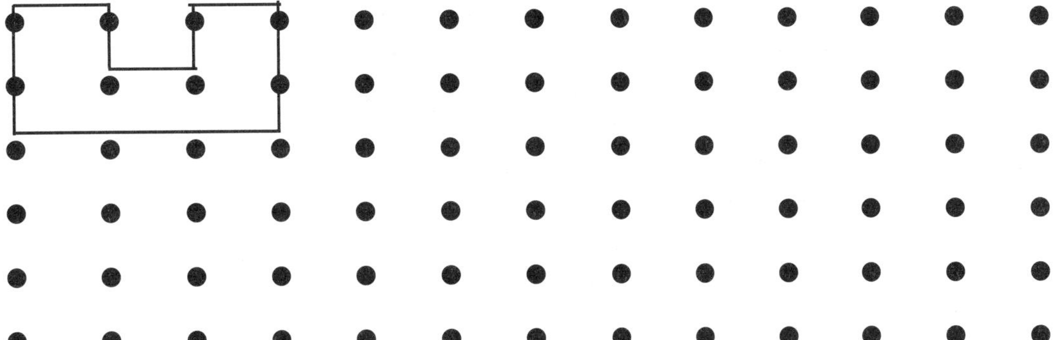

Figure A

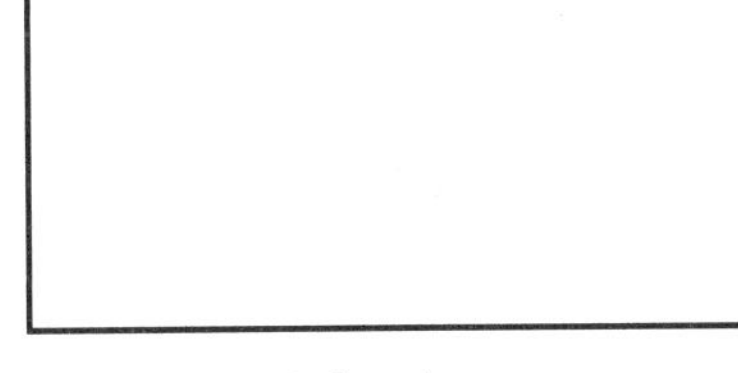

10 inches

20 inches

Figure B

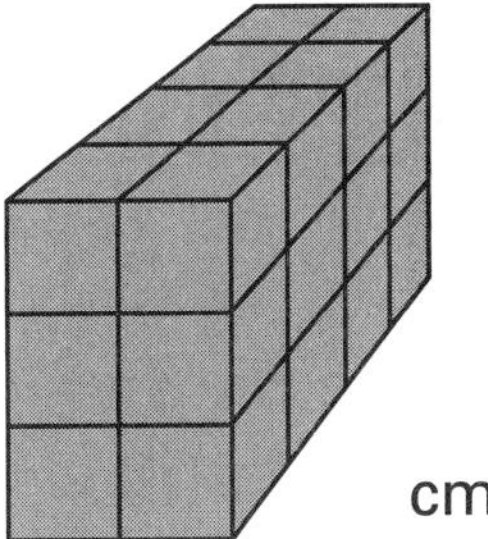

cm

8) Find the perimeter and area of figure A. Find the volume of figure B. 2 pts.

9) Give the missing numerator or denominator. 4 pts.

$\frac{3}{9} = \frac{9}{n}$ $\frac{2}{3} = \frac{28}{n}$ $\frac{6}{8} = \frac{n}{64}$ $\frac{1}{9} = \frac{9}{n}$

(10) Find the sum or difference. Make sure the answer is in lowest terms. 6 pts.

$\frac{2}{3} + \frac{1}{3} =$ ________ $\frac{8}{10} - \frac{4}{10} =$ ________ $\frac{9}{12} - \frac{3}{12} =$ ________

$\frac{5}{7} + \frac{1}{7} =$ ________ $\frac{7}{14} + \frac{6}{14} =$ ________ * $\frac{7}{9} + \frac{6}{9} =$ ________

(11) Find the sum. Make sure the answer is in lowest terms. 6 pts.

$\frac{1}{4} + \frac{2}{8} =$ ________ $\frac{5}{15} + \frac{1}{3} =$ ________ $\frac{6}{10} + \frac{1}{5} =$ ________

$\frac{2}{12} + \frac{2}{4} =$ ________ $\frac{2}{3} + \frac{1}{12} =$ ________ * $\frac{2}{5} + \frac{1}{3} =$ ________

57 points total

① Find the sum or difference. Reduce to lowest terms. 5 pts.

$$5\frac{2}{6} + 3\frac{1}{6}$$

$$12\frac{3}{7} + 16\frac{2}{7}$$

$$9\frac{5}{6} - 9\frac{2}{6}$$

$$38\frac{7}{12} - 28\frac{3}{12}$$

$$* \; 16\frac{5}{9} - \frac{5}{9}$$

② <, >, or =. 8 pts.

4.9  4.1   1.9 ○ 1.90   9.03 ○ 9.33   0.06 ○ 0.060

0.711 ○ 0.710   2.050 ○ 2.500   0.77 ○ 0.077   0.809 ○ 0.9

③ Find the sum or difference. 4 pts.

48.902	465.001	30.956	7. 76
+ 4.342	+ 233.021	− 29.824	− 0. 94

Write the numbers vertically and find the sum. 3 pts.

3.458 + 0.45 =   45.904 + 7.89 =   541.90 + 354.805 =

4

12 in	=	1 foot (ft)
3 ft	=	1 yard (yd)
1 yard	=	36 inches
5,280 ft	=	1,760 yards (yd) = 1 mile (mi)

Complete. 6 pts.

48 inches = ______ feet   12 feet = _______ yards   15,840 feet = _____ miles

108 inches = _____ yards   63 feet = _______ yards   3,520 yards = _____ miles

1 cup = 8 fluid ounces	2 pints = 1 quart
2 cups = 1 pint	4 quarts = 1 gallon

5 Complete. 6 pts.

10 cups = _____ pints   20 cups = ______ quarts   68 pints = ______ quarts

24 quarts = _____ gallons   64 fluid ounces = ______ cups   32 cups = ______ gallons

6

boiling	freezing	bitter cold day	room temperature

Match the words in the answer box with the appropriate temperature. 4 pts.

1. 0°C ___________   2. −10°C ___________   3. 100°C ___________   4. 22°C ___________

7 Complete. 6 pts.

Kilo	Hecto	Deka	Basic Unit (Meter, Liter or Gram)	deci	centi	milli

890 mm = _________ cm   78.89 m = _________ cm

587 mm = _________ m   8.54 Km = _________ dm

656 m = _________ mm   7.001 m = _________ cm

(8) Plot the following information on the bar graph and on the circle graph.
125 people were polled to see what kind of music they preferred.
The results follow: 30% gospel, 10% rock, 20% classical, 30% folk, and 10% rap.
The first one has been done for you. 8 pts.

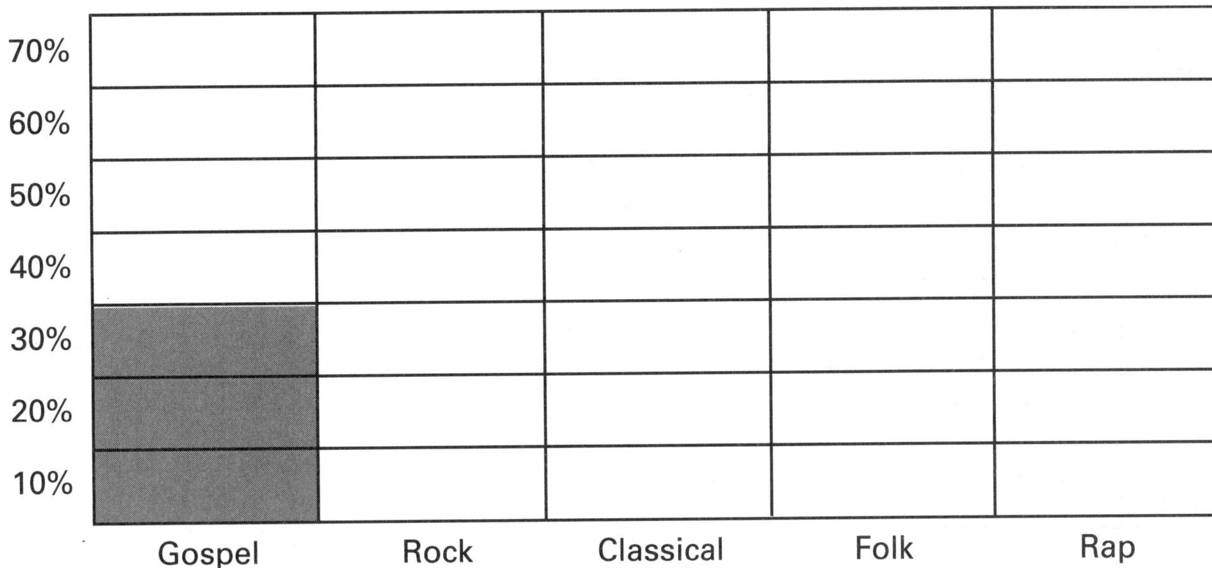

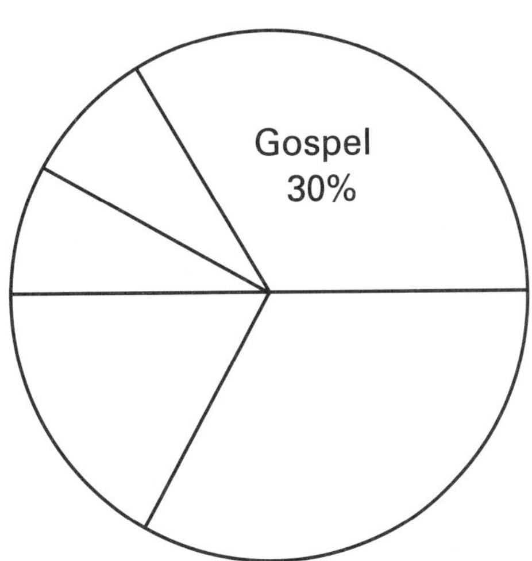

(9) Complete the chart with equivalent ratios. 10 pts.

cars	1					6	7
wheels	4						

(10) Divide by 3 to find equal ratios. 12 pts.

$\frac{3}{9}$	
$\frac{6}{18}$	
$\frac{30}{60}$	
$\frac{6}{9}$	

$\frac{300}{600}$	
$\frac{18}{36}$	
$\frac{9}{12}$	
$\frac{6}{12}$	

$\frac{12}{18}$	
$\frac{12}{21}$	
$\frac{3}{33}$	
$\frac{6}{30}$	

72 points total

1. Solve. 4 pts.

a. $\begin{array}{r} 5,138 \\ +\ 1,259 \\ \hline \end{array}$

b. $\begin{array}{r} 204 \\ 52 \\ +\ 602 \\ \hline \end{array}$

c. $\begin{array}{r} 268 \\ -\ 40 \\ \hline \end{array}$

d. $\begin{array}{r} \$49.55 \\ -\ \$13.79 \\ \hline \end{array}$

2. Round to the nearest dollar and add. 1 pt.

$\begin{array}{r} \$804.65 \\ +\ \ 210.03 \\ \hline \end{array}$

3. Ken purchased a calculator for $15.99, a TV for $179.95, and a video game for $49.95. How much did all of these items cost? If Ken gave the cashier $300.00, how much change would he receive? 2 pts.

4. Color the prime numbers silver. Color the composite numbers blue. 2 pts.

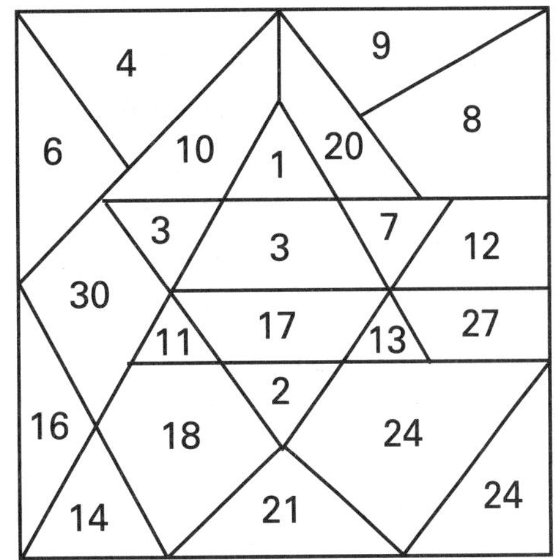

5. Divide. 2 pts.

$40 \overline{)166}$

$15 \overline{)\$75.00}$

(6) Multiply. Put <, >, or = in the circle. 6 pts.

$\begin{array}{r} 851 \\ \times\ 25 \\ \hline \end{array}$	◯	$\begin{array}{r} 1{,}208 \\ \times\ 200 \\ \hline \end{array}$
$\begin{array}{r} 135 \\ \times\ 9 \\ \hline \end{array}$	◯	$\begin{array}{r} 196 \\ \times\ 21 \\ \hline \end{array}$

(7) Round the 3-digit numbers to the hundreds and the 4-digit numbers to the thousands. 5 pts.

561	891	702	1,250	8,251
____	____	____	____	____

(8) Multiply. 1 pt.

200 x 300 =

(9) Underline the data that is not needed. Solve the problem. 2 pts.

For lunch Kathy purchased a slice of pizza and a drink for $1.00 each. She then bought a candy bar for dessert at a cost of $0.65. On the way home, she picked up a container of ice cream for a late night snack. She also rented a movie to watch before going to bed. How much did Kathy spend on lunch?

(10) Solve for *n*. 2 pts.

$(4 + 5) \times n = 27$ $\qquad\qquad$ $n + 5 = 16 - 4$

(11) Find the number. 4 pts.

9,348,160,925

_____ is in the hundreds' place

_____ is in the ten thousands' place

_____ is in the millions' place

_____ is in the billions' place

(12) Write in expanded and standard form. 1 pt.

Twenty-four thousand, five hundred twenty-six =

__________ + ___________ + ___________ + ________ + _____ = ______________

(13) Fill in the 4 steps which are used in the 4 Step Problem Solving Process.
Use the Four Step Problem Solving Process to solve the following questions. 7 pts.

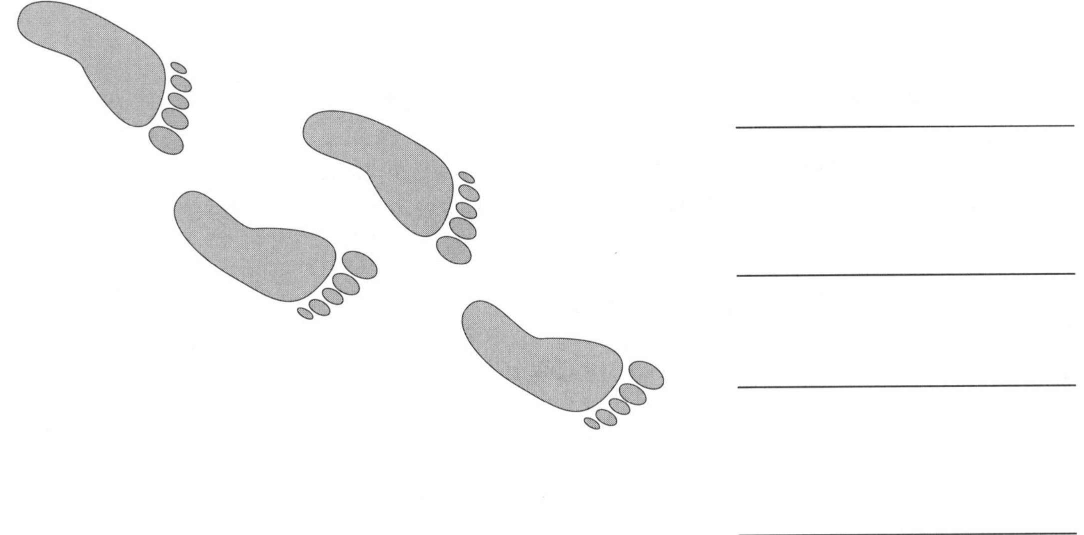

____

____

____

____

Carolyn had $400.00 in her checking account. She received a paycheck for $800.00. How much money does she have now?

Kitty went to the store and purchased a new computer program at a cost of $69.99. If she gave the cashier a $100.00 bill, how much change should she receive?

Thomas paid a workman to cut his grass and clean out his gutters. If the workman took 7 hours to complete this job, and Thomas paid him $5.00 per hour, how much money did the workman earn?

(14) Convert the Roman Numerals. 2 pts.

XXV = ______

LXX = ______

(15) Divide. 1 pt.

$6\overline{)102}$

(16) Find the quotient. 4 pts.

$5\overline{)\$44.75}$ $7\overline{)\$6.86}$ $13\overline{)\$92.82}$ $11\overline{)\$61.82}$

(17) Pair the words in the solution box with the definitions. 9 pts.

pentagon	hexagon	octagon	triangle	quadrilateral
rhombus	parallelogram	trapezoid	square	

1. A ______________ is a five-sided figure.
2. A ______________ is a figure with four equal sides and four right angles.
3. A ______________ is an eight-sided figure.
4. A ______________ has four sides and four angles.
5. A ______________ is a quadrilateral with all sides the same length. The angles are not all the same.
6. A ______________ is a six-sided figure.
7. A ______________ is a three-sided figure.
8. A ______________ has two pairs of sides the same length and two pairs of parallel sides.
9. A ______________ has one pair of parallel sides.

(18) Find the perimeter and area. 3 pts.

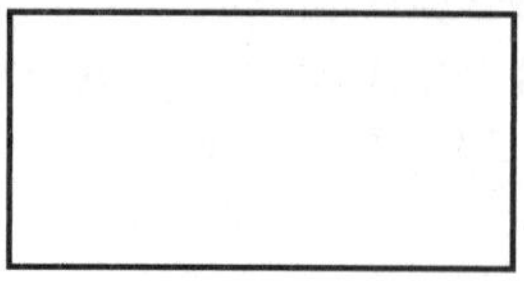

5 cm

10 cm

The perimeter is ____________

The area is ______________

Find tl

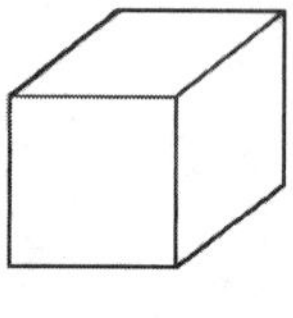

6 cm

cm

8 cm

The volume is ______________
(L x W x H)

(19) Match. 3 pts.

acute angle

right angle

obtuse angle

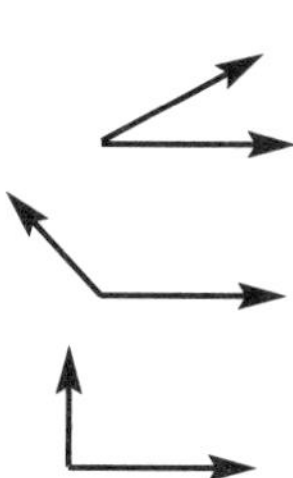

(20) Give the missing numerator or denominator. 4 pts.

$\frac{3}{4} = \frac{6}{n}$ $\frac{2}{5} = \frac{14}{n}$ $\frac{4}{9} = \frac{n}{81}$ $\frac{1}{9} = \frac{7}{n}$

(21) Find the sum or difference. Make sure the answer is in lowest terms. 6 pts.

$\frac{2}{3} + \frac{1}{6} =$ ______ $\frac{8}{12} - \frac{4}{12} =$ ______ $\frac{9}{10} - \frac{3}{10} =$ ______

$\frac{3}{4} + \frac{1}{8} =$ ______ $\frac{2}{3} + \frac{1}{9} =$ ______ * $\frac{2}{3} + \frac{1}{4} =$ ______

(22) Write the numbers vertically and find the sum. 3 pts.

8.356 + 0.26 = 45.801 + 6.49 = 600.01 + 3.705 =

(23) <, >, or =. 4 pts.

4.8 ◯ 4.70 8.9 ◯ 8.90 8.08 ◯ 8.80 0.05 ◯ 0.050

(24) Complete. 6 pts.

12 in	=	1 foot (ft)
3 ft	=	1 yard (yd)
1 yard	=	36 inches
5,280 ft	=	1,760 yards (yd) = 1 mile (mi)

36 inches = __________ feet 24 feet = __________ yards

10,560 feet = __________ miles 3,520 yards = __________ miles

72 inches = __________ yards 330 feet = __________ yards

25 4 pts.

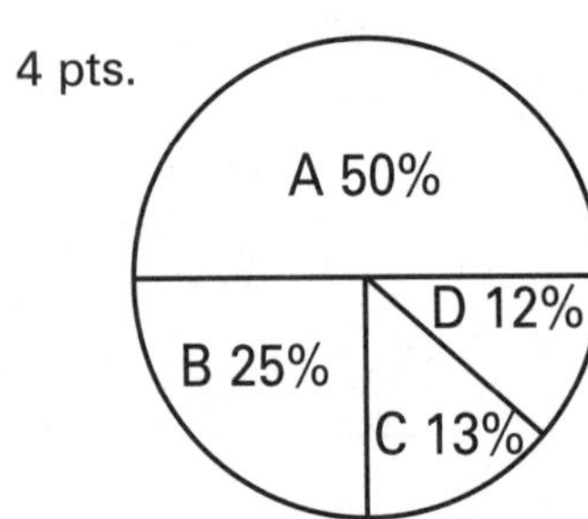

What percent of the class got an A or a B?

If 30 people took the test, how many got an A?

What percent of the class got a C or a D ?

What percent of the class got a D?

26 Complete the chart with equivalent ratios. 10 pts.

pizza	1			4		6		
cups of cheese	3			12				

27 Complete. 3 pts.

Kilo	Hecto	Deka	Basic Unit (Meter, Liter or Gram)	deci	centi	milli

890 mm = __________ cm

78.89 m = __________ cm

8.37 m = ____________ mm

101 points total

Horizons Mathematics 4

Unit Tests

Answer Key

Quarter Test 1 Lesson 40

1. Addend Addend Sum
   Minuend Subtrahend Difference
   Zero Property
   Grouping Property of Addition
   Opposites Property
   Zero Property of Addition
   Order Property of Addition

2. 2; 1; 8; 3; 2
   5; 4; 7; 10; 5
   ANSWERS: JESUS; SAVES

3. Answers: Understand, Plan, Work, Answer/Check
   Answers: $400.00 + $800.00 = $1,200.00
   $100.00 – $69.99 = $30.01
   $5.00 x 5 = $25.00

4. Answers: 8,000 + 900 + 20 + 6; 8 is in the thousands' place
   30,000 + 2,000 + 0 + 60 + 5; 5 is in the ones' place
   800,000 + 70,000 + 4,000 + 200 + 30 + 1; 8 is in the hundred thousands' place

5. 15; 7; 27; 31; 61; 40
   20 > 10 30 = 30 60 > 40

6. 27; 483; 6,397; 858

7. 960; 4,000; $292.00; 0; $7.00
   260; 400; $595.00; 3,000
   BELIEVING

8. Answers will vary. Example: How many more verses does he need to memorize?
   50 – 28 = 22

   Answers will vary. Example: How much more money will Kirby have left?
   $175.00 – $125.00 = $50.00

Quarter Test 2 Lesson 80

1. $36.00; $4.00; $87.00; $75.00

2. $1.00 = 1-1 dollar bill
   $13.00 = 3-1 dollar bills, 1-10 dollar bill
   $25.00 = 1-5 dollar bill, 1- 20 dollar bill

3. 1. Zero Property of Multiplication
   2. Order Property of Multiplication
   3. One Property of Multiplication
   4. Grouping Property of Multiplication

   5. Division of a Number by Itself
   6. Multiplication and Division are Related
   7. Division by Zero
   8. Division by One

   9. Dividend
   10. Divisor
   11. Quotient
   12. Multiplicand
   13. Multiplier
   14. Product

4. 2; 6 2; 8 1; 7 3; 9
   2, 2, 3 2, 2, 4 3; 3; 3
   2, 2, 2, 2
   Answers: 3 x 2 x 2 = 12 (example)
   2 x 2 x 2 x 2 =16
   1 X 7 = 7
   3 X 3 X 3 = 27

5. 119; 15,000; 6,279; 3,460
   264; 669; 24,000,000

6. 1. $2.25 + 0.95 + 0.95 + 0.95 + 0.95 + 0.95 = $7.00
      $7.00 ÷ 2 = $3.50

   2. $3.00 + $0.60 + $0.60 = $4.20
      $4.20 ÷ 2 = $2.10

7. 28; 39; 66

8. 4 r 6; 7; 6 r 27
   4; 2 r 10; 5
   45 r 41; 63 r 43

Quarter Test 3 Lesson 120

1. $6.02; $1.19; $7.89; $2.37; $5.18

2. 70; 90; 10; 20; 40

3. Tami

4. 1. j
   2. i
   3. b
   4. h
   5. m

4. (cont.)

6.	g
7.	c
8.	l
9.	d
10.	a
11.	k
12.	o
13.	e
14.	f
15.	n

5.
1. ∠RXS, ∠ XSQ
2. ∠ RXQ, ∠ RXP
3. $\overleftrightarrow{PQ}$ and $\overleftrightarrow{AB}$
4. $\overleftrightarrow{AB}$ and $\overleftrightarrow{CD}$

6.
1. Circle x
2. 2 cm
3. 2 cm
4. cd
5. 8 cm

7.

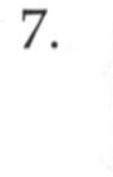

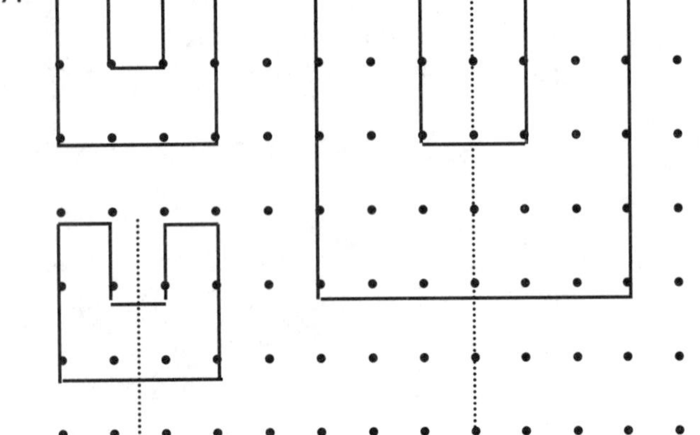

8. Figure A – perimeter 60 in; area 200 in^2
Figure B – 24 cm^3

9. 27; 42; 48; 81

10. 3/3 = 1; 4/10 = 2/5; 6/12 = 1/2
6/7; 13/14; 13/9 = 1 4/9

11. 4/8 = 1/2; 10/15 = 2/3; 8/10 = 4/5
8/12 = 2/3; 9/12 = 3/4; 11/15

Quarter Test 4 Lesson 160

1. 8 3/6 = 8 1/2; 28 5/7; 3/6 = 1/2;
10 4/12 = 10 1/3; 16

2. > = < =
> < > <

3. 53.244; 698.022; 1.132; 6.82

3.908; 53.794; 896.705

4. 4; 4; 3
3; 21; 2

5. 5; 5; 34
6; 8; 2

6.
1. freezing
2. bitter cold day
3. boiling
4. room temperature

7. 89.0; 7,889
0.587; 85,400
656,000; 700.1

8. Teacher check

9. 2/8 3/12 4/16 5/20 6/24 7/28

10. 1/3; 100/200; 4/6
2/6; 6/12; 4/7
10/20; 3/4; 1/11
2/3; 2/4; 2/10

Final Exam (Lessons 1-160)

1. 6,397

   858

   228

   $35.76

2. $1,015.00

3. $245.89 total
   $300.00 - $245.89 = $54.11

4. Teacher check

5. 4 r 6

   $5.00

6. 21,275 (<) 241,600

   1,215 (<) 4,116

7. 600; 900; 700; 1,000; 8,000

8. 60,000

9. $1.00 + $1.00 + $0.65 = $2.65
   On the way home, she picked up a container of ice cream for a late night snack. She also rented a movie to watch before going to bed.

10. $n = 3$

    $n = 7$

11. Answers: 9; 6; 8; 9

12. 20,000 + 4,000 + 500 + 20 + 6 = 24,526

13. Answers: Understand; Plan; Work, Answer/Check

    $400.00 + $800.00 = $1,200.00

    $100.00 – $69.99 = $30.01

    $5.00 x 7 = $35.00

14. 25

    70

15. 17

16. $8.95; $0.98; $7.14; $5.62

17. 1. pentagon
    2. square
    3. octagon
    4. quadrilateral
    5. rhombus
    6. hexagon
    7. triangle
    8. parallelogram
    9. trapezoid

18. 1. 30 cm
    2. 50 cm^2
    3. 240 cm^3

19. acute angle
    obtuse angle
    right angle

20. 8; 35; 36; 63

21. 5/6; 4/12 = 1/3; 6/10 = 3/5
    7/8; 7/9; 11/12

22. 8.616; 52.291; 603.715

23. >; =; <; =

24. 3; 8
    2; 2
    2: 110

25. 1. 75%
    2. 15 students
    3. 25%
    4. 12%

26. 2/6 3/9 4/12 5/15 6/18 7/21 8/24

27. 89.0; 7,889; 8,370